THE ANIMAL MIND

THE MACMILLAN COMPANY
NEW YORK · BOSTON · CHICAGO
ATLANTA · SAN FRANCISCO

MACMILLAN & CO., Limited
LONDON · BOMBAY · CALCUTTA
MELBOURNE

THE MACMILLAN CO. OF CANADA, Ltd.
TORONTO

THE ANIMAL MIND

A Text-book of Comparative Psychology

BY

MARGARET FLOY WASHBURN, Ph.D.

ASSOCIATE PROFESSOR OF PHILOSOPHY
IN VASSAR COLLEGE

New York

THE MACMILLAN COMPANY

1908

Norwood Press
J. S. Cushing Co. — Berwick & Smith Co.
Norwood, Mass., U.S.A.

PREFACE

THE title of this book might more appropriately, if not more concisely, have been "The Animal Mind as Deduced from Experimental Evidence." For the facts set forth in the following pages are very largely the results of the experimental method in comparative psychology. Thus many aspects of the animal mind, to the investigation of which experiment either has not yet been applied or is perhaps not adapted, are left wholly unconsidered. This limitation of the scope of the book is a consequence of its aim to supply what I have felt to be a chief need of comparative psychology at the present time. Although the science is still in its formative stage, the mass of experimental material that has been accumulating from the researches of physiologists and psychologists is already great, and is also for the most part inaccessible to the ordinary student, being widely scattered and to a considerable extent published in journals which the average college library does not contain. While we have books on animal instincts and on the interpretation of animal behavior, we have no book which adequately presents the simple facts.

Probably no bibliography seems to one who carefully examines it entirely consistent in what it includes and what it excludes. Certainly the one upon which this book is based contains inconsistencies. The design has been to exclude works bearing only upon general physiology, upon the morphology of the nervous system and sense organs, or upon the nature of animal instinct as such, and to include those which bear upon the topics mentioned in the chapter headings.

Within these limits, the collection of references upon no topic is as full as would be necessary for the bibliography of a special research upon that topic. Doubtless there are omissions for which no excuse can be found. In one or two cases, where the literature upon a single point is very large, as for example, in the case of the function of the semicircular canals, only a few of the more important references have been given.

One further comment may be made. The book throughout deals with comparative rather than with genetic psychology.

I gratefully acknowledge help from a number of sources. To Professor Titchener I owe, not only my share of that genuine psychological spirit which he so successfully imparts to his pupils according to their ability, but various helpful criticisms upon the present work, about half of which he has read in manuscript. Dr. Yerkes has given me much invaluable aid in securing access to material, and has very kindly permitted me to see the proofs of his book on "The Dancing Mouse." As editor of the series he has reviewed my manuscript to its great advantage. Professors Georges Bohn and George H. Parker have showed especial courtesy in making their work accessible to me. Professor Jennings has kindly allowed the use of a number of illustrations from his book on "The Behavior of the Lower Organisms." My colleague Professor Aaron L. Treadwell has generously helped me in ways too numerous to specify. But perhaps my heaviest single obligation is to Professor I. Madison Bentley, who has read the manuscript of the entire book, and whose advice and criticism have been of the utmost benefit to every part of it.

M. F. W.

VASSAR COLLEGE, POUGHKEEPSIE, N.Y.
October 1, 1907.

TABLE OF CONTENTS

CHAPTER I

THE DIFFICULTIES AND METHODS OF COMPARATIVE PSYCHOLOGY

CHAPTER II

THE EVIDENCE OF MIND

CHAPTER III

THE MIND OF THE SIMPLEST ANIMALS

CHAPTER IV

SENSORY DISCRIMINATION: METHODS OF INVESTIGATION

CHAPTER V

CHAPTER VI

CHAPTER VII

CHAPTER VIII

Spatially Determined Reactions and Space Perception

CHAPTER IX

Spatially Determined Reactions and Space Perception (*continued*)

CHAPTER X

CHAPTER XI

CHAPTER XII

CHAPTER XIII

THE ANIMAL MIND

THE ANIMAL MIND

CHAPTER I

THE DIFFICULTIES AND METHODS OF COMPARATIVE PSYCHOLOGY

§ 1. *Difficulties*

THAT the mind of each human being forms a region inaccessible to all save its possessor, is one of the commonplaces of reflection. His neighbor's knowledge of each person's mind must always be indirect, a matter of inference. How wide of the truth this inference may be, even under the most favorable circumstances, is also an affair of everyday experience: each of us can judge his fellow-men only on the basis of his own thoughts and feelings in similar circumstances, and the individual peculiarities of different members of the human species are of necessity very imperfectly comprehended by others. The science of human psychology has to reckon with this unbridgable gap between minds as its chief difficulty. The psychologist may look into his own mind and study its workings with impartial insight, yet he can never be sure that the laws which he derives from such a study are not distorted by some personal twist or bias. For example, it has been suggested that the philosopher Hume was influenced by his tendency toward a visual type of imagination in his discussion of the nature of ideas, which to him were evidently visual images. As is well known, the experimental method in psychology has aimed to minimize the danger of confusing individual peculiarities with general mental laws. In a psychological experiment, an unbiassed observer is asked to study his own experience under certain definite conditions, and to put it into words so that the experimenter may know what the contents of another mind are like in the circumstances. Thus language is the essential apparatus in experimental psychology; language with all its defects, its ambiguity, its substitution of crystallized concepts for the protean flux of actually lived experience, its lack of terms to express those parts of experience which are of small practical importance in everyday life, but which may be of the highest importance to mental science. Outside of the psychological laboratory language is not always the best guide to the contents of other minds, because it is not always the expression of a genuine wish to communicate thought. "Actions speak louder than words," the proverb says; but when words are backed by good faith they furnish by far the safest indication of the thought of others. Whether, however, our inferences are made on the basis of words or of actions, they are all necessarily made on the hypothesis that human minds are built on the same pattern, that what a given word or action would mean for my mind, this it means also for my neighbor's mind.

If this hypothesis be uncertain when applied to our fellow human beings, it fails us utterly when we turn to the lower animals. If my neighbor's mind is a mystery to me, how great is the mystery which looks out of the eyes of a dog, and how insoluble the problem presented by the mind of an invertebrate animal, an ant or a spider! We know that such minds must differ from ours not only in certain individual peculiarities, but in ways at whose nature we can only guess. The nervous systems of many animals vary widely from our own. We have, perhaps, too little knowledge about the functions of our own to conjecture with any certainty what difference this must make in the conscious life of such animals; but when we find sense organs, such as the compound eyes of insects or crustaceans, constructed on a plan wholly diverse from that of ours; when we find organs apparently sensory in function, but so unlike our own that we cannot tell what purpose they serve, — we are baffled in our attempt to construct the mental life of the animals possessing them, for lack of power to supply the sensation elements of that life. "It is not," said Locke, "in the power of the most exalted wit or enlarged understanding, by any quickness or variety of thought, to invent or frame one new simple idea in the mind" (232, Bk. II, ch. 2); we cannot imagine a color or a sound or a smell that we have never experienced; how much less the sensations of a sense radically different from any that we possess! Again, a bodily structure entirely unlike our own must create a background of organic sensation which renders the whole mental life of an animal foreign and unfamiliar to us. We speak, for example, of an "angry" wasp. Anger, in our own experience, is largely composed of sensations of quickened heart beat, of altered breathing, of muscular tension, of increased blood pressure in the head and face. The circulation of a wasp is fundamentally different from that of any vertebrate. The wasp does not breathe through lungs, it wears its skeleton on the outside, and it has the muscles attached to the inside of the skeleton. What is anger like in the wasp's consciousness? We can form no adequate idea of it.

To this fundamental difficulty of the dissimilarity between animal minds and ours is added, of course, the obstacle that animals have no language in which to describe their experience to us. Where this unlikeness is greatest, as in the case of invertebrate animals, language would be of little use, the slide had been accidentally left open for some little while. When I came to shut it, I found that there was an unusual resistance. As I looked more closely, I found that the spider had drawn a large number of thick threads directly under the lifted door, and that these were preventing my closing it. . . ."

"What was going on in the spider's mind?" Wundt asks, and points out that it is unnecessary to assume that she understood and reasoned out the mechanical requirements of the situation. The whole matter can be explained, he thinks, in a simpler way. "I imagine that as the days went by there had been formed in the mind of the spider a determinate association on the one hand between free entry into the cage and the pleasurable feeling attending satisfaction of the nutritive impulse, and on the other between the closed slide and the unpleasant feeling of hunger and inhibited impulse. Now in her free life the spider had always employed her web in the service of the nutritive impulse. Associations had therefore grown up between the definite positions of her web and definite peculiarities of the objects to which it was attached, as well as changes which it produced in the positions of certain of these objects, — leaves, small twigs, etc. The impression of the falling slide, that is, called up by association, the idea of other objects similarly moved which had been held in their places by threads properly spun; and finally there were connected with this association the other two of pleasure and raising, unpleasantness and closing, of the door" (446, pp. 351–352).

The Peckhams remark in criticism of this observation: "Had Wundt been familiar with the habits of spiders, he would have known that whenever they are confined they walk around and around the cage, leaving behind them lines of web. Of course many lines passed under his little sliding door, and when he came to close it there was a slight resistance. These are the facts. His inference that there was even a remotest intention on the part of his prisoner to hinder the movement of the door is entirely gratuitous. Even the simpler mental states that are supposed to have passed through the mind of the spider were the products of Wundt's own imagination " (322, p. 230). The fact that the anecdote was a recollection of childhood, so that it would probably be impossible to bring any evidence from the character of the web or other circumstance against the suggestion of Mr. and Mrs. Peckham, is a further instance of the unscientific use of anecdotal testimony.

An illustration of the third objection mentioned above, the disadvantage of ignorance of the animal's individual history, is furnished by Lloyd Morgan. In describing his futile efforts to teach a fox terrier the best way to pull a crooked stick through a fence, he says that the dog showed no sign "of perceiving that by pushing the stick and freeing the crook he could pull the stick through. Each time the crook caught he pulled with all his strength, seizing the stick now at the end, now in the middle, and now near the crook. At length he seized the crook itself and with a wrench broke it off. A man who was passing . . . said, 'Clever dog that, sir; he knows where the hitch do lie.' The remark was the characteristic outcome of two minutes' chance observation " (282, pp. 142–143). How many anecdotes of animals are based on similar accidents?

It will be seen that in both the cases just criticised the error lies in the interpretation of the animal's behavior. Indeed, a root of evil in the method of anecdote consists in the fact that observation in this form is imperfectly divorced from interpretation. The maker of an anecdote is seldom content with merely telling one what the animal did and leaving future investigation and the comparative study of many facts to decide what the animal's conscious experience in doing it was like. The point of the anecdote usually consists in showing that a human interpretation of the animal's behavior is possible. Here is shown the desire to tell a good story, which we mentioned among the pitfalls of the anecdotal method; the wish to report something unusual, not to get a just conception of the normal behavior of an animal. As Thorndike has forcibly put it: "Dogs get lost hundreds of times and no one ever notices it or sends an account of it to a scientific magazine. But let one find his way from Brooklyn to Yonkers and the fact immediately becomes a circulating anecdote. Thousands of cats on thousands of occasions sit helplessly yowling, and no one takes thought of it or writes to his friend, the professor; but let one cat claw at the knob of a door supposedly as a signal to be let out, and straightway this cat becomes the representative of the cat-mind in all the books" (393, p. 4).

All this is not to deny that much of the testimony to be found in Romanes's "Animal Intelligence" and Darwin's "Descent of Man" is the trustworthy report of trained observers; but it is difficult to separate the grain from the chaff, and one feels toward many of the anecdotes the attitude of scepticism produced, for example, by this tale which an Australian lady reported to the Linnæan Society. The burial of some deceased comrades was accomplished, she says, by a nest of "soldier ants" near Sydney, in the following fashion. "All fell into rank walking regularly and slowly two by two, until they arrived at the spot where lay the dead bodies. . . . Two of the ants advanced and took up the dead body of one of their comrades; then two others, and so on until all were ready to march. First walked two ants bearing a body, then two without a burden; then two others with another dead ant, and so on, until the line was extended to about forty pairs, and the procession now moved slowly onward, followed by an irregular body of about two hundred ants. Occasionally the two laden ants stopped, and laying down the dead ant, it was taken up by the two walking unburdened behind them, and thus, by occasionally relieving each other, they arrived at a sandy spot near the sea." A separate grave was then dug for each dead ant. "Some six or seven of the ants had attempted to run off without performing their share of the task of digging; these were caught and brought back, when they were at once attacked by the body of ants and killed upon the spot. A single grave was quickly dug and they were all dropped into it." No funeral procession for them! Of this story Romanes says, "The observation seems to have been one about which there could scarcely have been a mistake" (364, p. 91). One is inclined to think it just possible that there was.

§ 3. *Methods of Obtaining Facts: The Method of Experiment*

Diametrically opposed to the Method of Anecdote and its unscientific character is the Method of Experiment. An experiment, properly conducted, always implies that the conditions are controlled, or at least known; whereas ignorance of the conditions is, as we have seen, a common feature of anecdote. The experimenter is impartial; he has no desire to bring about any particular result. The teller of an anecdote wishes to prove animal intelligence. The experimenter is willing to report the facts precisely as he observes them, and is in no haste to make them prove anything. The conduct of an experiment upon an animal will, of course, vary according to the problem to be solved. If the object is to test some innate reaction on the animal's part, such as its ordinary responses to stimulation or its instincts, one need merely place the animal under favorable conditions for observation, make sure that it is not frightened or in an abnormal state, supply the appropriate stimulus unmixed with others, and watch the result. If it is desired to study the process by which an animal learns to adapt itself to a new situation, one must, of course, make sure in addition that the situation really is new to the animal, and yet that it makes sufficient appeal to some instinctive tendency to supply a motive for the learning process.

As one might expect, among the earliest experiments upon animals were those made by physiologists with a view to determining the functions of sense organs. The experimental movement in psychology was slow in extending itself into the field of the animal mind.

Romanes, whose adherence to the anecdotal method we have noted, made in 1881, rather as a physiologist than as a psychologist, a number of exact and highly valued experiments on cœlenterates and echinoderms, which were summarized in his book entitled " Jelly-fish, Star-fish, and Sea-urchins," published in 1885. He has also recorded some rather informal experiments on the keenness of smell in dogs. Sir John Lubbock, in 1883, reported the results of some experiments on the color sense of the small crustacean Daphnia, and his book on "Ants, Bees, and Wasps," containing an account of experimental tests of the senses and "intelligence" of these insects, appeared in the same year. A German entomologist, Vitus Graber, experimented very extensively at about this period on the senses of sight and smell in many animals. Preyer, the authority on child psychology, published in 1886 an experimental study of the behavior of the starfish. Loeb's work on the reactions of animals to stimulation began to appear in 1888. Bethe's experiments on ants and bees were published in 1898. Max

Verworn, the physiologist, published in 1899 an exhaustive experimental study of the behavior of single-celled animals. With the exception of Preyer and Romanes, all these men had but a secondary interest in comparative psychology: Bethe, indeed, as we shall see, wholly rejects it. Lloyd Morgan, who has written instructively on comparative psychology, makes but a limited use of the experimental method. Wesley Mills, professor of physiology in McGill University, has studied very carefully the mental development of young animals such as cats and dogs, but is inclined to criticise the use of experiment in observing animals. The work of E. L. Thorndike, whose "Animal Intelligence" appeared in 1898, represents, perhaps, the first definite effect of the modern experimental movement in psychology upon the study of the animal mind. Thorndike's aim in this research was to place his animals (chicks, cats, and dogs) under the most rigidly controlled experimental conditions. The cats and dogs, reduced by fasting to a state of "utter hunger," were placed in boxes, with food outside, and the process whereby they learned to work the various mechanisms which let them out was carefully observed. Since the appearance of Thorndike's work the performance of experiments upon animals has played much part in the work of psychological laboratories, particularly those of Harvard, Clark, and Chicago universities. The biologists and physiologists have continued their researches by this method, so that a very large amount of experimental work is now being done in comparative psychology.

Despite the obvious advantages of experiment as a method for the study of animal behavior, it is not without its dangers. These were clearly stated by Wesley Mills in a criticism of Thorndike's "Animal Intelligence" (273). They may be summed up by saying that there is a risk of placing the animal experimented upon under abnormal conditions in the attempt to make them definite and controllable.[1] Did not, for example, the extreme hunger to which Thorndike's cats and dogs were reduced, while it simplified the conditions in one sense by making the strength of the motive to escape as nearly as possible equal for all the animals, complicate matters in another sense by diminishing their capacity to learn? Were the animals perhaps frightened and distracted by the unusual character of their surroundings? Thorndike thinks not (396); but whether or no he succeeded in averting these dangers, it is clear that they are real. It is also obvious that they are the more threatening, the higher the animal with which one has to deal. Fright, bewilderment, loneliness, are conditions more apt to be met with among the higher vertebrates than lower down in the scale, and the utmost care should be taken to make sure that animals likely to be affected by them are thoroughly trained and at home in their surroundings before the experimenter records results.

§ 4. *Methods of Obtaining Facts: The Ideal Method.*

The ideal method for the study of a higher animal involves patient observation upon a specimen known from birth, watched in its ordinary behavior and environment, and occasionally experimented upon with proper control of the conditions and without frightening it or otherwise rendering it abnormal. The observer should acquaint himself with the individual peculiarities of each animal studied, for there is no doubt that striking differences in mental capacity occur among the individuals of a single species. At the same time that he obtains the confidence of each individual

[1] Cf. also Kline (222), and Vaschide and Rousseau (413).

animal, he should be able to hold in check the tendency to humanize it and to take a personal pleasure in its achievements if it be unusually endowed. This is, to say the least, not easy. Absolute indifference to the animals studied, if not so dangerous as doting affection, is yet to be avoided.

§ 5. *Methods of Interpreting Facts*

We may now turn from the problem of discovering the facts about animal behavior to the problem of interpreting them. If an animal behaves in a certain manner, what may we conclude the consciousness accompanying its behavior to be like? As we have seen, the interpretation is often confused with the observation, especially in the making of anecdotes; but theoretically the two problems are distinct. And at the outset of our discussion of the former, we are obliged to acknowledge that *all psychic interpretation of animal behavior must be on the analogy of human experience.* We do not know the meaning of such terms as perception, pleasure, fear, anger, visual sensation, etc., except as these processes form a part of the contents of our own minds. Whether we will or no, we must be anthropomorphic in the notions we form of what takes place in the mind of an animal. Accepting this fundamental proposition, the students of animals have yet differed widely in the conclusions they have drawn from it. Some have gone to the extreme of declaring that comparative psychology is therefore impossible. Others have joyfully hastened to make animals as human as they could. Still others have occupied an intermediate position.

Descartes and Montaigne are the two writers antedating the modern period who are most frequently quoted in this connection. The latter had evidently a natural sympathy with animals. In that most delightful twelfth chapter of the

second book of Essays, "An Apology of Raymond Sebonde,"
he gives free rein to the inclination to humanize them. I
quote Florio's translation: "The Swallowes which at the
approach of spring time we see to pry, to search and ferret
all the corners of our houses; is it without judgment they
seeke, or without discretion they chuse from out a thousand
places, that which is fittest for them, to build their nests and
lodging? . . . Would they (suppose you) first take water
and then clay, unlesse they guessed that the hardnesse of the
one is softned by the moistness of the other? . . . Why
doth the spider spin her artificiall web thicke in one place and
thin in another? And now useth one, and then another
knot, except she had an imaginary kind of deliberation, fore-
thought, and conclusion?" To ascribe such behavior to the
working of mere instinct, "with a kinde of unknowne,
naturall and servile inclination," is unreasonable. "The
Fox, which the inhabitants of Thrace use " to test the ice on a
river before crossing, which listens to the roaring of the water
underneath and so judges whether the ice is safe or not;
"might not we lawfully judge that the same discourse pos-
sesseth her head as in like case it would ours? And that it is
a kinde of debating reason and consequence, drawne from
natural sense? 'Whatsoever maketh a noyse moveth,
whatsoever moveth, is not frozen, whatsoever is not frozen,
is liquid; whatsoever is liquid, yeelds under any weight?'"
(277).

Descartes, on the other hand, writing some sixty years
later, takes, as is well known, the opposite ground. He
says in a letter to the Marquis of Newcastle, "As for the understanding or thought attributed by Montaigne and others to
brutes, I cannot hold their opinion." While animals surpass
us in certain actions, it is, he holds, only in those "which
are not directed by thought. . . . They act by force of

nature and by springs, like a clock, which tells better what the hour is than our judgment can inform us. And doubtless when swallows come in the spring, they act in that like clocks. All that honey bees do is of the same nature " (99, pp. 281–283). The statement of Descartes, contained in the letter to Mersenne of July 30, 1640, that animals are automata, is often misunderstood. Descartes does not assert that animals are unconscious in the sense which that term would carry to-day, but only that they are without thought. Sensations, feelings, passions, he is willing to ascribe to them, in so far as these do not involve thought. "It must however be observed that I speak of thought, not of life, nor of sensation," he says in the letter to Henry More, 1649; "I do not refuse to them feeling . . . in so far as it depends only on the bodily organs " (99, p. 287). In this he does not go so far as some modern writers, who decline to assert the presence of any psychic process in the lower forms of animal life.

Turning to recent times, we find arguments very like those of Montaigne used by the earlier evolutionary writers. Darwin, for instance, says in "The Descent of Man," "As dogs, cats, horses, and probably all the higher animals, even birds, have vivid dreams, and this is shown by their movements and the sounds uttered, we must admit that they possess some power of imagination" (89, p. 74). "Even brute beasts," says Montaigne, ". . . are seen to be subject to the power of imagination; witnesse some Dogs . . . whom we ordinarily see to startle and barke in their sleep" (277, Bk. I, ch. 20). "Only a few persons," Darwin continues, "now dispute that animals possess some power of reasoning. Animals may constantly be seen to pause, deliberate, and resolve." And he states that his object in the third chapter of the work quoted is "to show that there is no fundamental difference between man and the higher mammals in their mental faculties" (89, p. 66). Romanes is evidently guided by the same desire to humanize animals.

Now these writers were not led to take such an attitude merely out of general sympathy with the brute creation, like Montaigne; they had an ulterior motive; namely, to meet the objection raised in their time against the doctrine of evolution, based on the supposed fact of a great mental and moral gulf between man and the lower animals. They wished to show, as Darwin clearly states, that this gulf is not absolute but may conceivably have been bridged by intermediate stages of mental and moral development. While this argument against evolution was being pressed, the evolutionary writers were very unsafe guides in the field of animal psychology, for they distinctly "held a brief for animal intelligence," to use Thorndike's phrase. In more recent times interest in both the positive and the negative sides of the objection drawn from man's superiority has died out, and such special pleading has become unnecessary.

On the other hand, the fact that the greater part of the experiments on animals were until the last ten or fifteen years performed by physiologists has given rise to an opposite tendency in interpreting the animal mind: the tendency to make purely biological concepts suffice as far as possible for the explanation of animal behavior and to assume the presence even of consciousness in animals only when it is absolutely necessary to do so. Loeb in 1890 suggested the theory which he has since elaborated, that the responses of animals to stimulation, instead of being signs of "sensation," are in every way analogous to the reactions of plants to such forces as light and gravity; hence unconscious "tropisms" (235). Bethe in 1898 attempted to explain all the complicated behavior of ants and bees, which the humanizing writers had compared with our own civilization, as a result of reflex responses, chiefly to chemical stimulation, unaccompanied by any consciousness whatever (30). This revival, in an altered form, of the Cartesian doctrine has met with energetic opposition, especially from writers having philosophical interests. At the present time the parties in the controversy may be divided into three groups: those who believe that consciousness should be ascribed to all animals; those who hold that it should be ascribed only to those animals whose behavior presents certain peculiarities regarded as evidence of mind; and those who hold that we have no trustworthy evidence of mind in any animal, and should therefore abandon comparative psychology and use only physiological terms.

To the first group belong, among others, the French writer Claparède, the Swiss naturalist Forel, and the Jesuit Wasmann. The physiologist W. A. Nagel also takes a friendly attitude toward the animal mind. In the second group may be classed Loeb and H. Jordan. In the third belong the physiologists Beer, Bethe, H. E. Ziegler, von Uexküll, and J. P. Nuel.

Claparède, Forel, and Wasmann maintain the existence of consciousness in animals from widely different philosophical points of view. The first-named is what is called a parallelist; that is, he believes that mental processes and bodily processes are not causally related, but form two parallel and non-interfering series of events. In the study of animals, both the physical and the psychical series should, he thinks, be investigated. Biology should use two parallel methods: the one ascending, attempting to explain animal behavior by physical and chemical laws; the other descending, giving an account of the mental processes of animals. Ultimately, it may be hoped, according to Claparède, that both methods will be applied throughout the whole range of animal life. At present the ascending method is most successful with the lowest forms, the descending method with the highest forms. We cannot afford to abandon the psychological study of animals, for our knowledge of the nervous processes underlying the higher mental activities is very slight; physiology here fails us, and psychology must be left in command of the field. The danger besetting the attempt at a purely physical explanation of animal behavior is that the facts shall be unduly simplified to fit the theory. Thus Bethe's effort at explaining the way in which bees find their way back to the hive as a reflex response, or tropism, produced by "an unknown force," is highly questionable; the facts seem to point toward the exercise of some sort of memory by the bees. It is always possible, further, that the tropism is accompanied by consciousness. A physiologist from Saturn might reduce all human activities to tropisms, says Claparède in a striking passage. "The youth who feels himself drawn to medical studies, or he who is attracted to botany, can no more account for his profoundest aspirations than the beetle which runs to the odor of a dead animal or the butterfly invited by the flowers; and if the first shows a certain feeling corresponding to these secret states of the organism (a feeling of 'predilection' for such a career, etc.), how can we dare to deny to the second analogous states of consciousness?" (75). If it is argued that we have no direct, but only an inferential, knowledge of the processes in an animal's mind, the argument is equally valid against human psychology, for the psychologist has only an inferential knowledge of his neighbor's mind (77).

Wasmann defends the animal mind from a different point of view. For one thing, he believes that mental processes may act causally upon bodily states. He accepts, in other words, what is called interactionism, as opposed to parallelism. Further, although he strongly opposes the doctrine that the reactions of animals are unconscious tropisms, and constantly emphasizes their variability and modifiability through experience, he nevertheless believes that a gulf separates the human from the animal mind. The term "intelligence" which most writers use to designate merely the power of learning by individual experience, Wasmann would reserve for the power of deducing and understanding relations, and would assign only to human beings (425, 426). Although animals have their instincts modified by sense experience, man "stands through his reason and freedom immeasurably high above the irrational animal that follows, and must follow, its sensuous impulse without deliberation" (425).

Forel, in the third place, is what is called a monist in metaphysics. That is, he does not believe either that mind and body are parallel, or that they interact causally, but that they are two aspects of the same reality. "Every psychic phenomenon is the same real thing as the molecular or neurocymic activity of the brain-cortex coinciding with it" (132, p. 7). The psychic and the physical, on this theory, should be coextensive; not merely should consciousness in some form belong to all living things, but every atom of matter should have its psychic aspect. On such a basis, Forel takes highly optimistic views of the animal mind. In insects, of which he has made a special study, it is, he thinks, "possible to demonstrate the existence of memory, associations of sensory images, perceptions, attention, habits, simple powers of inference from analogy, the utilization of individual experience, and hence distinct, though feeble, plastic individual deliberations or adaptations" (132, p. 36).

The second of the three groups into which we divided present-day writers on the interpretation of animal behavior contains those who maintain not that all animals are conscious, but that those whose behavior meets a certain standard may be so considered. The nature of this test is a difficult problem. We shall therefore devote the next chapter to its consideration; and as it necessarily plays an important part in determining views regarding the animal mind, we shall postpone for the present the discussion of the second group.

The third group contains those biologists, conservative or radical according to one's own position, who deny to comparative psychology the right to exist. The eminent neurologist Bethe is a typical representative of the class. In his study of the behavior of ants and bees he refuses to allow these animals any "psychic qualities" whatever, and suggests the term "chemo-reception" instead of "smell," to designate the influence which directs most of their reactions, — "smell" implying a psychic quality (30). From his argument for the probable absence of consciousness in ants and bees, as well as in the crab (28), one might be inclined to put Bethe in the second of the above-mentioned classes, for it is the lack of one definite characteristic in the behavior of these animals, namely, modification by individual experience, that makes him think them unconscious. It becomes clear from other passages in his writings, however, that he considers the presence of consciousness even in animals that can learn by experience, a highly problematical and improper assumption. In a footnote to a later article he says: "Psychic qualities cannot be demonstrated. Even what we call sensation is known to each man only in himself, since it is something subjective. We possess the capacity of modifying our behavior [*i.e.* of learning], and every one knows from his own experience that psychic qualities play a part connected with this modifying process. Every statement that another being possesses psychic qualities is a conclusion from analogy, not a certainty; it is a matter of faith. If one wishes to draw this analogical inference, it should be made where the capacity for modification can be shown. When this is lacking, there is not the slightest scientific justification for assuming psychic qualities. They *may* exist, but there is no probability of it, and hence science should deny them. Hence if one ventures to speak of a Psyche in animals at all, one should give the preference to those which can modify their behavior" (29). But that Bethe himself prefers not to make the venture is evident from statements in the text of the same article. The psychic or subjective, he says, is unknowable, and the only thing we may hope to know anything about is the chemical and physiological processes involved. "These chemo-physical processes and their consequences, that is, the objective aspect of psychic phenomena, and these alone, should be the object of scientific investigation" (29).

Together with Beer and von Uexküll, Bethe shortly afterward published "Proposals for an Objectifying Nomenclature in the Physiology of the Nervous System." The main purpose of this paper was to suggest that all terms having a psychological implication, such as sight, smell, sense-organ, memory, learning, and the like, be carefully excluded from discussions of animal reactions to stimulation and animal behavior generally. In their stead the authors propose such expressions as the following: for responses to stimulation where no nervous system exists, the term *antitypes;* for those involving a nervous system, *antikineses;* the latter are divided into *reflexes,* where the response is uniform, and *antiklises,* where the response is modifiable. A sense-organ becomes a *reception-organ,* sensory nerves are *receptory-nerves,* and we have *phono-reception, stibo-reception, photo-reception,* instead of hearing, smell, and sight. The after-effect of a stimulus upon later ones is the *resonance* of the stimulus (20).

This attempt at an objective terminology meets the cordial approval of H. E. Ziegler and J. P. Nuel. The former declares that the concept of consciousness is worthless in the study of animals, as no one knows whether an animal is conscious or not. He suggests as additions to the new vocabulary the term *pleronomic* to designate inherited reactions, and *enbiontic* to signify acquired reactions (476). Nuel also thinks that our ignorance of the mental states of animals renders comparative psychology unscientific. He prefers the "kinetic" to the psychic point of view; a sense-organ, in man or beast, is an apparatus for reactions (297). In a book on vision Nuel has suggested an objective terminology of his own, where "ikonoreaction," for example, takes the place of sight (296).[1]

It would seem that no serious objection could be raised against the use of a purely objective nomenclature in physiology, and that confusion might thereby be avoided, without prejudicing the case of comparative psychology, which might exist side by side with the other science, and reserve the terms with psychic implications for itself. Wasmann, it is true, objects to the new terminology on its own account, as cumbrous and scholastic, and says that if Ziegler cannot use such words as sensation, perception, seeing, and the like, without anthropomorphism, the fault is his own, and the fact should not lead him to impose a new set of words on others (428). These criticisms, however, are those of the conservative who objects to anything new; all technical vocabularies are pedantic, but it is impossible to take too many precautions against confusion of ideas.

What attitude, now, shall we assume upon the broader question raised by these writers, as to whether comparative psychology is possible at all? Must we accept the statement

[1] Another instance of an attempt to use terminology without psychic implications is to be found in R. Semon's "Die Mneme als erhaltendes Princip im Wechsel des organischen Geschehens" (379).

that no knowledge whatever of the animal mind is obtainable? If so, we must also admit that human psychology is impossible. Our acquaintance with the mind of animals rests upon the same basis as our acquaintance with the mind of our fellow-man; both are derived by inference from observed behavior. The actions of our fellow-men resemble our own, and we therefore infer in them like subjective states to ours: the actions of animals resemble ours less completely, but the difference is one of degree, not of kind. This argument in behalf of comparative psychology, which is brought forward by Claparède (77), is opposed by Nuel with the denial that human and animal psychology rest upon the same basis (297); but no cogent proofs accompany Nuel's statement. The physiologists would doubtless accept the other horn of the dilemma, and reject human psychology along with animal psychology; but a scientific rigor which requires of us to abandon the assertion of mind in our fellow-beings and the study of that mind has pushed itself to absurdity. As Jordan says, inferences upon a basis of probability form a legitimate part of science (216). The mental processes in other minds, animal or human, cannot indeed be objectively ascertained facts; the facts are those of human and animal behavior; but the mental processes are as justifiable inferences as any others with which science deals. The prime necessity is merely that they shall be properly guarded. Certain precautions are necessary when we infer the state of our neighbor's mind; certain added precautions are necessary when we infer states in the mind of an animal, and our assertions should certainly diminish in dogmatism. As we go down the scale of animal life. But the psychologist, to whom, as Titchener has put it, "the facts and laws of mind are the most real things that the world can show" (400), will never consent to abandon the effort to probe the mysteries of other minds, human or animal, until science consents to abandon all hypotheses and inferences based on anything short of perfect identity between instances.

Is it possible to state briefly the special precautions that must be observed in interpreting animal behavior as accompanied by consciousness, granted that such interpretation is admissible? Jordan, while holding that the existence of the animal mind may fairly be inferred under certain circumstances, holds that we are not justified in inferring the actual *quality* of mental processes in animals. For this reason he objects to the term "comparative psychology" (216). There is no doubt that great caution should be used in regarding the quality of a human conscious process as identical with the quality of the corresponding process in the animal mind. For example, we might say with a fair degree of assurance that an animal consciously discriminates between light and darkness; that is, receives conscious impressions of different quality from the two, yet the mental impression produced by white light upon the animal may be very different from the sensation of white as we know it, and the impression produced by the absence of light very different from our sensation of black. Black and white may, for all we know, depend for their quality upon some substance existing only in the human retina.

A second precaution concerns the simplicity or complexity of the interpretation put upon animal behavior. Lloyd Morgan, in his "Introduction to Comparative Psychology," formulated a conservative principle of interpretation which has often been quoted as "Lloyd Morgan's Canon." The principle is as follows: "In no case may we interpret an action as the outcome of the exercise of a higher psychical faculty, if it can be interpreted as the outcome of the exercise of one which stands lower in the psychological scale" (280, p. 53).

In other words, when in doubt take the simpler interpretation. For example, a dog detected in a theft cowers and whines. One possible mental accompaniment of this behavior is remorse; the dog is conscious that he has fallen below a moral standard, and grieved or offended his master. A second is the anticipation of punishment; the dog has a mental representation of the consequences of his action upon former occasions, and imagining himself likely to experience them anew, is terrified at the prospect. A third possibility is that the dog's previous experience of punishment, instead of being revived in the form of definite images, makes itself effective merely in his feelings and behavior; he is uncomfortable and frightened, he knows not definitely why. It is evident that these three possibilities represent three different grades of complexity of mental process, the first being by far the highest. Lloyd Morgan's canon enjoins upon us in such a case to prefer the third alternative, provided that it will really account for the dog's behavior.

Now why should the simplest interpretation be preferred? We must not forget that the more complex ones remain in the field of possibility. Positive assertions have no place in comparative psychology. We cannot say that the simplicity of an hypothesis is sufficient warrant of its truth, for nature does not always proceed by the paths which seem to us least complicated. The fact is that Lloyd Morgan's principle serves to counterbalance our most important source of error in interpreting animal behavior. It is like tipping a boat in one direction to compensate for the fact that some one is pulling the opposite gunwale. We must interpret the animal mind humanly if we are to interpret it at all. Yet we know that it differs from the human mind, and that the difference is partly a matter of complexity. Let us therefore take the least complex interpretation that the facts of animal behavior will admit, always remembering that we may be wrong in so doing, but resting assured that we are, upon the whole, on the safer side. The social consciousness of man is very strong, and his tendency to think of other creatures, even of inanimate nature, as sharing his own thoughts and feelings, has shown itself in his past to be almost irresistible. Lloyd Morgan's canon offers the best safeguard against this natural inclination, short of abandoning all attempt to study the mental life of the lower animals.

CHAPTER II

THE EVIDENCE OF MIND

§ 6. *Inferring Mind from Behavior*

IN the last chapter we saw that some recent writers upon animal behavior and its interpretation, while refusing to admit the presence of consciousness in all forms of animal life, yet hold that it can be proved to exist in certain forms. The latter, it is maintained, display certain peculiarities of behavior that may be regarded as proofs of a psychic accompaniment. Into the nature of these proofs we may now inquire.

To begin with, can it be said that when an animal makes a movement in response to a certain stimulus, there is an accompanying consciousness of the stimulus, and that when it fails to move, there is no consciousness? Is *response to stimulation* evidence of consciousness? In the case of man, we know that absence of visible response does not prove that the stimulus has not been sensed; while it is probable that some effect upon motor channels always occurs when consciousness accompanies stimulation, the effect may not be apparent to an outside observer. On the other hand, if movement in response to the impact of a physical force is evidence of consciousness, then the ball which falls under the influence of gravity and rebounds on striking the floor is conscious. Nor is the case improved if we point out that the movements which animals make in response to stimulation are not the equivalent in energy of the stimulus applied, but involve the setting free of energy stored in the animal as well. True, when a microscopic animal meets an obstacle in its swimming, and darts backward, the movement is not a mere rebound; it implies energy contributed by the animal's own body. But just so an explosion of gunpowder is not the equivalent in energy of the heat of the match, the stimulus. Similarly it is possible to think of the response made by animals to external stimuli as involving nothing more than certain physical and chemical processes identical with those existing in inanimate nature.

If we find that the movements made by an animal as a result of external stimulation regularly involve withdrawal from certain stimuli and acceptance of others, it is natural to use the term " *choice* " in describing such behavior. But if consciousness is supposed to accompany the exercise of choice in this sense, then consciousness must be assumed to accompany the behavior of atoms in chemical combinations. When hydrochloric acid is added to a solution of silver nitrate, the atoms of chlorine and those of silver find each other by an unerring "instinct" and combine into the white precipitate of silver chloride, while the hydrogen and the nitric acid similarly "choose" each other. Nor can the fact that behavior in animals is adapted to an end be used as evidence of mind; for "purposive" reactions, which contribute to the welfare of an organism, are themselves selective. The search for food, the care for the young, and the complex activities which further welfare, are made up of reactions involving "choice" between stimuli; and if the simple "choice" reaction is on a par with the behavior of chemical atoms, so far as proof of consciousness goes, then *adaptation to an end,* apparent purposiveness, is in a similar position.

Thus the mere fact that an animal reacts to stimulation, even selectively and for its own best interests, offers no evidence for the existence of mind that does not apply equally well to particles of inanimate matter. Moreover, there is some ground for holding that the reactions of the lowest animals are unconscious. This ground consists in the apparent lack of variability which characterizes such reactions. In our own case, we know that certain bodily movements, those of digestion and circulation, for example, are normally carried on without accompanying consciousness, and that in other cases where there is consciousness of the stimulus, as in the reflex knee-jerk, it occurs after the movement is initiated, so that the nervous process underlying the sensation would seem to be immaterial to the performance of the movement. These unconscious reactions in human beings are characterized by their relative uniformity, by the absence of variation in their performance. Moreover, when an action originally accompanied by consciousness is often repeated, it tends, by what is apparently one and the same process, to become unconscious and to become uniform. There is consequently reason for believing that when the behavior of lower animals displays perfect uniformity, consciousness is not present. On the other hand, an important reservation must be made in the use of this negative test. It is by no means easy to be sure that an animal's reactions are uniform. The more carefully the complexer ones are studied, the more are variability and difference brought to light where superficial observation had revealed a mechanical and automatic regularity. It is quite possible that even in the simple, apparently fixed response of microscopic animals to stimulation, better facilities for observation might show variations that do not now appear.

This matter of uniformity *versus* variability suggests a further step in our search for a satisfactory test of the presence of mind. Is mere *variability* in behavior, mere irregularity in response, to be taken as such a test? Not if we argue from our own experience. While that portion of our own behavior which involves consciousness shows more irregularity than the portion which does not, yet the causes of the irregularity are often clearly to be found in physiological conditions with which consciousness has nothing to do. There are days when we can think clearly and recall easily, and days when obscurities refuse to vanish and the right word refuses to come; days when we are irritable and days when we are sluggish. Yet since we can find nothing in our mental processes to account for this variability, it would be absurd to take analogous fluctuations in animal behavior as evidence of mind. So complicated a machine as an animal organism, even if it be nothing more than a machine, must show irregularities in its working.

Behavior, then, must be variable, but not merely variable, to give evidence of mind. The criterion most frequently applied to determine the presence or absence of the psychic is *a variation in behavior that shows definitely the result of previous individual experience.* "Does the organism," says Romanes, "learn to make new adjustments, or to modify old ones, in accordance with the results of its own individual experience?" (364, p. 4). Loeb declares that "the fundamental process which occurs in all psychic phenomena as the elemental component" is "the activity of the associative memory, or of association," and defines associative memory as "that mechanism by which a stimulus brings about not only the effects which its nature and the specific structure of the irritable organ call for, but by which it brings about also the effects of other stimuli which formerly acted upon the organism almost or quite simultaneously with the stimulus in question." "If an animal can be trained," he continues, "if it can learn, it possesses associative memory," and therefore mind (243, p. 12). The psychologist finds the term "associative memory" hardly satisfactory, and objects to the confusion between mental and physical concepts which renders it possible to speak of a "mechanism" as forming an "elemental component" in "psychic phenomena," but these points may be passed over. The power to learn by individual experience is the evidence which Romanes, Morgan, and Loeb will accept as demonstrating the presence of mind in an animal.

Does the absence of proof that an animal learns by experience show that the animal is unconscious? Romanes is careful to answer this question in the negative. "Because a lowly organized animal," he says, "does *not* learn by its own individual experience, we may not therefore conclude that in performing its natural or ancestral adaptations to appropriate stimuli, consciousness, or the mind element, is wholly absent; we can only say that this element, if present, reveals no evidence of the fact " (364, p. 3). Loeb, on the other hand, writes as if absence of proof for consciousness amounted to disproof, evidently relying on the principle of parsimony, that no unnecessary assumptions should be admitted. "Our criterion," he remarks, "puts an end to the metaphysical ideas that all matter, and hence the whole animal world, possesses consciousness" (243, p. 13). If learning by experience be really a satisfactory proof of mind, then its absence in certain animals would indeed prevent the positive assertion that all animals are conscious; but it could not abolish the possibility that they might be. Such a possibility might, however, be of no more scientific interest than any one of a million wild possibilities that science cannot spare time to disprove. But we shall find that learning by experience, taken by itself, is too indefinite a concept to be of much service, and that when defined, it is inadequate to bear the whole weight of proving consciousness in animals. Such being the case, the possibility that animals which have not been shown to learn may yet be conscious acquires the right to be reckoned with.

The first point that strikes us in examining the proposed

test is that the learning by experience must not be too slow, or we can find parallels for it in the inanimate world. An animal may be said to have learned by experience if it behaves differently to a stimulus because of preceding stimuli. But it is one thing to have behavior altered by a single preceding stimulus, and another to have it altered by two hundred repetitions of a stimulus. The wood of a violin reacts differently to the vibrations of the strings after it has "experienced" them for ten years; the molecules of the wood have gradually taken on an altered arrangement. A steel rail reacts differently to the pounding of wheels after that process has been long continued; it may snap under the strain. Shall we say that the violin and the rail have learned by individual experience? If the obvious retort be made that it is only in living creatures that learning by experience should be taken as evidence of mind, let us take an example from living creatures. When a blacksmith has been practising his trade for a year, the reactions of his muscles are different from what they were at the outset. But this difference is not merely a matter of more accurate sense-discrimination, a better "placing" of attention and the like; there have been going on within the structure of his muscles changes which have increased their efficiency, and with which consciousness has had nothing to do. These changes have been extremely slow compared to the learning which does involve consciousness. In one or two lessons the apprentice learned what he was to do; but only very gradually have his muscles acquired the strength to do it as it should be done. Now among the lower animal forms we sometimes meet with learning by experience that is very slow; that requires a hundred or more repetitions of the stimulus before the new reaction is acquired. In such a case we can find analogical reasons for suspecting that a gradual change in the tissues of the body has taken place, of the sort which, like the attuning of the violin wood or the slow development of a muscle, have no conscious accompaniment.

We must then ask the question: *What kind of learning by experience never,* so far as we know, *occurs unconsciously?* Suppose a human being shut up in a room from which he can escape only by working a combination lock. As we shall see later, this is one of the methods by which the learning power of animals has been tested. The man, after prolonged investigation, hits upon the right combination and gets out. Suppose that he later finds himself again in the same predicament, and that without hesitation or fumbling he opens the lock at once, and performs the feat again and again, to show that it was not a lucky accident. But one interpretation of such behavior is possible. We know from our own experience that the man could not have worked the lock the second time he saw it, unless he consciously remembered the movements he made the first time; that is, unless he had in mind some kind of idea as a guide. Here, at least, there can have been no change in the structure of the muscles, for such changes are gradual; the change must have taken place in the most easily alterable portion of the organism, the nervous system; and further, it must have taken place in the most unstable and variable part of the nervous system, the higher cortical centres whose activity is accompanied by consciousness. In other words, we may be practically assured that consciousness accompanies learning only when the learning is so rapid as to show that the effects of previous experience are recalled in the guise of an idea or mental image of some sort. But does even the most rapid learning possible assure us of the presence of an idea in the mind of a lower animal? Where the motive, the beneficial or harmful consequence of action, is very strong, may not a single experience suffice to modify action without being revived in idea? Moreover,

D

animals as high in the scale as dogs and cats learn to solve problems analogous to that of the combination lock so slowly that we cannot infer the presence of ideas. Are we then to conclude that these animals are unconscious, or that there is absolutely no reason for supposing them possessed of consciousness? Yerkes has criticised the "learning by experience" criterion by pointing out that "no organism . . . has thus far been proved incapable of profiting by experience." It is a question rather of the rapidity and of the kind of learning involved. "The fact that the crayfish needs a hundred or more experiences for the learning of a type of reaction that the frog would learn with twenty experiences, the dog with five, say, and the human subject with perhaps a single experience, is indicative of the fundamental difficulty in the use of this sign" (463). Nagel has pointed out that Loeb, in asserting "associative memory" as the criterion of consciousness, offers no evidence for his statement (294). The fact is that while proof of the existence of mind can be derived from animal learning by experience only if the learning is very rapid, other evidence, equally valid on the principle of analogy, makes it *highly improbable that all animals which learn too slowly to evince the presence of ideas are therefore unconscious.* This evidence is of a *morphological* character.

§ 7. *Inferring Mind from Structure*

Both Yerkes and Lukas urge that the resemblance of an animal's nervous system and sense-organs to those of human beings ought to be taken into consideration in deciding whether the animal is conscious or not. Lukas suggests that the criteria of consciousness should be grouped under three heads: morphological, including the structure of the brain and sense-organs, physiological, and teleological. Under the second rubric he maintains that "individual purposiveness" is characteristic of the movements from which consciousness may be inferred; that individual purposiveness pertains only to voluntary acts, and that voluntary acts are acts "which are preceded by the intention to perform a definite movement, hence by the idea of this movement." We have reached the same conclusion in the preceding paragraph. The third test of the presence of consciousness, the teleological test, rests on the consideration: "What significance for the organism may be possessed by the production of a conscious effect by certain stimuli?" (252). This test, however, being of a purely *a priori* character, would seem to be distinctly less valuable than the others.

Yerkes proposes "the following six criteria in what seems to me in general the order of increasing importance. The functional signs are of greater value as a rule than the structural; and within each of the categories the particular sign is usually of more value than the general. In certain cases, however, it might be maintained that neural specialization is of greater importance than modifiability.

    I. Structural Criteria.
        1. General form of organism (Organization).
        2. Nervous system (Neural organization).
        3. Specialization in the nervous system (Neural specialization).
    II. Functional Criteria.
        1. General form of reaction (Discrimination).
        2. Modifiability of reaction (Docility).
        3. Variability of reaction (Initiative)" (463).

The terms "discrimination," "docility," and "initiative" in this connection are borrowed from Royce's "Outlines of Psychology" (372).

If resemblance of nervous and sense-organ structure to the

human type is to be taken along with rapid learning as co-ordinate evidence of consciousness, it is clear that here also we have to deal with a matter of degree. The structure of the lower animals differs increasingly from our own as we go down the scale. At what degree of difference shall we draw the line and say that the animals above it may be conscious, but that those below it cannot be? No one could possibly establish such a line. The truth of the whole matter seems to be this: *We can say neither what amount of resemblance in structure to human beings, nor what speed of learning, consti-tutes a definite mark distinguishing animals with minds from those without minds, unless we are prepared to assert that only animals which learn so fast that they must have memory ideas possess mind at all.* And this would conflict with the argu-ment from structure. For example, there is no good experi-mental evidence that cats possess ideas, yet there is enough analogy between their nervous systems and our own to make it improbable that consciousness, so complex and highly developed in us, is in them wholly lacking. We know not where consciousness begins in the animal world. We know where it surely resides — in ourselves; we know where it exists beyond a reasonable doubt — in those animals of structure resembling ours which rapidly adapt themselves to the lessons of experience. Beyond this point, for all we know, it may exist in simpler and simpler forms until we reach the very lowest of living beings.

CHAPTER III

The Mind of the Simplest Animals

§ 8. *The Structure and Behavior of Amœba*

WE have seen in the last chapter that no one can prove the absence of consciousness in even the simplest forms of living beings. It is therefore perfectly allowable to speculate as to what may be the nature of such consciousness, provided that the primitive organisms concerned possess it. Perfectly allowable, yet also perfectly useless, many authorities would argue; the remoteness of the creatures from ourselves in structure and behavior renders theorizing about their conscious experience, which is probably non-existent and certainly unimaginable in any definite terms by us, the idlest form of mental exercise.

Undeniably the formation of a positive notion regarding the character and content of psychic states in the mind, say of an Amœba, is next door to an impossibility. Yet it may not be wholly a waste of time if we spend a few pages in the attempt to discover *wherein the simplest type of mind, supposing it to be that belonging to the simplest type of animal, necessarily differs from our own.* Some light, perhaps, may be cast upon the growth of mental life in complexity if we try to make clear to ourselves what primitive consciousness is not, though we may not be able to find in our own experience any elements that shall properly represent what it is.

The first need is evidently information about the structure and the behavior of a primitive animal. For this purpose the

Amœba presents itself as a good subject. Structurally, it consists of a single cell, as do all the Protozoa, the lowest group
of animals; it is so small that it can be studied only through
the microscope; its form, at least that of *Amœba proteus*, the
most typical species, is irregular and constantly changing in
locomotion or in response to stimulation. While the internal
substance of its body shows a certain amount of differentiation,
there is no trace whatever of special modifications that might
be supposed to serve for the conduction of stimuli to different
parts of the body, and thus represent the prototype of a nervous system. Nor have any structures been found that could
conceivably be used for the special reception of stimuli; that
is, there are no sense organs. So far as the anatomy of the
animal is concerned, then, it differs so widely from our own
that we could only conclude from it the absence of all those
features which our conscious experience involves.

Turning from structure to behavior, we find the external
activities of Amœba, that is, those not confined to the inner
processes of its cell body, to be superficially, at least, divisible
into two classes: movements of locomotion and responses to
stimulation. Amœba, though a water-dwelling animal, is
not a free-swimming one, but moves by crawling on a solid
body. This method of locomotion involves in *Amœba proteus*
changes of form on the animal's part, projections, called pseudopodia, being sent out in advance of the movement of the
whole body. The protoplasm of the body shows in this process certain flowing movements which are differently described
by different observers, and doubtless vary in different species:
thus Rhumbler finds that the protoplasmic currents move
backward along the sides of the animal and forward through
the middle in a way quite comparable to the behavior of currents in a drop of any fluid where the tension of the surface
is diminished in front, *i.e.*, at the point toward which the drop,

in consequence of the diminished tension there, rolls. Such movements, Rhumbler shows, can be reproduced by placing, say, a drop of clove oil under the proper conditions of surface tension (361, 362). Jennings, on the other hand, has observed, at least in certain species of Amœba, that the protoplasmic currents are all forward in direction, the movement being really one of rolling, complicated by the attachment of the lower part of the body to the solid object on which the animal crawls. Mechanical conditions of surface tension would not account for such currents (204, 206, 211). Dellinger, finally, rejects both the surface tension and the "rolling" theories, and from a study of side views of the moving Amœba concludes that progression occurs through the advancement of the front end freely through the water and its subsequent attachment, the rest of the body following through active contraction brought about by a contractile substance (98). The problem is of great interest to the student of vital phenomena, but its bearing on the question of mind in the Amœba is so obscure that we need not consider it further, but may pass at once to the study of the animal's reactions to special stimulation.

These are, according to Jennings (206, 211), the foremost authority on the behavior of the lowest organisms, three in number; namely, the negative, the positive, and the food-taking reactions. First, if an Amœba comes into strong contact with a solid obstacle in its movements, or if a solution of different composition from the water in which it lives strikes against it, or if one side of it is heated, the animal responds by contracting the part stimulated, releasing it from the substratum, and moving in another direction, usually one forming only a small angle with the preceding one. If the whole of one side or end receives a strong stimulus, if light falls on one side, or an electric current is passed through the water, the side stimulated — in the case of the electric current, the side toward the positive pole — contracts as a whole, and the movement takes place in the opposite direction. These phenomena constitute the *negative* reaction (Fig. 1).

Secondly, the reaction to solid bodies sometimes takes a *positive* form. In this case a pseudopodium is pushed forward in the direction of the stimulus, and the animal moves toward the solid. As the negative reaction serves the purpose of avoiding obstacles, so the positive reaction is useful in securing contact with a support on which to creep, and with food. It seems to be given in response to weak mechanical stimuli, stronger ones producing the negative reaction. No chemicals have been found to occasion it, but weak chemical stimulation very likely coöperates with mechanical stimulation when the positive reaction is given to food.

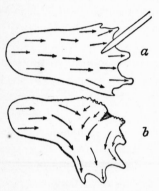

FIG. 1. — Negative reaction of Amœba to stimulation by a glass rod. *a*. Application of the stimulus. *b*. Change of direction of movement. After Jennings (211).

Thirdly, there is the *food-taking reaction*. This consists, for *Amœba proteus*, in the pushing forward of a pseudopodium on either side of the particle of food that has come into contact with the animal; the bending over of the ends of the pseudopodia so as to grasp the food, while "a thin sheet of protoplasm" spreads from the upper surface of the animal over it; and the final fusion of the ends of the pseudopodia and the ends of this sheet, so as to take the food directly into the animal's body. The reaction may occur anywhere on the body surface, there being no specialized mouth. It appears to be made only in response to edible substances, hence there is doubtless some chemical peculiarity about the stimulus which makes it effective (Fig. 2).

These three reactions make up, together with the ordinary crawling locomotion, the variety of the Amœba's experience as displayed in behavior, with the addition of a peculiar set of movements occurring in the *absence of all mechanical stimulation*. When an Amœba is floating in the water, through some chance, unattached to any solid, "such a condition," says

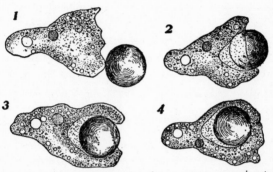

FIG. 2. — Food-taking reaction of Amœba. 1, 2, 3, 4, successive stages.
After Jennings (211).

Jennings, "is most unfavorable for its normal activities; it cannot move from place to place, and has no opportunity to obtain food." Its mode of getting out of the difficulty is to send out "long, slender pseudopodia in all directions," until "the body may become reduced to little more than a meeting point for these pseudopodia" (211, p. 8). As soon as one of these "feelers" comes in contact with a solid, it attaches itself, and the whole animal following soon takes up its normal crawling locomotion.

§ 9. *The Mind of Amœba*

Now what light does the behavior of Amœba, thus described in its various forms by Jennings, throw upon the nature of the animal's possible consciousness? The first thought which strikes us in this connection is that *the number of different sensations occurring in an Amœba's mind,* if it has one, *is very much smaller than the number forming the constituent elements of our own experience.* We human beings have the power to discriminate several thousand different qualities of color, brightness, tone, noise, temperature, pressure, pain, smell, taste, and other sensation classes. Thus the content of our consciousness is capable of a great deal of variety. It is hard to see how more than three or four qualitatively different processes can enter into the conscious experience of an Amœba. The negative reaction is given to all forms of strong stimulation alike, with the single exception of food. We shall in the following chapter discuss more fully the nature of the evidence that helps us to conjecture the existence of different sensation qualities in an animal's mind; but it is clear that where an animal so simple in its structure as the Amœba makes no difference in its reactions to various stimuli, there can be no reason for supposing that if it is conscious, it is aware of them as different. The reaction to edible substances is, however, unlike that to other stimulations. The peculiarity of edible substances which occasions this difference must be a chemical one. In our own case, the classes of sensation which result from the chemical peculiarities of food substances are smell and taste; evidently to a water-dwelling animal smell and taste would be practically indistinguishable. We may say, then, that supposing consciousness to exist in so primitive an animal as the Amœba, we have evidence for the appearance in it of a specific sensation quality representing the chemical or food sense, and standing for the whole class of sensations resulting from our own organs of smell and taste. The significance of the positive reaction is harder to determine. It seems to be given in response not to a special kind of stimulus, but to a mechanical or food stimulus of slight intensity. In our own experience, we do not have stimuli of different intensity producing sensations of different quality, except in the cases of temperature and visual sensations. We do, however, find that varying the strength of the stimulus will produce different *affective* qualities; it is a familiar fact that moderate intensities of stimulation in the human organism are accompanied by pleasantness, and stronger intensities by unpleasantness. The motor effects of pleasantness and unpleasantness in ourselves are opposite to each other in character. Pleasantness produces a tonic and expansive effect on the body, unpleasantness a depressive and contractive effect. In the Amœba, the positive and negative reactions seem to be opposed. The essential feature of the negative reaction is the checking of movement at the point stimulated; that of the positive reaction is the reaching out of the point stimulated in the direction of the stimulus. This much evidence there is for saying that besides a possible food sensation, the Amœba may have some dim awareness of affective qualities corresponding to pleasantness and unpleasantness in ourselves. It should, however, be borne in mind that wide differences must go along with the correspondence. In us, pleasantness brings a thrill, a "bodily resonance," due to its tonic effect upon the circulation, breathing, and muscles; unpleasantness has also its accompaniment of vague organic sensation, without which we can hardly conceive what it would be like. In an Amœba, it is clear that this aspect, as found in human consciousness, must be wholly lacking. Again, in the human mind pleasantness and unpleasantness are connected with various sensation qualities or complexes; we are pleased or displeased usually "at" something definite. The vagueness of the affective qualities in an Amœba's consciousness can only be remotely suggested by our own vague, diffused sense of bodily well-being or ill-being; and this is undoubtedly given its coloring in our case by the structure and functioning of our internal organs.

As for the peculiar behavior of an Amœba suspended in the water and deprived of solid support, the stimulus for this must lie within the cell body itself. If any consciousness accompanies it, then the nearest human analogy to such consciousness is to be found in organic sensations, and these, as has just been said, must necessarily be in the human mind wholly different in quality from anything to be found in an animal whose structure is as simple as the Amœba's.

A consequence of this lack of qualitative variety in the sense experiences of an Amœba is a lack of what we may call complexity of structure in that experience. The number of stimulus differences which are in the human mind represented by differences in the quality of sensations is so great that at any given moment our consciousness of the external world is analyzable into a large number of qualitatively different sensations. At the present instant the reader's consciousness "contains," apart from the revived effects of previous stimulation, many distinguishable sensation elements, visual, auditory, tactile, organic, and so on. The Amœba's consciousness, if it possesses one, must have a structure inconceivably simpler than that of any moment of our own experience.

A second point in which the mind of an Amœba must, if it exists, differ from that of a human being, consists in its *entire lack of mental imagery of any sort*. Not only has the Amœba but three or four qualitatively different elements in its experience, but none of these qualities can be remembered or revived in the absence of external stimulation. How may we be sure of this? If our primitive animal could revive its experiences in the form of memory images, it would give some evidence of the influence of memory in its behavior. Indeed, as we shall learn, it is possible, in all probability, for an animal's conduct to be influenced by its past experience even though the animal be incapable of reviving that experience in the form of a memory image. Therefore, if we find no evidence that the Amœba learns, or modifies its behavior as the result of past stimulation, we may conclude *a fortiori* that it does not have memory images.

Now it would be stating the case too strongly to say that past stimulation does not affect the behavior of Amœba at all. In the first place, this animal shows, in common with all other animals, the power of "getting used" to certain forms of stimulation, so that on long continuance they cease to provoke reaction. "Thus," Jennings says, "Amœbæ react negatively to tap water or to water from a foreign culture, but after transference to such water they behave normally" (211, p. 20). Such cessation of reaction occurs when the continued stimulus is not harmful. In a sense, it may be called an effect of experience; but there is clearly no reason for supposing that it involves the revival of experience in the form of an idea or image. We have parallel phenomena in our own mental life. A continued stimulus ceases to be "noticed," but the process involves rather the disappearance of consciousness than the appearance of a memory image. Jennings, however, is inclined to think that preceding stimulation may modify the Amœba's behavior in a way more nearly suggesting memory in a higher type of mind. He describes an interesting observation to illustrate this. A large Amœba, *c*, had swallowed a smaller one, *b*, but had left a small canal open, through which the swallowed one made efforts to escape, which were several times foiled by movements on the part of the large Amœba toward surrounding it again. Finally it succeeded in getting completely out, whereupon the large Amœba "reversed its course, overtook *b*, engulfed it completely again, and started away." The small Amœba contracted into a ball and remained quiet until through the movements of the large one there chanced to be but a thin layer of protoplasm covering it. This it rapidly pushed through, escaped completely, and was not pursued by the large Amœba (211, pp. 17–18), (Fig. 3).

Of this performance Jennings says, "It is difficult to conceive each phase of action of the pursuer to be completely determined by a simple present stimulus. For example . . . after Amœba *b* has escaped completely and is quite separate from Amœba *c*, the latter reverses its course and recaptures *b*. What determines the behavior of *c* at this point? If we can imagine all the external physical and chemical conditions to remain the same, with the two Amœbæ in the same relative positions, but suppose at the same time that Amœba *c* has never had the experience of possessing *b*, — would its action be the same? Would it reverse its movement, take in *b*, then return on its former course? One who sees the behavior as it occurs can hardly resist the conviction that the action at this point is partly determined by the change in *c* due to the former possession of *b*, so that the behavior is not purely reflex" (211, p. 24).

If it is true that an Amœba which had not just "had the experience of possessing *b*" would not have reversed its movement and gone after *b* when the latter escaped, still we cannot think it possible that *c*'s movements in so doing were guided by a memory image of *b*. It may be supposed that the recent stimulation of contact with *b* had left a part of *c*'s protoplasm in a condition of heightened excitability, so that the weak stimulus offered perhaps by slight water disturbances due to *b*'s movements after escaping produced a positive reaction, although under other circumstances no reaction would have been possible. In any case, there is no evidence that Amœba's

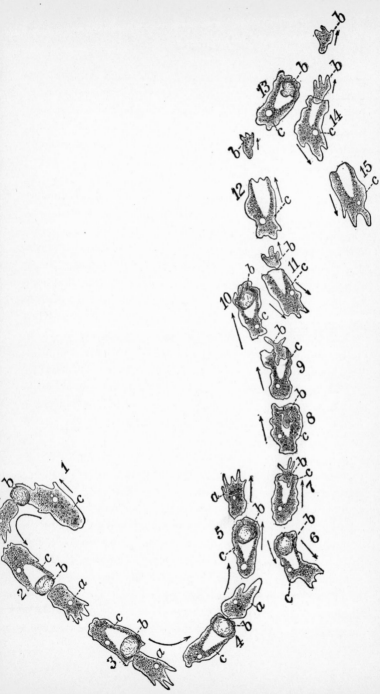

FIG. 3.—Pursuit, capture, and ingestion of one Amœba by another; escape of the captured Amœba and its recapture; final escape. *b*, the captured Amœba, was originally a fragment of another; *a*. After Jennings (211).

behavior is influenced by stimulation occurring earlier than the moments just preceding action; no proof of the revival of a process whose original effects have had time to die out; and it is upon such revival that the memory images which play so much part in our own conscious life depend.

Let us consider for a moment some of the results of the absence of this kind of material in the possible mental processes of Amœba. In the first place, such a lack profoundly affects the character of the experiences which the animal might be supposed to receive through external stimulation. If we call the possible conscious effect of a mechanical stimulus upon the Amœba a touch sensation, the term suggests, naturally, such sensations as we ourselves experience them. In normal human beings touch sensations are accompanied by visual suggestions, more or less clear, of course, according to the visualizing powers of the individual, but always present in some degree. Fancy, for example, one of us entering a room in the dark and groping about among the furniture. How constantly visual associations are brought into play! Not once is a mere touch impression apprehended without being translated into visual terms; the forms and positions of the articles encountered are thought of immediately as they would appear if the room were lighted. The difficulty we have in thinking of a touch sensation with no visual associations illustrates the difference between our sense experience and that of an animal incapable of recalling images of past sensations.

It is equally obvious that in the absence of memory ideas, not only must the Amœba lack processes of imagination and reasoning, but there can be nothing like the continuous self-consciousness of a human being, the "sense" of personal identity, which depends upon the power to revive past experiences. It is even possible that the "stream of consciousness" for an

Amœba may not be a continuous stream at all. Since its sensitiveness to changes in its environment is less developed than that of a human being, and there are no trains of ideas to fill up possible intervals between the occurrences of outside stimulation, the Amœba's conscious experience may be rather a series of "flashes" than a steady stream. And for the Amœba, again, we must remember that even such a series would not exist as such; the perception of a series would involve the revival of its past members. Each moment of consciousness is as if there were no world beyond, before, and after it.

Another consequence of that simplicity of structure which results both from the rudimentary powers of sensory discrimination and from the absence of memory ideas in the Amœba's mind is that there can be no distinction, within a given mental process, between that which is attended to and that which is not attended to, between the focus and the margin of consciousness. Given a consciousness which at a certain moment is composed of the qualitatively different elements A, B, C, and D, we can understand what is meant by saying that A is attended to, is in the foreground of attention, while B, C, and D remain in the background. But given, on the other hand, a creature whose conscious content at a certain time consists wholly of the qualitatively simple experience A, it is evident that attention and inattention are meaningless terms. Different moments of its consciousness may differ in intensity; but attention, involving, as it does, clearness rather than intensity, arises only when mental states have become complex and possess detail and variety within their structure.

§ 10. *The Structure and Behavior of Paramecium*

Although Amœba represents in structure the simplest form of animal life, its behavior in response to stimulation is rather

E

more complex than that of some other members of the type Protozoa. There is a large group of single-celled animals called Ciliata, from the fact that their bodies are covered with little hairlike protoplasmic filaments or cilia which serve as organs of locomotion by acting like tiny oars. A common representative of the group is Paramecium. The structure of this animal is distinctly more specialized than that of Amœba. Not only are the cilia modified locomotory structures, but there is a definite region for food-taking. A groove extends obliquely down one side of the body, terminating at its lower end in a mouth. The cilia along this oral groove beat with especial vigor and create currents which sweep food particles to the mouth. Paramecium swims rapidly through the water with a spiral motion of its body, due to the facts that the aboral cilia beat more strongly than the rest, and that the animal compensates for the turning thus occasioned by turning on its long axis. Its reactions to stimulation Jennings has shown to be only two in number. First, there is a very definite avoiding or negative reaction. This is given in response to decided mechanical stimulation at the anterior end, as when the animal swims rapidly against an obstacle, and also in response to chemical stimulation, to strong ultra-violet rays (167), and to temperatures above or below a certain middle region called in this case, as in analogous cases with other animals, the *optimum*. For Paramecium it lies between 24° and 28° C. The negative reaction consists, according to Jennings, of the following process: the animal darts backward, reversing the beat of its cilia, turns toward the aboral side (that opposite to the oral groove) by increasing the beat of the oral cilia and lessening the compensating rotation, and continues on a forward course that is now at an angle with its former line of motion. If this new course carries it clear of the stimulus, it continues on its way; if not, repeated contact with the stimulus causes a second reaction, the Paramecium always turning in the same direction, so that ultimately it avoids the source of stimulation (194, 211) (Fig. 4). Differing strengths of stimulus produce the reaction with different degrees of violence. When a very strong stimulus is encountered, the animals "respond first by swimming a long way backward, thus removing themselves as far as possible from the source of stimulation. Then they turn directly toward the aboral

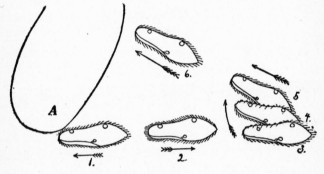

FIG. 4. — Negative reaction of Paramecium. *A* is the source of stimulation. 1–6 are the successive positions of the animal. After Jennings (211).

side, — the rotation on the long axis completely ceasing. In this way the animal may turn directly away from the drop [the stimulus] and retrace its course" (211, p. 50). On the other hand, when the stimulus is very weak the reaction may be reduced to the following form: the Paramecium "merely stops, or progresses more slowly, and begins to swing its anterior end about in a circle." As long as it does not thus get out of range of the stimulus, the movement is continued. "When the anterior end is finally pointed in a direction from which no more of the stimulating agent comes, the Paramecium swims forward " (211, p. 51). Evidently, however, these are but differing degrees of a reaction whose essential features are the same.

While Paramecium definitely avoids by means of this negative reaction certain chemicals introduced into the water, it shows a tendency to collect in the neighborhood of others. Such is the case with weak acids, with a bubble of oxygen if air has been long excluded from the slide, and with carbon dioxide, which in water of course produces acid (214). Jennings pointed out that the inclination of Paramecium to gather in groups is very likely due to the attraction for them of the carbon dioxide which they excrete. But he has also shown that this "attraction" to certain chemicals does not mean the presence of a special positive reaction. The fact is that when the animals collect in a drop of weak acid, for example, they are not drawn toward the acid. They simply happen, in their ordinary movements, to swim into it, and on entering it show no disturbance whatever. But when they come to the edge of the drop on their way out, they give the negative reaction to the surrounding water. In this way they are, as it were, trapped within the drop.

The nearest analogue to a positive reaction in Paramecium consists in the fact that sometimes, when they come into contact with a solid, instead of darting backward, the animals merely cease moving, and extending stiffly the cilia which touch the object, remain at rest (Fig. 5). The utility of this behavior is that around decaying vegetable matter, the kind of solid oftenest found in the animal's ordinary environment, there is apt to be a supply of food in the way of bacteria; it is a good anchorage. What characteristics of the stimulus determine that this "contact reaction," rather than the negative reaction, shall be given? Does weak mechanical stimulation occasion it, as happens with Amœba's positive reaction? Evidence in favor of this is offered by the fact that the contact reaction is more likely to occur if the animal comes against the solid when swimming rather slowly. Jennings reports also that individuals vary. "Often all the individuals in a culture are thus inclined to come to rest, while in another culture all remain free-swimming, and give the avoiding reaction whenever they come in contact with a solid " (211, p. 60). This would suggest that some individuals are in a state of greater excitability than others, so that a given stimulus acts more strongly upon them. On the other hand, there is a possibility that qualitative as well as intensive differences in the stimulus are responsible for the contrasting reactions. "In general," says Jennings, Paramecium "shows a tendency to come to rest against loose or fibrous material; in other words, it reacts thus to material with which it can come in contact at two or more parts of the body at once.

FIG. 5. — Positive thigmotaxis in Paramecium. After Jennings (211).

To smooth, hard materials, such as glass, it is much less likely to react in this manner " (211, p. 61). Perhaps, then, the spatial distribution of the stimulus over several points of the body surface increases the probability of a contact rather than an avoiding reaction.

Certain other forms of behavior in Paramecium involve the taking up of a definite position with reference to some constant stimulus, and are therefore termed by Jennings "orienting reactions." In the first place, if there is a current in the water, the animals will head up-stream. Jennings explains this as due to the giving of avoiding reactions in response to the disturbing effects of the current on the cilia until, with the Paramecium's head up-stream, the current no longer tends to reverse the cilia. Analogous reaction is given to gravity; the animals direct their heads upward, and swim in that direction. The cause of this has been the subject of some dispute, which we shall discuss in a later chapter; but the response to gravity seems in any case not to involve a new form of reaction. Further, Paramecium reacts to the centrifugal force produced by whirling a horizontal tube around a vertical axis just as it does to gravity; that is, it orients itself in such a way as to swim toward the axis, in the opposite direction to the pull of the force (211, p. 78).

To an electric current the response of Paramecium is more complicated. When the current is weak the animals move toward the cathode. This appears to be caused simply by the giving of the negative reaction so long as the front end of the animal is turned toward the anode, and is thus being stimulated. But if the current is made gradually stronger, the movement toward the cathode grows slower and finally stops. Further increase in the intensity of the current causes the animal to swim backward toward the anode, and finally to burst into pieces. This reversal of movement Jennings has found to be due to the fact that the cilia nearest the cathode have their direction reversed; as the current is made stronger, this effect is increased, until finally it balances and prevails over the beat of the forward cilia (211, pp. 82 ff.). The animal's movements are thus really discoördinated by the action of the strong current. The effect seems a pathological one, and probably need not be taken into account in considering the normal life of the infusorian; as Jennings says, "The reaction to electricity is purely a laboratory product" (211, p. 168).

§ 11. *The Mind of Paramecium*

If we now compare the behavior of Paramecium with that of Amœba in order to draw conclusions with regard to the possible consciousness of the former, we find that although the mechanism of reaction is decidedly more complicated in Paramecium than in Amœba, there is rather less possibility of variety in the conscious experience of the ciliated protozoön. The reversal of cilia, the rolling toward the aboral side, form a more elaborated and specialized mode of withdrawal than does the simple checking of protoplasmic flow at one region of the body. But, supposing Paramecium to be conscious, the significance for its consciousness of the negative or avoiding reaction is even less clear than that of the corresponding behavior in Amœba. The negative reaction in Amœba is contrasted on the one hand with a positive reaction, opposite in character, given to stimuli of less intensity, so that the opposition of unpleasantness and pleasantness in the human mind is clearly suggested; and on the other hand with a food-taking reaction, given to edible substances, and hinting at a differentiation corresponding to that between touch and taste in our own experience. The only approach to a positive reaction in Paramecium is the coming to rest in contact with solids, and this does not present any very striking analogy with such expressions of pleasantness as we are acquainted with. Further, Paramecium has no special food-taking reaction at all. The fact seems to be that its greater speed of motion has developed its negative reaction at the expense of the others. It does not need to reach out in a typical positive reaction, for its rapid dashing through the water greatly increases its natural chance of getting food. The whirling of the oral cilia brings it edible as well as inedible substances. It does, however, much need in its headlong career a means of avoiding the dangers into which it may rush, and so we find the very definite and well-adapted negative reaction dominating the field. If, then, the mind of an Amœba is thought of as capable of three or four qualitatively different experiences, that of a Paramecium must be even less favored.

Is there any evidence of the presence in Paramecium of the revival of past experiences in any form? The answer to this question must be negative, as in the case of Amœba. Immediately preceding stimulation does have some effect upon the response to present stimulation, but these effects are all of such a character as to suggest rather the disappearance of possible consciousness than the recall of a memory image. Jennings mentions several instances. "If a Paramecium is subjected to a strong induction shock, it fails for some time thereafter to react to weak shocks, though at the beginning it reacted to these" (211, p. 100). Such a result is due probably to fatigue. "Paramecia which have been living at the usual temperatures show a temperature optimum of about 24 to 28 degrees; if they are kept for some hours at a temperature from 36 to 38 degrees, the optimum rises to 30 or 32 degrees. A change in the individuals induced in this way is commonly spoken of as acclimatization" (211, p. 101). Further, "if a bit of filter paper is placed in a preparation of Paramecia, the following behavior may often be observed. An individual swims against it, gives the avoiding reaction in a slightly marked way, swimming backward a little; then it swims forward again, jerks back a shorter distance, then settles against the paper and remains. After remaining a few seconds, it may move to another position, still remaining in contact with the paper. Then it may leave the paper and go on its way" (211, p. 101). Behavior of this type, where a stimulus at first occasions the negative reaction, but on immediate repetition ceases to do so, we shall find very common among the lower forms of animals; it suggests simply that the stimulus acts less and less strongly on repetition, not that the effects of its earlier application are consciously recalled.

Jennings's work on other ciliate Protozoa, as well as on the group known as Flagellata, the members of which have in place of cilia a long whiplike protoplasmic filament, and move by lashing it to and fro in the water, indicates that in all of them the negative reaction is the principal feature of behavior (199, 211), and that if any of them possess minds, those minds are of quite as rudimentary a type as that of Amœba, and very likely rendered even more so, as far as qualitative variety of experience goes, by the predominance of the negative reaction due to greater speed of motion.

§ 12. *Definitions of Tropisms*

Before passing to the study of higher forms of animal life, we may note the meaning of a few technical terms used in describing the behavior of simple animals especially. The direct motor response of an animal to an external stimulus is known as a *tropism*, from the Greek word meaning "to turn." Various prefixes are attached to this term to indicate the nature of the stimulus concerned; thus *phototropism* means the reaction of an animal to light; *chromotropism*, reaction to color; *thigmotropism*, reaction to contact; *chemotropism*, reaction to chemical stimulation; *rheotropism*, reaction to currents; *geotropism*, reaction to gravity; *electrotropism*, reaction to the electric current; *anemotropism*, reaction (*e.g.*, in winged insects) to wind. Some writers have used instead of *tropism* the word *taxis*, from the Greek word meaning "to arrange," speaking of chemotaxis, thigmotaxis, and so on. *Phototaxis* has, as we shall see, a rather special significance distinct from phototropism. When an animal gives a positive reaction in response to a stimulus, it is said to be *positively chemotropic*, or *phototropic*, as the case may be; when its reaction is negative, it is called *negatively chemotropic*, *phototropic*, and so on.

CHAPTER IV

§ 13. *Preliminary Considerations*

ONE of the most important points in which the human mind differs from the mind of the lowest animal forms consists, we have seen, in the enormously greater number of different sensations which enter into human experience, as compared with the small number of sensory discriminations possible to the simpler animals. Much of the experimental work that has been done on animals has been directed toward discovering what discriminations they make among the stimuli acting upon them, and to the results of this work we shall give our attention in the next chapters. But first we ought to get a clearer idea of just what kind of evidence is needed to indicate the existence of a variety of sensations in an animal's mind.

At the outset, we must remind ourselves that, in the absence of any satisfactory proof that the lower animal forms have minds at all, and the equal absence of any proof that they have not, all our conclusions about the number and kind of their possible sensations must remain subject to the proviso that they possess consciousness. Further, a point that was mentioned on page 24 must again be emphasized. No evidence of discrimination between two stimuli on an animal's part can do more than show us that for the animal they are different; just what the quality of the sensation resulting from each may be, whether it is identical with any sensation quality entering into our own experience, we cannot say. The light rays which to us are red and blue may for an animal's consciousness also differ from each other, and yet if our experience could be exchanged for the animal's, we might find in the latter nothing like red and blue as we know them.

Thus much being premised, what sort of evidence can be obtained that an animal does discriminate between two stimuli? Again, as in considering the evidence for the existence of consciousness in general, there is an argument from structure and an argument from behavior.

§ 14. *Structure as Evidence of Discrimination*

The *argument from structure* consists primarily in the fact that an animal possesses sense organs recognizably like our own. If a creature has an organ suggesting strongly the construction of the human cochlea, or an organ with a lens and a membrane composed of rods and cones, it is highly probable that auditory stimuli in the one case and light in the other produce specific sensations. This argument from the morphology of sense organs is, however, limited in two ways. First, it is only a small part of the animal world whose sense organs resemble ours closely enough to make the analogy safe. And secondly, we do not after all know very much about the relation of our own sense-organ structure to function. We know, for example, that our own organ with a lens and retina gives us visual sensations, but we cannot say with certainty which structures in the retina furnish brightness sensations and which color sensations, nor do we know anything about the retinal structures that underlie different qualities of color sensations. We can say that sensations of hearing come from the ear, but no one can tell us how to judge from the structure of the ear what range and fineness of pitch discriminations exist in its possessor's mind. No investigator has yet succeeded in relating the different qualities of smell and taste to differences in the end organs.

§ 15. *Behavior as Evidence of Discrimination*

The *argument from behavior* is as follows: If an animal reacts in a different way to two qualitatively unlike stimuli, then, providing that it is conscious at all, it may be supposed to receive qualitatively unlike sensations from them. If it always reacts in the same way to both, then both may be supposed to be accompanied by the same sensation quality. Obviously these statements need further discussion. For one thing, it may be urged that in our own case the same external reaction is often made to stimuli that are nevertheless consciously discriminated. A man may eat with relish and without observable difference in behavior, for example, foods that yet give him perfectly distinguishable smell and taste sensations. Precisely this objection holds against a method of experimentation, formerly a good deal used, which may be called the Preference Method of testing discrimination. Vitus Graber, for instance, attempted to find whether animals belonging to a variety of species could discriminate colors, by offering them the choice of two compartments illuminated each with a different color. Clearly, if the animals chose one compartment as often as the other, it would be rash to conclude that the two lights produced for them indistinguishable sensation qualities. There might simply be the absence of any preference, along with perfect discrimination. The fact is that in all experiments upon animals, whether to determine their power of distinguishing stimuli or their power of learning by experience, the first requisite is to give the animal what we commonly call a *motive.* That is, the conditions of the experiment must be so arranged that some already present tendency to act, whether inborn in the animal or acquired by previous experience, shall be appealed to.

This is increasingly the case, the higher the animal worked with stands in the scale. The higher animals have what might be called a large reserve fund of discriminations. That is, they are capable of making many more selective reactions to stimuli than they need at a given moment actually to use. Hence in their case the experimenter must make a careful adjustment of conditions to bring out exactly the discrimination wanted. He must either make the performance of the reaction pleasant or its non-performance unpleasant to the animal. A monkey, for example, confronted by a set of glass tumblers covered each with a differently colored paper, may behave toward them all in precisely the same way; yet if food be put regularly in the blue tumbler, whose position in the row is varied, it becomes worth the monkey's while to make use of his discriminative powers, and he may show by his different behavior toward the blue tumbler that it produces on him a different impression from the others.

With simpler animals the problem is less difficult. If an animal is capable only of a half dozen different ways of responding to stimulation, we may with comparative safety assume that it has less opportunity to hold them in reserve; and if such an animal invariably reacts in the same way to two different forms of stimulus, or if the variations in its response are not correlated with differences in the stimulation, it becomes probable that the two stimuli produce in its assumed consciousness identical sensation qualities. Thus it is not the number of stimuli to which an animal reacts that can be taken as evidence of the qualitative variety of its sensations, but the number of stimuli to which it gives different reactions. When Jennings, for instance, says that Amœba "reacts to all classes of stimuli to which higher animals react" (211, p. 19), we cannot conclude that it possesses all classes of sensations that higher animals possess, for its reactions to these different stimuli are but little varied according to the kind of stimulus.[1]

§ 16. *Evidence from Structure and Behavior Combined*

As a matter of fact, the argument from structure needs confirmatory evidence from behavior. For clearly the mere presence of a sense organ bearing sufficient likeness to our own to admit of conjecturing its function would be of no value as proof unless it were shown that the sense organ actually functioned. In order to do this, it would be necessary to show that the animal reacted to the stimulus conjectured as appropriate to the sense organ, and that removal of the organ profoundly modified the reaction. Thus we shall find that many experiments to test sensory discrimination have been made by the *method of extirpating a sense organ* and studying the effect on behavior. The method has many disadvantages, the chief of which lies in the fact that it is hard to say which disturbances in behavior are due actually to the loss of the organ and which to the more widespread effects of the operation. Yet this much may be said for the combination of proof from structure and behavior involved in the Method of Extirpation, if we may so call it: where an animal reacts to a certain stimulus, for instance light, when a sense organ is intact, and fails to react to light, though otherwise normal, when the organ is removed, there arises a possibility that light

[1] One of many reasons for the unsatisfactoriness of a recent article by A. Ölzelt-Newin, entitled "Beobachtungen über das Leben der Protozoen" (299), lies in the author's uncritical acceptance of the hypothesis that reaction to a special kind of stimulus means a special kind of sensation.

may produce in the animal's consciousness a specific sensation quality, *even although the animal ordinarily reacts to light in a manner indistinguishable from that of its responses to other stimuli.* Though light and mechanical stimulation, for example, both ordinarily produce a negative reaction, yet if light brings about its effect only through the medium of a specialized structure with which mechanical stimuli are not concerned, then along with the probable unpleasantness accompanying the negative reaction there may go a quality peculiar to the functioning of that special structure.

Another mode of combining evidence from structure with evidence from behavior is by the *use of localized stimuli.* If an animal gives a response, which in itself may have nothing to mark it off from responses to other stimuli, when a special kind of stimulation is applied to certain regions of the body, and only then; while the other stimuli produce better reactions when applied elsewhere, then the suggestion is given that different sense organs are involved, and the same possibility arises of different sensation qualities.

Two other forms of evidence whereby from behavior a differentiation of sensory structures can be argued, and from differentiation of sensory structures possible differences of sensation quality, may be mentioned. The first of these consists in showing that reactions to different stimuli may be *independently fatigued.* The natural inference is that a specific nervous apparatus belongs to each stimulus. The second lies in demonstrating that the reactions to different stimuli occur with different degrees of rapidity. If there is a marked *difference in the reaction times* of an animal to different forms of stimulation, each, again, may be supposed to affect its own nervous pathway. A modification of this method consists in noting the influence of a stimulus upon the time of reaction to another nearly simultaneous stimulus.   If such an influence can be shown, it is evident that the force producing it has some effect on the nervous system.   By combining this method with that of extirpating a sensory structure, indications may be obtained that the nervous effect of the auxiliary stimulus is dependent on a definite receptive apparatus, and hence is probably accompanied by a special sensation.   This method was used by Yerkes to demonstrate hearing in frogs (456, 462, 464).

One further consideration offers itself to the student of animal responses to stimulation.   It has been the special endeavor of Jennings to point out the fact that these responses, instead of being wholly accounted for by the characteristics of the stimulus, are determined in part by the internal, physiological condition of the animal (211).   We shall therefore note often in the course of the following pages cases where difference of reaction is due to internal rather than to external causes.

§ 17. *Evidence for Discrimination of Certain "Lower" Sensation Classes*

Bearing all these points in mind, let us proceed to survey the evidence for variety in the sensations of animals.   In the lowest forms, such evidence must be derived entirely from behavior.   That from the presence of a sense organ is almost wholly lacking.   And although various stimuli, as we have seen, produce reactions in Amœba, yet there is only one case where these reactions are strikingly different according to the quality of the stimulus applied.   This instance consists in the distinction between food-taking reactions, given to edible substances, and the responses to mechanical stimulation.   The sense of touch, undoubtedly, must play a part in the mental life of the lowest animals that have consciousness at all.

But the earliest distinction between a touch quality and a quality that is other than touch seems to occur when food sensation and contact sensation are differentiated. It is possible that warmth and cold also appear as distinct sensation qualities in the experience of low forms of animals, but we have little real evidence of the fact. No organs of temperature sensation are definitely known even in human beings. And the responses of low animals to thermal stimulation are not specialized. They consist usually of negative reactions, given when the animal is subjected to a temperature either above or below, but especially above, the "optimum"; and these reactions are not different from the ordinary negative type, suggesting unpleasantness rather than a specific sensation quality. In some cases the sensibility to thermal stimulation has been found to be differently distributed from that to other classes of stimuli. But in any case, sensations of warmth and cold are probably in no member of the animal kingdom differentiated into any greater number of qualitatively distinct sensations.

The sense of touch, also, shows but little internal differentiation. Its importance, so far as we can judge, is rather on the spatial than on the qualitative side. The sense quality of pain we naturally think of as the accompaniment of the negative reaction in its more violent forms, given to a stimulus that is injuring the organism. Organic and kinæsthetic sensations are hard to trace in the lower animals; for animals whose structure differs widely from our own, the qualities of these two classes must remain beyond the power of our imagination. That differences in physiological condition such as are produced by hunger, satiety, or fatigue involve differences of accompanying organic sensation in the consciousness of the animal manifesting them is possible. Kinæsthetic sensations, as we shall see, are apparently con-

F

cerned in the processes whereby many animals have learned to traverse a labyrinth path.

The three classes of sensation whose existence in the animal mind can be most satisfactorily traced are the chemical sense, under which smell and taste belong, the sense of hearing, and the sense of sight. To the study of these the following chapters will be devoted. Since the manifestations of the chemical sense in the lowest forms of animals consist chiefly in a differentiation of response to food and to mechanical stimulation, the contact sense or sense of touch will, in discussing these forms, be considered along with the chemical sense.

CHAPTER V

Sensory Discrimination: the Chemical Sense

§ 18. *The Chemical Sense in Cœlenterates*

We have already discussed the responses to mechanical, chemical, and food stimulation in those members of the Protozoa whose behavior has been most carefully studied, and may begin the present chapter with an account of the corresponding reactions in the lowest of the Metazoa, or many-celled animals, the cœlenterates. Although externally the forms of different families of cœlenterates differ widely, yet the general plan of structure is the same in all: the body of the typical cœlenterate is a hollow sac, whose walls consist of two layers of cells, food being taken into a mouth at one end of the sac, and the arrangement of cells being on the plan of circular symmetry. In the phylum of the cœlenterates are included sea-anemones, jellyfish, the little green or yellow Hydra, sponges, corals, and ctenophores.

Hydra (Fig. 6), one of the simplest cœlenterates, shows a food reaction distinct from the contact reaction. Mechanical stimulation is followed by withdrawal of the tentacles, and by contraction of the stem. This behavior may be called a negative or avoiding reaction, and no positive reaction to a mechanical stimulus has been observed. The food-taking reaction, on the other hand, consists in the seizing of the food by the tentacles. It seems to be given in response to a combination of chemical with mechanical stimulation, such as is offered by contact with a solid edible object (418). Shall we say that Hydra possesses, then, a food sensation and a contact sensation that are distinguishable in its consciousness, provided such consciousness exists? It may be that the contrast between the two is more nearly analogous to that between pleasantness and unpleasantness in our own experience, for the food-taking reaction in Hydra

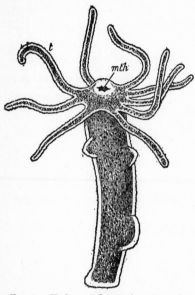

is the only form of the positive reaction, and the response to mere contact is distinctly negative in character. The influence of *physiological condition* in Hydra's reactions is shown by the fact that although ordinarily the food response is brought about only by contact with food, if the animal is very hungry any chemical stimulation, even quinine, will produce it (418). This blunting of discrimination has, of course, the adaptive aspect that the

FIG. 6.—Hydra. *mth*, mouth; *t*, tentacle. After Parker.

starved animal can afford to lose no chances, and suggests the analogy from our own experience of the loss of intellectual discrimination in moments of intense emotion. For the emotion too represents a situation where the organism cannot afford to lose chances by hesitating in reaction long enough for nice discrimination.

In *Tubularia crocea*, a cœlenterate belonging to the family of hydroids which form colonies of many individuals on a common stem, food and contact stimuli do not produce different reactions, but have different degrees of efficiency in bringing about response. When a grain of sand was placed in contact with the tentacles on one side and a bit of meat in a corresponding position on the other side, the reaction was almost invariably in the direction of the meat. Filtered meat juice allowed to flow upon the distal tentacles produced a reaction 82 per cent of the time, while carmine water was effective only 15 per cent of the time. Further, if the distal tentacles were touched several times with a needle, they remained closed; but if the second stimulus used was a piece of meat, the tentacles opened out and waved about (319). Whether in such a case as this the possible conscious accompaniments of the responses are to be regarded as qualitatively different sensations, or only as different degrees of intensity of the same sensation, it is difficult to say. Another hydroid, *Corymorpha palma*, gives no response whatever to meat juice; only irritating chemicals produce reactions, whose character appears to be tactile (402).

In the sea-anemones or actinians we find behavior in response to food stimulation as distinguished from contact stimulation varying in different representatives of the group. Generally speaking, the food reaction seems to be more marked than the contact reaction. W. H. Pollock a number of years ago reported his observation that certain unnamed sea-anemones opened out if food were suspended near them in the water, and referred the phenomenon to "a sense of smell" (343). *Adamsia rondeleti* winds its tentacles around bits of sardine meat and passes them from tentacle to tentacle toward the mouth. When balls of filter paper softened with sea water are substituted, the feeding reaction is wholly lacking. Either the tentacles fail to react at all, or the ball is "felt of" slowly with no attempt to seize it, or it is momentarily seized and then dropped. If the paper ball be soaked in fish juice, on the other hand, it is seized as eagerly as the fish meat. A negative reaction, consisting in the withdrawal of the tentacles affected, may be produced by applying a bit of paper soaked in quinine solution or by the discharge of quinine solution from a pipette near the tentacles (237, 288). A peculiar form of negative reaction has been observed in Adamsia, and more strikingly in Cerianthus, when a paper ball soaked in fish juice has been passed from tentacle to tentacle till it has nearly reached the mouth. The process is suddenly reversed, and the ball is passed back from one tentacle to another till it reaches the outside edge and is dropped off. Nagel, the observer, thinks the stimulus for this change of reaction is the gradual wearing off of the "sapid parts" of the ball during its passage toward the mouth — it might be the squeezing out of the meat juice — and calls special attention to the fact that the reaction whereby the paper is got rid of is wholly different from the ordinary reaction of a tentacle to mechanical stimulation, which, as we have seen, does not involve seizing the object at all. A tentacle touched by a bit of moistened filter paper ordinarily responds, if at all, by a mere contraction without the winding seizure of the object. Touched by the same object "handed on" to it by a tentacle nearer the mouth than itself, it seizes the paper and passes it on to the tentacle beyond it. The cause of this difference in behavior seems to lie in the processes that have been taking place just previously. Nagel does not hesitate to say that a psychic process must be involved, but its details are not easy to construct (291).

Another sea-anemone, Aiptasia, has but one ring of tentacles, and like *Tubularia crocea*, instead of showing different responses to contact stimulation alone and to contact plus food stimulation, it merely reacts with greater emphasis to the latter. In both cases the tentacles wind around the object, contract, and direct themselves toward the mouth (291). Again the question arises whether the possible accompanying sensations differ in quality or only in intensity. One species of Aiptasia, *A. annulata*, however, does react differently to filter paper soaked in crab juice and to plain filter paper (207), showing that even within a genus the capacity for stimulus discrimination may differ. In like manner one sea-anemone, Actinia, will take filter paper soaked in acetic acid, while another, Tealia, rejects it (127).

Metridium, a common sea-anem-one of our coasts, has its tentacles covered with cilia which have a continual waving motion toward the tip of the tentacle (Fig. 7). If particles of an inedible substance are dropped on a tentacle, no definite reaction occurs, but the particles are carried by the ordinary motion of the cilia out to the tentacle tip, where they drop off. When a bit of crab meat, or some meat juice, is dropped on a tentacle, the latter contracts and curls over with the tip directed toward the mouth. The ciliary movement continuing in its usual direction now of course carries the food toward the mouth. Applying food to the lips on either side of the mouth causes a different response. The cilia on these lips ordinarily wave outwards; when food is brought in contact with them their motion is reversed, and the food is thus passed into the mouth. In Metridium, then, there is no specific rejecting reaction for inedible substances (303).

Fig. 7.—Metridium. After Parker.

Various instances of the *effect of physiological condition* upon response to food stimulation in sea-anemones have been noted. Adamsia loses the power to discriminate between edible and inedible substances when very hungry (291). *Sagartia davisi* will also swallow inedible substances if hungry enough (403). *Stoiachactis helianthus* will give either a positive or a negative reaction to food according to its condition of hunger or satiety (207). The reaction of Metridium to food may vary decidedly with the degree of hunger (3); although it will continue taking food as long as the process is mechanically possible (211). Fatigue has also been shown to affect the food responses of Metridium and other sea-anemones; specimens that have been fed meat and filter paper alternately will after a time refuse to take filter paper (207, 291, 303). This behavior was thought by Nagel to indicate that the animal had discovered the deception practiced upon it; but apparently the real cause is fatigue; showing itself first with reference to the weaker of the two stimuli (3).

As regards the localization of the sensitive elements, authorities, and probably species, differ. Nagel finds the tentacles most sensitive (291); Loeb observed that the stump of the animal has discriminative reactions (237), while Fleure and Walton state that in the species tested by them the mouth-region is most responsive to chemical stimulation (127).

A certain amount of discrimination between mechanical stimuli is asserted of these animals by Romanes. "I have observed," he says, "that if a sea-anemone is placed in an aquarium tank and allowed to fasten upon one side of the tank near the surface of the water, and if a jet of sea water is made to play continuously and forcibly upon the anemone from above, the result of course is that the animal becomes surrounded with a turmoil of water and air bubbles. Yet after a short time it becomes so accustomed to this turmoil that it will expand its tentacles in search of food, just as it does when placed in calm water. If now one of the expanded tentacles is gently touched with a solid body, all the others close around that body in just the same way as they would were they expanded in calm water " (366, p. 48), although the solid stimulus is decidedly less intense than that offered by the bubbles.   Similarly, Fleure and Walton find that certain species show little reaction to accidental contact with a pebble that is moved, but react quickly to a finger (127).

The body of a typical medusa or jellyfish consists of a bell-shaped " umbrella " from the edge of which tentacles depend. Hanging from the middle like the clapper of the bell or the handle of the umbrella is the manubrium, at the end of which is the mouth.   In the medusa *Carmarina hastata* no differentiation in reaction to contact and food stimulation appears, merely a readier response of the tentacles to the latter; but we do find whatever evidence for the existence of a specific sensation quality is furnished by localized sensitiveness, for the skin of the under side of the umbrella, and of the manubrium, is very sensitive to mechanical stimulation, and wholly insensitive to chemical stimulation, while the tentacles, as has just been stated, react, by shortening and twisting themselves about the object, more readily to chemical than to mechanical stimulation.   A mechanical stimulus applied to any part of the under edge of the umbrella produces after from one to three seconds a movement of the manubrium tip toward the point stimulated (289, 291).

The little medusa *Gonionemus murbachii* (Fig. 8) shows, on the other hand, two well-defined different responses to special stimulation: motor reactions and food-taking reactions.   The motor or swimming reactions are given in response to mechanical stimulation and to the presence of food near the animal in the water; but the food-taking reaction occurs only in response to food (solution of fish meat); very rarely a weak inorganic chemical stimulus will produce the beginning of the response.   An important exception to the usual inefficacy of mechanical stimuli in bringing about the feeding reaction occurs when a *moving* mechanical stimulus is used ; this very quickly produces the early stages of the food-taking response. Special reactions to stimuli in motion are widespread throughout the animal kingdom; their significance will be discussed in the chapter on Space Perception. The food-taking response in Gonionemus shows a marked coördination of movements; if the food touches one or more tentacles, these contract and twist about it; they then bend toward the manubrium, and the margin of the bell also

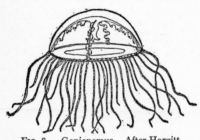

FIG. 8. — Gonionemus. After Hargitt.

bends in; the manubrium swings over toward the bell and envelops the food with its lips (451).

Another cœlenterate whose reactions to chemical stimulation have been observed is the ctenophore *Beroe ovata*. Its body is an elongated oval, with longitudinal ciliated ridges, having the mouth slit at the end which is normally uppermost when the animal is at the surface of the water, and at the opposite end an otolith or statolith organ lying between two flattened "polar plates." The significance of this organ will be considered later. The aboral region is far more sensitive than any other to mechanical stimulation; the slightest touch on one of the polar plates causes the animal to shorten itself and fold in the plates. The aboral end, being the hind end of the creature, is not usually brought into contact with objects. Nagel, who studied the animal, suggests that this region, being sensitive to changes in pressure, may enable the animal to right itself when it rises to the surface with the aboral end up, as the change from water to air pressure could not fail to stimulate the polar plates. Nagel apparently made no experiments on the behavior of Beroe with reference to food stimuli; for chemical stimulation he used picric acid, dilute hydrochloric acid, quinine, strychnine, saccharine, coumarin, vanillin, and naphthalin. To all these unwonted stimuli the animal responded by some form of negative reaction, indicating possible unpleasant feeling. The edges of the mouth, where the nerves end in bulblike structures, reacted to quinine, vanillin, and coumarin by stretching the mouth into a circular form instead of its usual slitlike shape; suggesting an effort to get rid of the stimulus. Precisely similar reactions were produced by stimulation with lukewarm water. Nagel concludes that the organs for chemical and thermal stimulation are identical; whether the sensation qualities are different is, he thinks, an open question. There is at least no evidence that they are different (289, 291).

§ 19. *The Chemical Sense in Flatworms*

Next to the cœlenterates zoölogists place the phylum of the Platyhelminthes or flatworms, which possess a bilaterally instead of a radially symmetrical structure. Many representatives of the group are parasitic, and so far as the writer is aware, no extended study of the reactions of these forms to stimulation has been made. Most of our knowledge in regard to the sensory life of the flatworms is confined to the class Turbellaria, including the common freshwater and marine planarians. These are small slow-moving creatures which crawl about on solid objects under water or on films covering the surface. The mouth is situated on the ventral side of the body, sometimes quite far removed from the head end (Fig. 9). One chief interest of planarians to physiologists has lain in their remarkable power to regenerate parts lost by mutilation.

Planaria maculata, a common freshwater planarian, responds to stimulation by two forms of negative reaction, a positive reaction, and a feeding reaction. The negative and positive responses are given either to mechanical or to chemical stimuli, the former being produced by strong, the latter by weak stimulation. Hence they do not suggest correlation with qualitatively different sensation contents, but rather with unpleasantness and pleasantness. The two forms of negative reaction correspond to differences in the location of the stimulus. If the head end of the body is stimulated strongly on one side, the head is turned away from that side. If the posterior part of the body is strongly stimulated, the animal makes powerful forward crawling movements. The significance of local differences in stimulation for response and for possible consciousness, again, will more properly be discussed in a later chapter. As has just been said, both weak chemical and weak mechanical stimulation cause *Planaria maculata* to give a positive reaction by turning its head in the direction of the stimulus, which need not be in actual contact with the body (316). A planarian will follow an object such as the point of a pin moved in front of it, and one planarian will follow the trail of another that happens to come within the proper distance. Similarly, the neighborhood of food will cause the animal to turn toward it. Bardeen has suggested that the so-called "auricular appendages," two small movable prominences on the animal's back near the head end, which are specially sensitive to touch, may be "delicate organs

FIG. 9.—Planarian, dorsal view. After Woodworth.

capable of stimulation by slight currents in the water set up by the minute organisms that prey" upon the animal's food; so that the positive reaction when given to food may be really a response to mechanical stimulation (10). As Pearl, however, found that chemicals, diffused in the water, would produce positive responses (316), it is probable that *Planaria maculata* is directly sensitive to chemical stimulation, though it responds thereto in the same way as to mechanical stimulation. A land planarian, *Geodesimus bilineatus*, is reported by Lehnert to perceive food at distances from four to five times the length of its body, and he does not describe the positive reaction as given in response to any other than food stimulation (231).

The food-taking reaction in *Planaria maculata* is made under the influence of combined mechanical and chemical stimuli, in contact with the pharynx or the ventral side of the animal. When an object which has occasioned the positive reaction is reached, the head folds over it and grips it, contracting so as to squeeze it. The substance being thus brought into contact with the pharynx, swallowing movements are produced if the proper stimulus is given. Bardeen was inclined to think that contact with a soft substance constituted the proper stimulus, as he found that hard particles placed on the pharynx were not swallowed (9). Pearl, however, believes that mechanical and chemical stimulation must combine. The former alone does not suffice, for swallowing movements are not evoked when one planarian crawls over another; the latter alone is insufficient, for placing the animal in a sugar solution has no effect. If chemical and mechanical stimulation are united, the reaction is given whether the chemical is edible or not; Pearl found it occurring in response to sodium carbonate (316).

Evidence of the *influence of physiological condition* upon the reactions of planarians is furnished by the fact that the resting planarian shows a decidedly lowered susceptibility to stimulation. Bardeen found that if the animal was not already in motion, it gave no positive response to food in its neighborhood (10).

§ 20. *The Chemical Sense in Annelids*

In our own experience, as has been said, the "food sense" is represented by the two senses taste and smell, the stimulus for the one being fluid, and that for the other gaseous, so that the latter enables us to perceive objects at a distance. For water-dwelling animals, such as most of those whose behavior we have been describing, the distinction evidently cannot well be drawn. If such an animal perceives food at a distance, the stimulus is necessarily diffused through the water, and Lloyd Morgan has proposed the term "telæsthetic taste" for the sense which makes such perception possible (279, p. 256). The term indicates that this sense corresponds to taste in an air-dwelling animal because the stimulus is fluid, but differs in that it allows perception of a distant object, as taste in the ordinary sense does not. In the most familiar representative of the Annelida or segmented worms, the common earthworm, as in the land planarian, a distinction analogous to that between smell and taste in our own sensory experience may be made; in the leeches and marine annelids it cannot.

Gentle and continuous mechanical stimulation produces in the earthworm "positive thigmotaxis"; that is, the animals have a tendency to crawl and lie along the surface of solids (387). That there is some discrimination of edible from inedible substances when in contact with the body Darwin thought probable from the apparent preference of the worm for certain kinds of food (91). In the earthworm *Allolobophora fœtida* we find a differentiated response to contact and chemical stimulation. These worms live in barnyard manure. When placed on scraps of shredded filter paper moistened with water they refuse to burrow; when the filter paper is wet with a decoction of the manure they burrow as soon as they come into contact with it. The adequate stimulus for burrowing is thus a combined mechanical and chemical one; the chemical stimulus alone is insufficient, for filter paper thus prepared has no effect on the worms unless they are actually in contact with it (387). Using the human terms, the case is one of taste rather than smell. Nagel suggests that the earthworm's chief use for a chemical sense is to help it find the moisture which is necessary to its life (292); but curiously enough *Allolobophora fœtida* seems to have no power of doing this from a distance. Smith found that a worm would crawl around a wet spot on paper until its skin dried, without crawling into it. If by accident it happened to touch the moist place, it would enter and remain there (387). There seems no satisfactory evidence that worms respond to chemical stimulation from a distance by positive reactions, although Darwin believed that they found buried food by "the sense of smell" (91). Chemical stimuli not in contact with the body do produce negative reactions (292), but these reactions do not differ from the responses to strong mechanical stimulation. They are of various forms — turning aside, withdrawing into the burrow if the tail is already inserted, squirming, and so on, the differences being correlated with differences in the intensity and location of the stimulus and in the excitability (physiological condition) of the animal. But nothing in the character of the response suggests that negative reaction to a chemical stimulus has a different conscious accompaniment from that of negative response to a mechanical stimulus. The most natural interpretation of them all on the psychic side is that of unpleasantness, increasing in intensity as the reaction takes a more violent form.[1] The *time occupied in reacting* has, however, recently been made a basis for differentiating the response to different chemicals. It was found that if the worms were suspended by threads, and their anterior ends dipped into solutions of sodium, ammonium, lithium, and potassium chlorides, the animals reacted to these substances with diminishing promptness in the order just given. The differences in reaction time were marked. Now all four of these substances produce in man nearly the same taste quality, salt, for which the common constituent chlorine is therefore held responsible. The sodium, lithium, ammonium, and potassium ions have apparently but little effect on the human taste organs. Since the earthworm reacts with decided time differences to the four, it may be that its taste organs are specifically affected by each, and that different taste qualities may be occasioned in its consciousness, supposing it to be conscious (314). In other members of the annelid family, such as the leeches and marine worms, we know little of the differentiation between food and contact senses. That some of them respond to odorous substances is stated by Nagel (292).

§ 21.　*The Chemical Sense in Mollusks*

In the case of the Mollusca, also, there is little satisfactory evidence on the subject of the chemical sense. The Acephala, to which the clam, oyster, and scallop belong, do not take

---

[1] W. W. Norman argued that the squirming reactions of worms, and the corresponding reactions of other animals to injurious stimulation, cannot be taken as evidence of an accompaniment of disagreeable consciousness, because of the fact that when the worm, for instance, is cut in two, the squirming movements are confined to the posterior piece, while the head end crawls away undisturbed. The head end, he urges, containing the cerebral ganglia, ought to be the part capable of suffering, but it gives no reaction (295). We cannot, however, conclude from the absence of a reaction under abnormal conditions that its possible conscious accompaniment in the normal state is also done away with.

food by active movements; hence, of course, they can have no specific feeding reactions. Chemical sensibility, distributed over the surface of the body, has been observed in lamelli-branchs, a branch of the Acephala (292). Gasteropods, including snails and slugs, have, owing to their active food taking, more use for a chemical sense; in marine snails it seems rather definitely localized in the feelers (292). Yung found in the snail *Helix pomatia* that smell was most acute at the end of the feelers, but that the animal even when deprived of its feelers could distinguish perfume. Taste he found best developed near the lips, and touch sensibility distributed over the body, but especially toward the end of the feelers (472, 474).

§ 22. *The Chemical Sense in Echinoderms*

In the phylum of the echinoderms, under which are classed starfish and sea-urchins, the "circular symmetry" of body structure characteristic of the cœlenterates reappears. Starfish were found by Romanes many years ago to show, besides pronounced negative reactions to strong or injurious mechanical stimulation, what he called a sense of smell. Its manifestations depended on the *physiological condition* of the animal; that is, upon its degree of hunger. If kept several days without food a starfish would immediately perceive its presence and crawl toward it. "Moreover, if a small piece of the food were held in a pair of forceps and gently withdrawn as the starfish approached it, the animal could be led about the floor of the tank in any direction." By cutting off various parts of the rays, Romanes found that "the olfactory sense was equally distributed throughout their length;" and he also showed that the ventral and not the dorsal surface of the body was concerned, by varnishing the latter, which left the reactions unaffected, and by observing that when a bit of food

G

was placed on the back it remained unnoticed (365, pp. 321–322). Preyer reported great individual differences in the responses of starfish to food stimulation; while certain specimens were unmoved by the neighborhood of food, an individual of another species came from more than six inches away and fell upon it (350). Whether the unlikeness of behavior was due to the species difference or to a difference in the degree of hunger, does not appear.

§ 23. *The Chemical Sense in Crustacea*

The highest invertebrate animals belong to the phylum of the Arthropoda, like the annelid worms in their segmented structure, but more highly organized in many respects. The body of a typical arthropod consists of a series of segments, one behind another, each segment with a pair of appendages. The higher an arthropod stands in the scale, the more modification and differentiation of function there is in the segments and appendages; the former often become consolidated, and the latter become modified for swimming, walking, or sensory purposes. The lowest grand division of the Arthropoda is that of the Crustacea.

As the animals of this group are covered with a hard outside shell, sensitiveness to touch and chemical stimulation is ordinarily referred to certain hairs scattered over the body, and to the modified appendages of the anterior segments which we commonly know as "feelers," the large and small antennæ. That mechanical contact stimuli in certain Crustacea give rise to specialized reactions is evidenced by observations on the hermit crab. This animal, as is well known, has acquired the instinct of taking up its abode in empty shells, most commonly those of some gasteropod mollusk. When wandering about in search of a dwelling, the crab's reactions to the objects it meets show adaptation to the character of the stimulus, for it will not investigate a glass tube or ball; the smooth surface seems not to be the adequate stimulus for beginning the movements involved in exploring and entering a shell (41).

The responses of Crustacea to food stimulation vary, as might be expected, with different genera and species. Nagel finds the rôle of the food sense in aquatic Crustacea very insignificant; they occasionally show antennal movements in the presence of food, he says, but are not guided to it (292). That general restlessness is shown by various Crustacea in the neighborhood of food, but not in contact with it, has been observed by Bell in the crayfish (22), by Holmes in the amphipod *Amphithoe longimana* (180), by Bateson in shrimps and prawns (11), and by Bethe in the green crab (28). Bethe arranged a series of aquaria one above the other, with a connection between them, and found that when food was placed in the uppermost compartment the crabs in the lower ones were successively excited as the food juices diffused themselves from each compartment to the one below. In the amphipod, the small antennæ and the mouth parts appeared to be the regions especially sensitive to food stimulation; if the food touched one of the former, the animal instantly made a dart for it. Touching the antennule with a needle very rarely caused such a reaction (180). Bateson's shrimps and prawns had their food sensibility located chiefly in the antennules, though if food was placed very near them they would show disturbance even though deprived of antennules (11). This was the case also with Holmes's amphipod. Bell, on the other hand, found the whole body of the crayfish sensitive to chemical stimulation, and no evidence that the small antennæ were especially concerned. The crayfish's reactions to contact with food were such as to direct the stimulus toward the mouth; negative reactions of rubbing, scratching, and pulling at the affected part were obtained by stimulation with acids, salts, and other irritants (22). Evidences of irritation by the neighborhood of asafœtida were observed also by Graber in Pagurus (152).

In some Crustacea the sense of smell is possibly concerned in guiding the male to the female. Certain copepods which daily migrate from near the surface of the water to greater depths and back again have had this behavior explained as a result of the reactions of the females to light, plus the tendency of the males to follow the females. That the latter is an affair of chemical stimulation is indicated by the fact that the females were sought even when concealed in tubes (304). In the case of some other Crustacea, however, the sexes do not seem to be aware of each other's neighborhood until they come into actual contact (182, 184).

§ 24. *The Chemical Sense in Arachnida*

The two most important divisions of the phylum Arthropoda, besides the Crustacea, are those of the Arachnida and Insecta. Spiders, as is well known, have highly developed responses to mechanical stimulation; the web-making species in particular are sensitive to very slight web vibrations. The food reactions of spiders have never, so far as the writer knows, been tested, but various observers report sensitiveness to chemical stimulations, such as those produced by odorous oils, not in contact with the body. Spiders of the family Attidæ would react to glass rods dipped in such oils and brought close behind them, but would not react to clean glass rods when similarly placed (320). The reactions seem to be of a negative character (351), and, of course, in all such cases it remains uncertain whether the possible conscious accompaniment is a specifically olfactory unpleasantness or an unpleasant irritation of the body surface. Pritchett found that irritating and non-irritating oils gave negative reactions (351);

but an oil that belongs, for us, to the latter class might belong to the former in the case of a spider. If the sensibility were sharply localized, that fact would point in the direction of a specific olfactory sensation; but while some authorities think the spider's feelers or palpi are smell organs (25), others believe that sensibility to chemical stimulation is distributed over the body (258, 351). Nagel finds no specific organ of smell and little smell sensibility in spiders (292).

A member of the Arachnida which presents but slight superficial resemblance to the spiders is Limulus, the horseshoe crab. Limulus shows taste reactions, but no response to smell stimuli. If the mandibles at the base of the legs be rubbed with inedible objects, there is no reaction. Similar negative results are obtained by holding strong-smelling food close to the mouth or jaws. But if an edible substance be rubbed on the mandibles, strong chewing movements take place. Ammonia or acid vapor will produce these same chewing reflexes, but the claws make snapping movements "as though to pick away some disagreeable object." If a wad of blotting paper wet with ammonia or acid be laid on the mandibles, the chewing movements are reversed and the object is sometimes picked up by the claws and removed. Patten found organs which he believed to be gustatory on both the mandibles and the claws (315). Pearl observed no gustatory reactions in the free-swimming embryo of Limulus (317).

§ 25. *The Chemical Sense in Insects*

Throughout all the branches of the animal kingdom thus far mentioned, the chemical sense has functioned chiefly as a food sense. There has been but little evidence of the development of qualitative discrimination within the sense itself. That is, while in many cases an animal can apparently distinguish the edible from the inedible, and gives negative reactions to irritating chemicals, one would hardly be justified in saying that it possesses more than one food sensation quality; while in our own case, of course, though we make comparatively little use of the sense of smell, the qualitative discriminations possible by its means are many. But we come now to a group of animals where there appears a remarkable development of qualitative variety in the sensations resulting from chemical stimulation; namely, the Insecta. As the reactions of animals to mechanical stimulation, on the other hand, offer evidence of little qualitative difference in the accompanying sensations, we shall give but slight attention to them in what follows.

To begin with, there is evidence that taste and smell are distinct in many insects. The water beetle *Dytiscus marginalis*, found apparently unresponsive to food at a distance, will bite with especial eagerness at filter paper soaked in what Nagel calls "a pleasant solution" (292). Ants fed honey mixed with strychnine will taste it and then stop, and will do this even when the antennæ and mouth palpi are removed, indicating that the taste organs are in the mouth itself (130). Similar results have been obtained from similar tests on wasps, and it has been observed that wasps so treated will hesitate when offered pure honey afterward (439).

Vitus Graber tested the reactions of various insects to odors by the method which we called on page 60 the Method of Preference. This was Graber's favorite mode of studying the effect of stimuli upon animals. Applied to olfactory stimuli it consisted in offering a choice between different compartments, containing each a different odor. The animal's power of discrimination was argued from the tendency to choose certain odors rather than others. Such preferences were shown by the insects (152). The method, however, as was noted above, is unsatisfactory, because discrimination might exist where preference did not. Another criticism urged against Graber's experiments is that the odors used were too strong and irritating. The insects displayed choice between odors even when their antennæ were removed; but there is much evidence to show that the antennæ are the true organs of smell in insects. Various flies and beetles which are in the habit of laying their eggs in putrefying flesh will not react to it when their antennæ are removed, and it has been shown that insects which seem to find their mates by response to olfactory stimulation, fail to do so when deprived of antennæ (130). Interesting "compensatory movements" have been seen in silkworm moths with one antenna removed; they turned, that is, in the direction of the remaining antenna (219). We shall note movements of this class later in insects with one eye blackened, and in fish with one auditory nerve cut. The exploring movements of the antennæ which certain insects make in seeking a proper place to lay their eggs in have been taken as evidence of the smell function of these organs (324). It may be, then, that the reactions of insects without antennæ observed by Graber were due rather to the irritating than to the properly olfactory character of the stimuli.

The function of the chemical sense in the mating processes of insects is one of the most remarkable phenomena connected with the sensory reactions of animals. Forel says he had a female Saturnia moth shut up in his city room, and that within a short time a number of males came and beat against the window (130). Riley hatched in Chicago some moths from the Ailanthus silkworm, which were carefully confined. No other specimens were known to exist within hundreds of miles. A virgin female was put in a wicker cage on an ailanthus tree, and a male, with a silk thread tied around the abdomen for identification, was liberated a mile and a half away. The next morning the two were together (363).

The most interesting observations on the sense of smell as used in the mating of insects, however, are those of Fabre. A cocoon of the "*Bombyx du chêne*," a species of which Fabre had not seen a specimen in the locality for twenty years, was brought to him, and from it a female hatched. Sixty males sought her within a few hours after she reached maturity. Fabre noticed in this and other cases that shutting the female in an air-tight box prevented the males from being guided to her, but that the smallest opening was enough to allow the odor to escape; that the males were not in the least confused or led astray by placing dishes of odorous substances about, and that they would seek anything on which the female had rested for a time, a fact which suggests that the stimulus is a secretion of the body, as it is known to be in silkworm moths. Fabre offers the suggestion that smell stimuli as they are operative in the animal kingdom generally may be of two classes: (1) substances which give off particles in vapor or gas, and (2) substances which give off a form of vibration. Our own olfactory sense is limited to the first class of stimuli, but some animals, notably insects, may be sensitive to both (115). Certainly the marvellous sensitiveness involved in these mating reactions suggests a kind of response to stimulation unknown in human experience.

§ 26. *How Ants find Food*

In many ways the Hymenoptera are the most interesting of insects, particularly those members of the order which have developed community life. Their reactions to chemical stimulation have been the subject of a large mass of literature, some of the more important results of which we may now undertake to survey, considering ants, bees, and wasps successively. Sir John Lubbock was among the earliest observers to indicate the great importance of chemical stimuli in the life of ants. In the first place, he demonstrated that it is by chemical stimulation that *ants are able to follow each other to supplies of food;* or to larvæ, for an ant's behavior to an ant larva found in the course of its wandering is like its behavior to food; the larva is picked up and carried to the nest. Lubbock put some larvæ on a glass plate at a little distance from one of his artificial ant nests, and set a similar empty plate beside it; he then made a bridge of a strip of paper leading from the nest toward the plates, and connected each of them with this bridge by a separate short paper strip. He placed a marked ant at the larvæ; she picked up one and returned to the nest. She soon appeared followed by several others; when she had reached the larvæ, and before the others had arrived at the dividing of the ways, Lubbock exchanged the short strips, so that the one over which the marked ant had passed now led to the empty plate. The following ants all took this path, indicating that they were guided by some trace which her footsteps had left. Lubbock was inclined to think, however, that some kind of communication must have passed between the marked ant and her fellows in the nest to induce them to follow her, and also that this communication might on occasion convey some notion of the quantity of food or larvæ to be had. He placed three glass plates near an ant nest, connecting each of them with the nest by means of a paper strip. On one plate he put a heap of several hundred larvæ, on the second two or three only; the third was empty. He put marked ants on each of the plates, and captured all the ants which they led back with them. Many more ants came to the plate with the larger heap of larvæ than to the others. Lubbock explained this by supposing that the ant from that dish had in some way communicated to the nest the greater numbers at her disposal (248, pp. 172 ff.). Obviously it would be enough to suppose that the smell of food or larvæ about an ant returning laden to the nest is a stimulus to her nestmates to follow her; that this smell is stronger, the larger the stock she has found, and hence acts as a more powerful stimulus.

§ 27. *How Ants find the Way Home*

Lubbock's experiments indicated also that in *finding their way back to the nest* ants make more use of smell than of sight. One only of these observations need be described. Lubbock placed larvæ in a dish on a table connected by a bridge with an ant nest. He accustomed the ants to go back and forth from the dish to the nest along a path which he diversified by artificial scenery, such as rows of bricks along either side, and a paper tunnel. When the path was thoroughly learned he moved the bricks and the tunnel so that they led in a different direction; the ants, however, were not at all disconcerted by this cataclysm of nature, but followed the same track as before, evidently guided by their own footprints (248, p. 259). The direction of the light is not without some influence, however. When two candles that had stood near the nest were moved to the opposite side, some of the ants were confused (248, p. 268). Bethe, whose object is to show that all ant behavior is a series of unconscious reflexes to chemical stimuli, made the following attempt to study the formation of a new ant path. He placed near the entrance to a nest a large sheet of paper covered with lampblack, on which the footsteps of the ants could be traced. On this paper he placed a supply of food. When an ant had found the food, in going back to the nest she always followed the path by which she had come, except that when the original path had crossed itself in loops, the ant omitted the loops in returning. Other ants followed the same path, though they all had a tendency to cut off curves (30). Wasmann, the ardent opponent of Bethe's reflex theory, looks with suspicion on this tendency gradually to straighten the path, and thinks an animal reflexly drawn along by a chemical stimulus on the ground would make no improvements in the route (426). The evidence that it is the sense of smell, if not a smell reflex, that guides the ants remains, however, strong. Bethe further points out that the chemical stimulus deposited by the feet of the ants is volatile. If a strip of paper be placed across an ant path, the ants on coming to it stop, quest about, and are delayed until one accidentally runs across the strip and others follow. (Why, asks Wasmann, if they are being reflexly drawn along, do they not merely stop short when the stimulus fails, instead of hunting for it?) The piece of paper is thus gradually adopted into the ant road; if it is subsequently removed, the ants stop and are bewildered at the place where it was, showing that the earlier traces of their footsteps, under the paper, have evaporated. Again, Bethe thinks he has evidence that the chemical stimulus left by the feet of ants going from the nest is different from that deposited by those going to the nest, and that ants on the way home will not follow a track made by the feet of other ants on the outward journey, and *vice versa* (30). That they will follow their own individual track in either direction is shown by the smoked paper experiment just described, and also by an experiment of Fielde's, where ants finding their way through a labyrinth from a heap of pupæ to the nest and back again followed each one its own trail without regard to the others (218). Bethe found that when the usual road to an ant nest had been interrupted by the removal of a heap of sand, and the road across the breach had been established solely by incoming ants, the outgoing ants refused to follow it, and made a new road for themselves (30). Wasmann thinks this may have been done merely on account of the faintness of the recently established path as compared with the old one (426). Bethe observed also that if a strip of paper had been adopted into an ant road, and was then while an ant was on it rotated through 180 degrees, the ant stopped and was disturbed on coming to the end of it (30). Experiments on rotating ants were made also by Lubbock (248), and seem to give puzzling and conflicting results; it is not clear why even on the assumption that there is a difference in odor between the road to the nest and that from the nest, an ant on a road which led both ways should have found her course interrupted by rotation. One fact, Bethe thinks, shows that even assuming two road smells is not enough. Ants of certain families (Lasius) which habitually make regular and frequented roads, can if they come upon one of these roads in wandering at once take the proper direction, either to or from the nest. Evidently the mere presence of two smells would not enable them to do this. Bethe suggests that the particles of the two chemical substances are also differently polarized, so that one of them can be followed only in one direction, the other in the opposite direction (30). Wasmann objects to this that an ant returning on its own traces would destroy them, as the opposite polarizations would cancel; and that similar confusion would occur on a narrow and much frequented road (426). He and Forel (132) both think that, granting the distinction between the outward and inward paths, which is made by only a few families of ants, the direction is most probably given by a perception of the "smell form" of the footsteps obtained through the antennæ.

Recently C. H. Turner has come to the conclusion that ants are not guided "slavishly" or reflexly by the odor of their tracks in finding the way to and from the nest. He made a small cardboard stage from which an inclined cardboard

bridge led down to the artificial ant nest. Ants and pupæ
were placed on the stage. After the ants had through
random movements learned the way down the incline
a second incline was placed so as to lead from the opposite
side of the stage to the nest. No ants went down this way.
The inclines were then exchanged so that the one bearing the
scent of the ants' footprints was on the opposite side and the
unscented incline in the old place; the ants continued to go
down in the old place. It is unsafe to criticise an experiment
without having actually seen it, but Turner's account does not
exclude the possibility that the ants were guided in setting
out on their homeward course by the scent of their footprints
on the cardboard stage, which seems to have remained un-
changed. He confirms Bethe's observation that the pathways to and from the nest are different, but does not find
that even a single ant follows her own footsteps in both directions. The direction of the light, not smell, is the ruling
factor in pathfinding, according to Turner, who offers the
following experimental evidence. When the stage with the
first incline was arranged as before and a 16 c.p. lamp
placed near the side to which the incline was attached, the ants
learned to go down the pathway to the nest. When the incline on the opposite side was added, and, after waiting a time
to make sure that no ants went down that way, the lamp
was moved to the other side, marked disturbance was shown
by the ants. "In most cases, some would finally go down
the new incline; in a few cases after the lapse of several
minutes all went down the new incline." Altering the intensity of the light had no effect; the disturbance was caused
by any decided change in its direction (408).

In all probability, different species of ants vary in the
degree to which they make use of smell as a guide. Piéron,
for example, finds that *Formica cinerea* depends more upon

vision than *Lasius fuliginosus*, which is guided largely by smell (325), and the same conclusion is reached by Wasmann (426). Piéron calls attention to still another factor which he calls muscular memory, influential in all the species he tested, but especially so in *Aphænogaster barbara nigra*. If an ant of this species is returning to the nest and steps on a bit of paper covered with earth, she may be moved bodily to some distance without seeming to notice the fact. In such a case, on being set down, she continues her march "in the new region, following a direction absolutely identical with that which she was following in her return to the nest, and she does not stop or seem disturbed until after a more or less prolonged march, often about equal to the distance that separated her, at the moment when she was displaced, from the entrance to the nest." Even if her displacement occurs near the entrance to the nest, she will go on past it and stop at a distance about equal to that which she would ordinarily have had to traverse. Evidently smell is not here concerned (325). The ant would seem to be like a little machine wound up to go just so far and to take just such turnings. We shall mention this observation again in a later chapter.

§ 28. *How Ants "recognize" Nest Mates*

Another problem of ant life to which smell appears to furnish the key is that of the *recognition of nest mates*. It has long been known that an ant entering a strange nest, though of the same species, is likely to meet with rough treatment, and even be put to death. Now Forel found in 1886 that ants of the genus Myrmica whose antennæ were removed would attack their own nest mates (130). It seems probable that each nest of ants has a peculiar odor which is the basis of the distinction between friends and foes. Bethe tested the smell theory by dipping an ant first in weak alcohol, then in water, and then in the juices obtained by crushing the bodies of a number of ants of another species. He found that an ant thus treated would be attacked and killed by its own nest mates, but could be introduced, though not so easily, into the nest whose odor it now presumably bore, even though its appearance was quite different from that of the ants therein (30). Wasmann repeated these experiments with much less success than Bethe; bathing Myrmica ants with essence of Tetramorium ant did not preserve them from final destruction at the jaws of the latter, though it delayed their fate; nor did much bathing with foreign nest odors induce their nest mates to attack ants of the species *Lomechusa strumosa*, though they seemed disturbed at first. Wasmann apparently thinks other factors besides smell, vision perhaps, enter into the recognition process (426). Bethe, in a later paper, suggests that Wasmann's negative results may have been due to the fact that the nest smell very quickly returns to the ants after it has been removed; he himself took account only of the first reaction of other ants toward the one subjected to treatment (31).

Fielde, as the result of a study of the genus Stenamma, concludes that each ant is the bearer of three distinct odors: the individual odor, which enables her to follow her own trail in a labyrinth, and the reception of which depends upon the tenth segment of the antennæ; the race odor, dependent on the eleventh segment; and the nest odor, dependent on the twelfth (118). In a later article she concludes that the nest odor of the worker ants is derived from their queen mother; that the odor of the queen is unchanging, and is imparted to her eggs. The worker, however, gradually changes its odor. Queens of diverse odors may be produced by the influence of males that are the offspring of worker mothers and have the differentiated worker odor. A young ant isolated from the pupa stage until many days old will single out its queen mother from queens of other species, but will show decided suspicion of older sister worker ants. A mixed nest formed of newly hatched ants of different species was separated for seven months. On rejoining each other, the ants showed hostility; their odor, Fielde argues, had changed. But young ants of one species were received by those of the other species. Fielde does not hesitate to introduce the psychic factor and say that the latter remembered the odor of the young ones, having been associated with it in their own youth. The suggestion might be made that the young ants had not as yet developed any specific odor, but this is opposed by the observation that newly hatched Lasius ants from a strange colony were not received by a nest of Stenammas, while young Lasius ants from a colony with which the Stenammas had been acquainted in youth were accepted eleven months after the latter had been segregated. It is an affair of the memory, Fielde is assured; and she says, "If an ant's experience be narrow, it will quarrel with many, while acquaintance with a great number of ant odors will cause it to live peaceably with ants of diverse lineage, provided the odors characterizing such lineage and age environ it at its hatching" (123). Bethe held that an ant's own nest odor offered no stimulus to it at all, but that fighting reflexes were occasioned by any foreign nest odor (30). Many facts, however, seem to tell against this view; among others, the early observation of Forel that a Myrmica ant deprived of its antennæ attacks everything in sight (130). It should, according to Bethe's theory, live peaceably with all.

Thus we see that in spite of some divergence of testimony, there is evidence that ants have a variety of qualitatively different smell experiences: the smell of food and of larvæ, probably distinct, though there is no experimental proof of the fact; the individual smell of an ant's own footsteps; a possible distinction, in some species, between the smell of the outgoing and that of the incoming paths; and the different odors which seem to be responsible for the discrimination between nest mates and foreigners. If it is true, as Fielde maintains, that loss of the eighth and ninth segments of the antennæ renders an ant incapable of caring for the young, then the recognition of larvæ and pupæ does depend upon a specific odor (118). Forel makes an interesting distinction between the sense of smell in insects with immovable antennæ and the same sense where the antennæ, as in ants, can be moved about over objects. In the former case it is as with us a qualitative sense pure and simple, giving information of objects at a distance; in the latter case it is a contact sense, and may give rise to spatial as well as qualitative perceptions. He compares the antennæ to a pair of olfactory hands, and points out how such organs may allow of the perception of the "smell form" of objects (132).

§ 29. *How Bees are attracted to Flowers*

In bees the sense of smell is equally well developed. But no topic in comparative psychology has been more hotly disputed than the use which bees make of this sense, and the extent to which they depend, rather, upon sight. Darwin (90) and H. Müller (284, 285) thought both color and fragrance influential in attracting insects. Plateau maintains that the chief influence attracting bees to flowers is smell, and that color has little effect. He made a number of experiments in which the brightly colored corollas of flowers were cut off without disturbing the nectaries, and claims to have found that the visits of bees to the mutilated flowers were as frequent as before (336–338, 339, 341). On the other

H

hand, Giltay obtained opposite results; the flowers whose corollas were removed were neglected by bees, while those which were covered so as to be invisible, but not so as to prevent the odor from escaping, were also unnoticed (144). Josephine Wéry found that the proportion of bees visiting flowers with intact corollas to those visiting flowers with the corollas removed was 66 : 18 (434). Kienitz-Gerloff criticises Plateau's figures and the accuracy of his experiments (220). Forel found that a bee with the antennæ and all the mouth parts removed, hence probably incapable of smell, returned to flowers for honey, though of course without success (130). Andreæ thinks that among diurnal insects those which live on the ground, and take but short flights, are more influenced by smell; while the freely flying insects are attracted by the sight of flowers (5).

§ 30. *How Bees find the Hive*

Most complicated of all is the problem as to how bees find their way back to the hive. It is obvious that the simple ant method of following a chemical trail is ruled out for insects that fly. Bethe abandons the puzzle as insoluble (30).

Von Buttel-Reepen attempts at length, and with a vast amount of apic lore, to refute his position. It would be impossible to give more than the briefest statement of the arguments of both sides. Bethe maintains that the smell of the hive does not guide the bees back to it, because he found that if the hive were rotated slowly enough to allow the cloud of nest smell at the opening to move with the opening, the bees returning would not follow it for more than 45°, but would go to the place where the opening had been. He thinks they are not guided by sight, because when he completely changed the appearance of the hive, masking it with branches, and other coverings, the bees were not disconcerted, but flew straight to the mouth of the hive. He brings other evidence against the vision hypothesis which we shall discuss in Chapter XI. An unknown force, he concludes, guides the bee in its homing flight (30). Von Buttel-Reepen believes that visual memory will explain all the facts; that the bees were not disturbed by the altered appearance of their hive because they knew their way so thoroughly that nothing could disturb them by the time they had come so nearly home. The visual memory required is, he admits, of a peculiar sort, which we shall consider in a later chapter. The odor of the hive does coöperate with vision in certain cases; when a stock of bees has been moved without their knowledge, they fly out without making any "orienting flight," as they commonly do on leaving a new place, a fact that is one of the evidences for the visual memory theory. Nevertheless, many of them succeed in finding their way back, and then, if their hive is placed among a number of others, von Buttel-Reepen thinks they "smell" their way back to the right one. He mocks at Bethe's unknown force, on the ground that it must sometimes lead the bee to the hive and sometimes back to the place where food has been found (72). Bethe attempts to answer this by saying that the force acts in coöperation with the physiological condition of the animal; the laden bee follows it to the hive, the bee with the empty crop is led back to the food supply (32). Of course one may say what one pleases about the *modus operandi* of an unknown force without fear of disproof, but also without carrying much conviction.

§ 31. *How Bees "recognize" Nest Mates*

The nest smell, which characterizes each hive and prevents the reception of strangers, who are treated precisely after the fashion of ants in similar circumstances, is composed according to von Buttel-Reepen of the following odors: the individual odor of different workers; the family odor, common to all the offspring of the same queen; the larval smell and food smell; the drone smell, the wax smell, and the honey smell. There are various ways in which the mode of reaction to a foreign nest smell is modified. If two bee stocks are placed side by side, and one has the queen and entire brood removed, it will go over to the other stock and be kindly received. One can understand that the attraction of the queen and brood odor may overcome the tendency of the foreign nest smell to repel the invaders, but it is harder to see why the more fortunate stock should allow itself to be invaded. Further, a bee laden with honey can get itself received by a foreign stock that has exchanged hives with it, where an unladen bee is attacked; here the smell of the honey may overcome the foreign smell. As is well known, two alien stocks may be united by sprinkling them with some odorous substance. The queen odor is the strongest factor in the nest smell; in swarming it overcomes the tendency to return to the old nest, and queenless swarms will join themselves to foreign swarms having a queen. The apparent attention paid to the queen while laying eggs, the gathering of workers around her trilling their antennæ toward her, suggest strongly that her odor is pleasant to them. The queen herself, however, is perfectly indifferent to any foreign nest smell, and will beg food of any bee, even those which are angrily crowded around her cage in a foreign hive. Drones also will go from stock to stock, and are always peacefully received until drone-killing time begins. It has usually been supposed that the unrest displayed by a bee stock when deprived of its queen is due to the absence of the queen odor, and it seems almost certain that this must be a powerful influence, though von Buttel-Reepen thinks it is not the only influence, for he has observed that if the queen be replaced in the honey space, removed from the rest of the hive, the bees will quiet instantly, before the smell has had time to diffuse itself. Also, bees sometimes behave as if they had lost their queen when she is only put in a cage, and her odor is perfectly accessible (72).

It is clear that bees as well as ants are capable of distinguishing a considerable number of smell qualities. Probably the same thing is true of the social wasps. In the solitary wasps, however, we find less evidence of a highly developed sense of smell, or rather of a great variety of smell reactions, and the solitary bees are very likely less influenced by smell than the social bees. In the interesting study of the solitary wasps by Mr. and Mrs. Peckham, it appears that sight plays a far more important rôle than smell for these insects and the return to the nest in particular seems to be almost entirely an affair of sight (322, 323). In general the greatest development of qualitative variety in the sense of smell is found in the social Hymenoptera, and is probably a product of the social state. Perris, however, noted that the solitary wasp Dinetus was much disturbed in finding its nest hole if he had placed his hand over the hole during the wasp's absence, and thought the odor of his hand was distracting to the insect (324).

§ 32. *The Chemical Sense in Vertebrates*

Although the vertebrates stand at the head of the animal kingdom, yet in point of complexity of structure and behavior the lowest vertebrate is far below the highest members of the invertebrate division. When we undertake to study the responses to special stimulation displayed by this same lowest vertebrate, the little Amphioxus or lancelet, it is like going back to the earthworm. The only kind of evidence that contact, chemical, and temperature stimuli

produce specific sensation qualities is found in the fact that
sensibility to them is differently localized, and may be independently fatigued. To weak acid, the head end of the
animal is most sensitive, the posterior end less, the middle
least; to contact with a camel's-hair brush, the two ends are
equally sensitive and more so than the middle; to a current
of warm water the order of sensitiveness is head end, middle, posterior end (311).

For fishes, as for all aquatic animals, the distinction between smell and taste becomes obscure. The neighborhood
of food not in actual contact with the body seems to stir fish
to activity, but not to direct their movements. Bateson
(12) and Herrick (165) both obtained evidence of this; Nagel,
on the other hand, declares that fish do not perceive food at a
distance except by sight, and that the function of the first pair
of cranial nerves in these animals must remain uncertain (292).
The well-developed character of these "olfactory" nerves
and lobes, whose function in higher vertebrates is certainly
connected with smell, would argue against the supposition that
smell can be wholly lacking in fishes. It is generally agreed
that a contact food sense exists in fish; Nagel, however,
holds that its organs are situated only about the mouth (292),
while Herrick has good experimental proof that fishes which
have "terminal buds," structures resembling taste buds,
distributed over the skin, are also sensitive to food stimulation
applied to different regions of the skin. He thinks that Nagel's
negative results were due to the fact that instead of food stimuli
in his experiments he used chemicals with which the fish
would not normally be acquainted (165). Nagel thinks the
rôle of the chemical sense in Amphibia also is negligible (292),
and there is no experimental evidence, to the writer's knowledge, indicating specific taste or smell sensations either in Amphibia or in reptiles. In birds the high development of both

sight and hearing, and the fact that almost all reactions are made in response to the stimuli for these senses, masks the presence of olfactory sensitiveness if it exists. Taste, birds seem to have; the chicks experimented on by Lloyd Morgan, for example, displayed disgust at picking up bits of orange peel instead of yolk of egg (281, pp. 40–41). Xavier Raspail is, so far as the writer knows, the only observer who has expressed a definite opinion in favor of the sense of smell in birds. He thinks they abandon eggs that have been handled because they detect the fact by smell; that they find buried grubs by smell, and are guided by this sense to concealed food and water. The last statement he supports by the observation that their tracks lead straight to hidden food on their first visit to it, showing that it was not found by accident (359).

When we come to the Mammalia, however, we find in the great majority of types a very high development of qualitative discrimination in the sense of smell. Hunters know it to be the chief defensive weapon of wild animals, and it has retained great keenness in many domesticated ones, — the cat, for instance, which will be awakened from slumber in the garret by the odor, quite unsuspected of human nostrils, of some favorite food being prepared in the kitchen, and is thrown into ecstasy at a faint whiff of catnip. The dog, however, is the hero of this field of mental prowess. The experiments of Romanes on the power of a favorite setter to track his scent are well known. In one of them he collected a number of men, and told them to walk in Indian file, "each man taking care to place his feet in the footprints of his predecessor. In this procession, numbering twelve in all," Romanes says, "I took the lead, while the gamekeeper brought up the rear. When we had walked two hundred yards, I turned to the right, followed by five of the men; and at the point where I had turned to the right, the seventh man turned to the left, followed by all the remainder. The two parties . . . having walked in opposite directions for a considerable distance, concealed themselves, and the bitch was put upon the common track of the whole party before the point of divergence. Following this common track with rapidity, she at first overshot the point of divergence, but quickly recovering it, without any hesitation chose the track which turned to the right." It had previously been ascertained that she would not follow the scent of any other man in the party save her master, and failing him, the gamekeeper. "Yet . . . my footprints," continues Romanes, "in the common track were overlaid by eleven others, and in the track to the right by five others. Moreover, as it was the gamekeeper who brought up the rear, and as in the absence of my trail she would always follow his, the fact of his scent being, so to speak, uppermost in the series, was shown in no way to disconcert the animal following another familiar scent lowermost in the series" (367). Such behavior indicates not only that the dog can experience a variety of smell qualities, which is also the case with us human beings, but that it has the power to analyze a fusion of different odors and attend exclusively to one component, a power that we lack almost entirely. When we experience two smell stimuli at the same time, it is but rarely that we can detect both of the two qualities in the mixture; usually one of them swamps the other, or else a new odor unlike both results. But the dog, and probably many other animals, can analyze a smell fusion as a trained musician analyzes a chord. In this respect, if not in the variety of smell qualities, the olfactory sense has undergone degeneration in us, and so far as we can judge, the fact is due to the habit of relying rather upon the sense of sight.

Even in the case of the monkey, Kinnaman reports that the animals he was testing with regard to their power of discriminating the size, shape, and color of vessels in one of which food was placed, always looked, never smelled, for the food (221).

CHAPTER VI

SENSORY DISCRIMINATION: HEARING

§ 33. *Hearing in Lower Invertebrates*

THE sense of hearing, in all air-dwelling animals, is that sense whose adequate stimulus consists in air vibrations; for human beings these vibrations may reach a frequency of 50,000 (single vibrations) in one second and still produce an auditory sensation. But the meaning of the term "hearing" for water-dwelling animals, and hence for most of the lowest forms of animal life, is more difficult to determine. In the Protozoa it seems to have no meaning at all; the reactions of these animals to water vibrations are indistinguishable from their reactions to mechanical stimulation. But in some of the cœlenterates the possibility of a specific auditory sensation quality has been suggested by the discovery of a peculiar sense organ. While varying in its structure in different genera and orders of cœlenterate animals, this organ consists typically of a small sac, filled with fluid and containing one or more mineral bodies. Apparently these latter could operate in connection with a stimulus only when the stimulus was constituted by shaking the animal, or in some way disturbing its equilibrium. They might then serve as means for the reception of water vibrations, as the ear serves for the reception of air vibrations; they might, in short, be primitive organs of hearing. Accordingly the term "otocysts" was given to organs of this type wherever they were found in the animal kingdom, and the mineral bodies in the otocysts were called otoliths.

But experiments upon cœlenterates have entirely failed to show that animals of this class react to sounds (111, 415, 291). And in some cœlenterates, as well as in higher animals having the same type of organ, the removal of the so-called otocysts has been found to involve disturbance of the animal's power to keep its balance and maintain a normal position. Hence Verworn has suggested that for "otocyst" and "otolith" the terms "statocyst" and "statolith" might appropriately be substituted (415). In jellyfish, indeed, even the balancing function of the statocyst organs appears doubtful; and it is possible that they function in response to shaking and jarring (286, 291). In any case, there is no evidence whatever of a specific auditory sensation in the consciousness, if such exists, of cœlenterate animals.

Nor has any reaction to sound been demonstrated in either the flatworms or the annelid worms; their sensitiveness to vibrations seems to be an affair of mechanical stimulation. Darwin's experiments on this point are well known. The earthworms which he observed were quite insensitive to musical tones, but when the flower pots containing their burrows were placed on a piano, the worms retreated hastily as soon as a note was struck (91). Most observers agree that mollusks also react only to mechanical jars (*e.g.*, 101), and that the statocyst organs found in some mollusks have no auditory function. Bateson, however, records that a certain lamellibranch, suspended by a thread in a tank, responded by shutting its shell when a sound was produced by rubbing a finger along the glass side of the tank (12), and Bethe demands to know of what possible use as static organs the statocysts in fixed mollusks can be (27). The echinoderms are apparently insensitive to auditory stimuli (350, 365).

§ 34. *Hearing in Crustacea*

In the Crustacea the function of the statocyst organs has been the subject of much dispute. They are in this group of animals sometimes closed sacs with statoliths, sometimes open sacs containing grains of sand. Most commonly the organs are situated in the basal segment of the small antennæ. There is usually inside the sac a projection bearing several ridges of hairs, graded in size, which tempt to the hypothesis that they respond to vibrations of different wave lengths, as the fibres of the basilar membrane of the human cochlea are supposed by the Helmholz theory to do. Hensen, indeed, placing under the microscope the tail of a small shrimp, Mysis, whose statocyst is situated in that region, observed that the long hairs of the tail vibrated in response to musical tones, from which he infers that the statocyst hairs may do so [1] (163). In 1899 he was still inclined to believe that the latter can serve no other than an auditory function (164). Nevertheless the weight of authority is in favor of regarding the "sac" in Crustacea as a static rather than an auditory organ. The only evidence of sound reaction in two shrimp-like forms, Palæmon and Palæmonetes, was a "flight reflex" given by some individuals when sounds were produced very near them in the water; and although this response ceased when the statocysts were destroyed, the fact is of little significance, as other reflexes also were abolished by the operation (19). To sounds made by tapping the wall of the aquarium Palæmonetes reacted by leaping away from the wall nearest to it, even though the leap was made toward the sound. When both statocysts were removed, the reactions were still made, but not so markedly nor at so great a distance from the

---

[1] This observation is sometimes incorrectly quoted as if the hairs concerned were actually the statocyst hairs. Cf., for example, Morgan, 279, p. 266.

sound. A similar response to the striking of a partially submerged glass jar was seen in a decapod, *Virbius zosteri- cola*, which has no statoliths (349). Mysis has been found to react to sounds when the statocysts are destroyed (27). The fiddler crab, which is amphibious, responds in water to vibrations by retreating slowly from the vibrating walls, and does the same when blinded and deprived of its statocysts, but gives no reaction when the antennæ and antennules are removed. On land these animals do not respond to sounds, only to vibrations produced in the earth, for instance by stamping (349). No sound reactions have been found in the crayfish (21). In short, such responses to vibrations as occur among the Crustacea seem affairs rather of mechanical than of true auditory stimulation; nevertheless Bethe (27) and Hensen (164) are both inclined to believe, as did Delage, who first called attention to the static function of the statocysts (97), that they may be auditory organs also. The "static sense" of Crustacea will be discussed later.

§ 35. *Hearing in Spiders*

In spiders the same difficulty arises, of deciding whether the reactions to sound are tactile or auditory. There are no statocysts, but the delicate hairs on the body and legs of the animal have been held to be auditory organs. Dahl, a number of years ago, found them responding to the tones of a violin (86, 87), but this test, which Hensen applied to Mysis, is of very doubtful significance; as Prentiss suggests, the hairs on the back of the human hand do the same (349). When various species of spiders were tested by holding tuning forks near them or their webs, only the web-making species gave any response. These latter would not react to ordinary noises, nor to the sound of a small fork, but to the humming of a large fork they responded always by raising the front legs, and sometimes by dropping from their webs (320). Two Texan species that were experimented upon by placing them in a cage free from vibration gave no response whatever to tuning forks of various pitches or to other sounds (351). It seems, then, highly probable that spiders are sensitive only to vibrations communicated to their webs, and very likely these furnish tactile rather than specific auditory stimulation. The observation of Boys may be quoted: "On sounding an A fork, and lightly touching with it any leaf or other support of the web or any portion of the web itself, I found that the spider, if at the centre of the web, rapidly slews around so as to face the direction of the fork, feeling with its fore feet along which radial thread the vibration travels. Having become satisfied on this point, it next darts along that thread till it reaches either the fork itself or a junction of two or more threads, the right one of which it instantly determines as before. If the fork is not removed when the spider has arrived it seems to have the same charm as any fly, for the spider seizes it, embraces it, and runs about on the legs of the fork as often as it is made to sound, never seeming to learn by experience that other things may buzz besides its natural food. If the spider is not at the centre of the web at the time that the fork is applied, it cannot tell which way to go until it has been to the centre to ascertain which radial thread is vibrating." If, however, it has followed the fork to the edge of the web, and the fork is then withdrawn and brought near again, the spider reaches out in its direction. If the spider is at the centre of the web and a sounding fork is brought near without touching the web, the spider does not reach for it, but drops down at the end of a thread. If the fork touches the web again, the spider climbs the thread and finds the spot very quickly (69).

§ 36. *Hearing in Insects*

The sense of hearing in insects also is problematical. When the insect makes a sound itself, which, as in the case of crickets, is connected with the mating process, it would seem *a priori* highly probable that it can hear. Various structures have been designated as auditory organs, the finely branched antennæ of mosquitos and gnats, on the same doubtful evidence that they have been found to vibrate in response to musical tones (264); and in the Orthoptera certain very peculiar structures situated on the front legs of grasshoppers and crickets, and in the first segment of the abdomen in locusts. These structures Graber called chordotonal organs, and he felt convinced from experimental tests that they were auditory. The cockroach, Blatta, while running about the room will stop, he says, for an instant when the strings of a violin are struck. A blinded specimen, hung by a thread, became violently agitated at a sudden tone from a violin. A water insect, Corixa, although undisturbed by the water vibrations produced by pushing a bone disk toward it in the water, gave decided reactions when the disk was connected with an electric bell. Other water beetles were still more sensitive. That they distinguished pitch differences Graber thought probable from the fact that he observed reactions of different degrees of violence to sounds of different pitch; and their discrimination of intensity changes he thought demonstrated by the fact that if a continuous tone, sounding while a water beetle is swimming about, be made suddenly louder, the speed of the insect's movements visibly increases. It is going rather far, however, to pass from the evidence that insects discriminate sounds made by their own species from other sounds to the conclusion that "they like us have the capacity to analyze, at least to a certain degree, these peculiar clangs or noises, and to distinguish clearly from one another the partial tones that compose them" (149).

Tower thought that he had observed the potato beetle reacting to the sound of a tuning fork (404). Will noted responses from a male beetle to the stridulation of a female of its species enclosed in a box 15 cm. away (439). Rádl has recently made the suggestion that the organs which Graber called chordotonal organs, and which contain a fibre stretched between two points of the integument, represent a kind of transition between "*Gemeingefühl*" and hearing. In support he offers the following evidence: the fibres resemble the tendons in which some muscles end, and are very likely developed from tendons; the organs exist in insects that have no use for hearing, such as grubs shut up in fruits; insects have not been shown to respond to pure tones, but only to noises such as the cricket's chirping, which for us affect *Gemeingefühl*. Further, there is no evidence that hearing ever guides insects to each other; in short, it is but a rudimentary sense, and its organs are those which serve also to register muscular activity. It is, in insects, a "refined muscular sense" (357).

The auditory sense, if it exists in insects, is very likely confined to those which produce sounds, and its qualities limited within the range of such sounds. Most species of ants, for instance, produce no sound that the human ear, even with the aid of a microphone 248), can detect, although certain East Indian species are reported to make a loud hissing noise when disturbed (424), and some American species are said to chirp (108, 437). Ch. Janet maintains that ants of the Myrmicidæ make a stridulating noise (190, 191). The weight of evidence is also against the existence of sound reactions in ants; careful experiments by Fielde and Parker on a number of species led to the conclusion that the only vibrations responded to were those which were communicated through the solid on which the ants stood, and received through the legs (125). It is probable that the observers who have come to opposite conclusions have not in every case been careful to exclude the possibility of such vibration of the substratum. Wasmann, for instance, thinks he has seen reactions to sound; he noted that ants in an artificial nest raised their antennæ and lifted the fore part of their bodies when he scratched with a needle on some sealing wax with which the nest had been mended (423). He also quotes Forel's account (129) of a species which makes an "alarm signal" by striking the ground with its abdomen: this, remarks Wasmann naïvely, must be perceived by the ants, "otherwise it would not be an alarm signal"! (424). If perceived, it may of course be as a tactile rather than an auditory sensation. Weld has observed reactions to the sound of whistles and tuning forks in several species of ants, and even concludes that they perceive the direction from which sounds come; but since, of the four observations upon which this latter opinion is based, two were cases where the ants hurried toward the sound and the others cases where they backed away from it, the possibility of mere coincidence seems not to be excluded (433).

As regards the auditory sense in bees, there is again a difference of opinion. They do, of course, make sounds, and sounds of different quality, under different conditions. Yet Lubbock entirely failed to get bees to respond to any kind of sounds artificially produced (248), while Bethe urges that the sounds produced by bees are involuntary, like the sounds of our own breathing and heart-beats, and that there is no more evidence that bees can hear them than that we can hear these sounds in our own case (32). Forel is positive that insects in general cannot hear (130). Von Buttel-Reepen,

I

on the other hand, who knows bees thoroughly, thinks that the sense of hearing plays a considerable part in their life. He believes that the disturbance produced by the loss of a queen is communicated to the whole hive by the peculiar wailing noise made by some members and instinctively imitated by the others, and that this disturbance is calmed by a similar dissemination of the "happy humming" produced on her restoration — hearing playing a more important part than smell. The starting of a swarm, he thinks, is also largely a matter of sound communication. The process begins by the coming out of certain bees which push in among the bees hanging at the entrance of the hive and stir them up to swarming by making sounds. The "swarm-tone" is peculiar and often disturbs the inhabitants of neighboring hives that are not ready to swarm. Also, a swarm can be guided to a new dwelling if a few bees are taken there; they call the others by loud humming. If during this process the new hive is moved, the bees will go on for a few moments in the direction in which they started, then slowly turn, guided by the tone. A few may keep on in the original direction. We may look with suspicion, however, upon von Buttel-Reepen's suggestion that these latter, having passed beyond hearing of the call, are guided by the recollection of the tone they heard at first ! He refers also to the shrill noise made by the young queens ready to swarm, and to the peculiar uneasiness produced when a strange queen is being attacked, and resulting, he thinks, from her "cries of pain" (72).

§ 37. *Hearing in Fishes*

Throughout the vertebrate animals there exist structures bearing analogy to our own ears, whose function might therefore be supposed to be auditory. But in the lowest vertebrates the only structures of the human ear represented are the semicircular canals, and these suggest a static rather than an auditory organ. The cyclostomes, eel-like and semi-parasitic forms classed below the true fishes, have a pair of sacs one on either side of the head, containing mineral bodies, and each leading into one or two semicircular canals. In the true fishes the sac has two chambers, marked off from each other by a constriction. Three semicircular canals open from the foremost chamber, two lying in the vertical plane, and one in the horizontal plane. The chambers contain "statoliths" and fluid.

That the semicircular canals in fishes have a static [1] function has been shown by experiments to be described later. Is the fish ear also an organ of hearing? Again authorities differ, and it is probable that species differ. Kreidl got no response from goldfish when vibrating rods were placed either in the water or in the air near the water. Only when the fish were made more sensitive by strychnine did they react, and only to noise, not to tone. They reacted quite as well, more-over, when the ears were removed; whence it was concluded that their sensitiveness to noise resided in the skin (227, 228). A similar negative conclusion regarding auditory sensation has been reached by F. S. Lee (230) and by O. Körner as a result of experiments on twenty-five species (223). On the other hand, Bigelow found that the goldfish on which he ex-perimented were sensitive in their normal condition, but in-sensitive when the auditory nerves were cut, and thinks that Kreidl's operation did not remove the whole of the fish's ear (33). Triplett thought both perch and goldfish were excited by the sound of whistling, which usually preceded their being fed (407). Parker tested the killifish, a species of minnow, using the sustained slow vibrations (40 complete swings per

[1] The word "static" is here used to mean "relating to equilibrium" in general, not to static equilibrium as distinguished from dynamic equilibrium.

second) of a bass viol string placed on one side of the aquarium as a sounding board. The fish cage was suspended in the aquarium from an independent support. Normal fish responded to the vibrations, usually by movements of the fin, 96 per cent of the time. Fish in which the nerves to the ears had been cut responded in 18 per cent of the tests; those in which the skin had been made insensitive, but the ears left, 94 per cent. Since causing the string to vibrate jarred the whole aquarium somewhat, these experiments were checked by others where the stimulus was produced by placing the stem of a vibrating tuning fork against the sounding board. The results were the same as in the first set of tests. Parker concludes that the ears of the minnow are certainly organs for the reception of sound; but as he obtained no such reactions from dogfish, he is inclined to think that different species vary (305, 306). Tests by Zenneck on *Leuciscus rutilus*, *L. dobula*, and *Alburnus lucidus* also led to the conviction that these fish, at least, could hear. A bell was struck by electricity under water, and occasionally a piece of leather was placed upon it at the point where the clapper struck. In the latter case the mechanical vibrations produced were, it was held, the same as those occasioned by the actual ringing of the bell, but the sound vibrations were destroyed. The fish reacted by swimming instantly away from the neighborhood of the bell when it was rung, but not when the leather was used; hence, apparently, they reacted to sound (475).

Widely distributed among fishes is a curious set of structures known as the lateral-line canals. Along each side of the fish, extending from head to tail, there is a row of pores opening into a long canal, which at the head divides into three branches, one going upward above the eye, a second below the eye, and a third down toward the lower jaw. The functions of these canals have given rise to much discussion among zoölogists, an exhaustive history of which will be found in Parker's mono-graph entitled "The Function of the Lateral-line Organs in Fishes." The problem seems to have been solved by Parker's own experiments. He first proved experimentally that the canals played no part in responses to the following stimuli: light, heat, salinity of the water, food, oxygen dis-solved in the water, carbon dioxide, foulness of the water, hydrostatic pressure, steady currents flowing through the water, and sound. When, however, the water in the aqua-rium was made to vibrate slowly, about six times per second, the fish made certain characteristic reactions, differing somewhat for the four or five species observed, but always failing to appear when the lateral-line nerve was cut. Parker concludes that "the stimulus for the lateral-line organs (a water vibration of low frequency) is a physical stimulus inter-mediate in character between that effective for the skin (de-forming pressure of solids, currents, etc.) and that for the ear (vibrations of high frequency), and indicates that these organs hold an intermediate place between the two sets of sense organs named" (309). The ear is thus regarded as actually derived from the lateral-line canal, as this in turn was derived from the skin. We may suppose that at least three different sensa-tion qualities result from stimulation of the skin, the canals, and the ear, where hearing can be shown to exist.

§ 38. *Hearing in Amphibia*

Emergence from the water, on the part of adult Amphibia, is accompanied by disappearance of the lateral-line canals, and consequently of whatever sensations these mediate. In the frog, the ear has a tympanic membrane lying at the sur-face of the head. A single bone, the columella, with one end against this membrane, lies across the middle ear. The internal ear is not essentially different in structure from that of the fish; there is no cochlea. Yerkes has made an interesting study of the reaction of frogs to sound. He found that they occasionally "straightened up and raised the head as if listening" when other frogs croaked or made a splash by jumping into the water. To no other sound did he get any apparent response, nor was it possible to make frogs in their native habitat jump or show any uneasiness by producing any sort of noise, so long as the experimenter remained invisible. "Apparently," Yerkes says, "they depend almost entirely upon vision for the avoidance of dangers." It is of course highly improbable that an organ should be adapted only to the reception of the croaking of other frogs and the splash of water, and not to noises made in imitation of these; and Yerkes suggests that the frogs may hear many sounds to which they respond by inhibiting movement as a measure of safety. This view is confirmed by the results of experiments where the breathing movements of the frog's throat were registered by means of a lever resting against it and recording on smoked paper. Evidence from change of the breathing rate was obtained of the hearing of sounds ranging from fifty to one thousand single vibrations a second (456). Later, it was shown that sounds, although they did not, when given alone, cause the frogs to react, modified the responses to other stimuli, reinforcing or inhibiting them according to the interval between the sound and the other stimulus. This effect was noticed both when the frogs were in the air and when they were under water. It was more marked in the spring (the mating season) than in the winter. That it concerned the special auditory sense-apparatus, and hence may have been accompanied by true auditory sensations, was shown by the fact that it disappeared when the auditory nerves were cut. Sounds ranging from fifty to ten thousand single vibrations a second were effective (462, 464). This, of course, does not mean that the frog perceives such sounds as differing in pitch. The absence of a cochlea throws doubt on such a supposition; the sensation differences are probably much cruder than would be the case for a human being.

§ 39. *Hearing in Higher Vertebrates*

The reptilian ear does not differ markedly from that of amphibians. The writer knows of no experiments upon the sense of hearing in reptiles.

The cochlea is supposed to be the portion of the human ear upon which the power to distinguish pitch differences rests. Yet birds have no cochlea, though if we grant that animals which produce sounds are those which are able to hear them, some birds at least must be capable of pitch discriminations of wide range and great acuteness. The powers of imitation so often evidenced in bird song are proof that this is the case.[1] The sense of hearing, so long absent or problematical in the ascending scale of animal forms, reaches great importance in the life of birds and mammals. How far various mammals have the same range of auditory qualities that a human being has, what their capacity for pitch discrimination may be, has been but little investigated. Raccoons have been taught to discriminate between the note A_1 on a harmonica and the note A''', climbing on a box to be fed when the high note was sounded and staying down when they heard the low one (82). It is probable that the variety of auditory qualities entering into the experience of the highest vertebrates is large.

[1] Interesting evidence of this power in a bird which might not have been supposed to possess it was obtained by Conradi, who found that English sparrows reared by canaries acquired recognizable bits of the canary song (83).

CHAPTER VII

Sensory Discrimination: Vision

§ 40. *Some Problems connected with Vision*

In this chapter we shall consider one aspect only of the reactions of animals to light stimulation; namely, the question whether such stimulation produces in the possible consciousness of a given animal any sensations qualitatively unlike those accompanying other forms of stimulation, and if so, how many such specifically visual sensations, qualitatively different from each other, the animal may be supposed to be capable of receiving. The spatial aspect of vision will for the present be neglected.

Even with this restriction, the photic reactions of animals present a series of problems of enormous complexity. One especially difficult question is, it is true, postponed: the question as to just what happens when an animal seeks or avoids light. The so-called orientation of animals, that is, their assumption of a definite position with reference to a force acting upon them at a certain point, is a subject more closely connected with spatial than with qualitative discrimination; and though, as we shall see, the seeking or avoiding of light by an animal by no means always involves orientation of the body, yet the complex distinctions that have to be drawn in connection with this subject will be more fully discussed under the head of orienting reactions. But puzzles enough are left for the present chapter. What, for instance, is the meaning of the fact that the rays beyond the violet end of the spectrum, invisible to us, produce effects upon certain animals?

Are they seen, or do the sensations accompanying them rather resemble those produced by an irritating chemical? What kind of sensation quality may we suppose exists in the consciousness of an animal whose responses to light are mediated by the skin, not by the eyes? When an animal discriminates in its reactions between rays that to our eye differ in color, is the discrimination one of color qualities, or of differences in brightness, such as the spectrum offers to a totally color-blind person? And if a colored ray does not produce a color sensation in the consciousness of a given animal, that is, if the animal is color-blind, does it produce the same brightness sensation that it would produce in a color-blind human being? These questions will constantly suggest themselves, but in most cases the evidence will be insufficient to settle them.

§ 41. *Vision in Protozoa*

Many of the Protozoa, as we know, react to light. Amœba gives a negative response when light falls upon it from the side; that is, it moves away from the light, and Jennings conjectures that this probably occurs by the contraction of the part of the body nearest the light, which is what would happen if the light were a mechanical stimulus (211, p. 11). Blue light has the same effect as white light, and red light has no effect at all; but the reactions of Amœba to light of different colors differ only in degree, and do not indicate any qualitative difference of accompanying conscious processes (162). Nor, if the reaction to light is really identical with the negative reaction in general, can we conclude that any specific visual sensation accompanies it. The same holds true of the responses of various ciliate and flagellate Protozoa to light. These all, so far as observed, take place by the ordinary negative or avoiding reaction; some of the animals give it on passing from a region of less to one of greater illumination, and thus "seek" the darker regions, while others give it when undergoing a change in the reverse direction, and hence are "positively phototropic." But if nothing distinguishes the negative reaction to photic stimuli from the negative reaction to any other stimulus, then nothing shows the existence of a sensation quality peculiar to the effect of light — *unless* a special receptive apparatus can be demonstrated. In a flagellate Protozoön called Euglena, a pigment spot exists near the anterior end. Now although pigment apparently is not, as Hesse (176) has emphasized, a necessary constituent of visual organs, yet its occurrence always suggests some relation to light, as it is essentially a kind of matter having the property of absorbing light. Euglena gives the negative reaction on entering a shadow. Is its pigment spot really an "eye spot" and concerned in this response? Apparently the reaction occurs before the pigment spot has entered the shadow, and as soon as the transparent tip lying in front of the pigment spot has been pushed into the shaded region (110). It is uncertain, then, what the function of the pigment spot is. But in another organism, which is structurally intermediate between the single-celled and the many-celled forms, pigment spots do play a rôle in light reactions. This organism is called Volvox, and it is really a colony of globular flagellates, each with its flagellum turned outward, and each with an "eye spot." Very weak light has no effect on the movements of Volvox; moderate light causes movement toward the source of light, and very strong light causes movement away from the source (183). Accurate observation of these movements indicates that the eye spots are essential to them; each individual responds to a change of illumination of its eye spot (262). This much evidence, then, we have that if Volvox possesses consciousness, changes of light intensity produce in it a specific sensation.

§ 42. *Vision in Cœlenterates*

Turning to the cœlenterates, we find that Hydra shows no response to light other than a tendency to come to rest in the more illuminated parts of the vessel containing it (406, 444). Very strong light, however, makes it wander about until it happens to reach a more shaded region. Thus if the animal is subjected to light either above or below a certain "optimum," it is restless. A "vague uneasiness" is the kind of psychic accompaniment to this behavior most naturally suggested; repeated strong mechanical stimulation will also make the animal wander about. Nothing points to the existence of a visual quality. Blue and green light are more frequented by Hydra than red and yellow light; this parallels the effect of colored rays on Amœba (444). Widely distributed through the animal kingdom is a kind of equivalence, for reaction purposes, between blue or violet and white light on the one hand, red light and darkness on the other.

On the hydroid colonies of Tubularia no change of light intensity operated as a stimulus (319). In Actinians the only evidence that the reactions due to light differ from those otherwise produced lies in the *greater slowness* of the former. Many sea-anemones are wholly unaffected by photic stimulation, *Sagartia luciæ* and Metridium, for example (160). Many others have been found to contract when illuminated (150, 207, 291). *Eloactis producta* expands its tentacles only in light of low intensity, taking about fifteen minutes to do so when covered with a hood, and retracting in five minutes when the light is restored. This retraction is decidedly slower than that produced by mechanical stimulation (160). That the responses to light are more marked in animals which have been living in comparative darkness than in those taken from illuminated spots, has been shown both for sea-anemones and for Hydra (127).

Many Medusæ or jellyfish also react to light more slowly than to other forms of stimulation. It is true that on Sarsia, a form tested by Romanes many years ago, light seemed to act as quickly as any other stimulus. If a flash of light were allowed to fall on the animal while it was moving about, "prolonged swimming movements" ensued; if it was at rest, it gave only a single contraction — another instance of the effect of physiological condition upon reaction. Sudden darkening produced no reaction, whence Romanes concluded that "it is the light *per se* and not the sudden nature of the transition from darkness to light which in the former experiment acted as the stimulus." There are, however, as we shall see, other animals in which an increase of illumination brings about response where a decrease fails, and *vice versa*. When a beam of light was thrown into a bell-jar containing many Sarsiæ and placed in a dark room, "they crowded into the path of the beam and were most numerous at that side of the jar which was nearest the light." "There can thus," concludes Romanes, "be no doubt about Sarsia possessing a visual sense" (365, p. 41). But as these reactions are not differentiated in any way, they cannot be taken as evidence of a specific sense, unless indeed they depend on a specialized sensory structure. This latter Romanes found to be the case; Sarsia has pigment spots on the margin of its bell, and its response to light ceased when these were destroyed. Tiaropsis, another jellyfish studied by the same observer, gave further evidence of "a visual sense" in the fact that it responded to light more slowly than to mechanical stimulation. In Gonionemus, both difference in reaction time and dependence of response on a special organ indicate that light may produce a specific sensation, always granting the presence of consciousness. Yerkes found that this jellyfish, unlike Sarsia, reacts in the same manner in passing either from sunlight to shadow or the reverse. In both cases it stops swimming and sinks to the bottom. A sudden change of illumination, therefore, checks its activity. On the other hand, if when the light falls upon it the animal is at rest, it becomes active again; but sudden decrease of illumination has no effect upon the resting animal. The inhibitory effect of strong light falling upon the jellyfish while in motion Yerkes explains as a special adaptation. For one case of such increase of illumination occurs when the animal swims, bell upward, to the surface on being disturbed; the light of the surface is of course normally stronger than that in the lower regions. The inhibition of activity resulting causes the animal, after turning over, to sink slowly, bell downward, with expanded tentacles. This is a position that gives it a better chance of catching food and carrying it to the lips than is offered by the right-side-up posture, where food would have to be carried downward against the upward current occasioned by the sinking of the animal. Light is not the only factor in producing the inversion at the surface, however, for it will occur in darkness. When swimming, Gonionemus moves toward the light if the latter is fairly intense, but comes to rest in the shaded portions of the vessel containing it. The reaction time to light is much slower than that to other stimuli, but the animal responds most promptly when certain pigmented bodies at the base of the tentacles are exposed to the stimulus. If the margin of the bell containing these bodies is cut off, no reaction to light can be obtained (451, 458, 470). A great variety of structures apparently sensory in function is found on the bell margin of different genera and species of Medusæ. Some of them are statocysts. Others suggest a visual function, and in the Cubomedusæ there are fairly well developed eyes.

§ 43. *Vision in Planarians*

In planarians, unmistakable eyes are present, yet apparently the reactions to light are not wholly dependent upon them. The general effect of photic stimulation on the planarian is to stimulate it to movement; it comes to rest in the shaded portions of a vessel (9, 239, 243, 169). To a certain extent, light directs the movement of the animal away from it (313). But Hesse found that one species of planarian with much more highly organized eyes than another reacted to light decidedly less; the strength of the light reaction does not, he concludes, correspond to the development of the light perception. The latter depends on the number of sensitive elements in the eye, the former on the habits of the animal and the feeling tone aroused by the light (169). This "feeling tone" may apparently be connected with a skin sensation. Decapitated and hence eyeless planarians respond to light, but more slowly (243), and with less definite reference to the direction of the light (313).

§ 44. *Vision in Annelids*

The earthworm's sensitiveness to light is also dermal, although Hesse believes that he has found visual organs in certain structures in the skin, especially at the upper lip and the tail end (168). However this may be, the effectiveness of light as a stimulus is not confined absolutely to any one region of the body. When the worms are in a normal condition, attached to their burrows, the combined effect of light and the contact stimulus at the tail produces the ordinary negative reaction of withdrawal into the burrow (91, 179). The only evidence that light is accompanied by a specific consciousness is to be derived again from the fact that the reaction time to light is much longer than that to mechanical stimulation.

If the worm is detached from the burrow, it will take a course leading it more or less obliquely away from the light; if it is crawling in passages between glass plates, which allow it the choice between only two paths, one straight toward the light and the other straight away, it takes the latter about 95 per cent of the time (387). Graber used his "Preference Method" on earthworms, employing a box with two compartments, one illuminated with diffused daylight, the other dark. At the end of every hour the number of worms in each compartment was counted. That in the darkness was on the average 5.2 times as great as that in the light. When ground glass was substituted for the dark screen, making the compartment under it about half as light as the other, the number in the lighter compartment was about .6 the number in the darker, though still moderately light, portion of the box, thus showing that the worms were sensitive to comparatively small differences in intensity. Graber also placed colored glasses over the compartments, with the following results: the worms preferred red to blue even when the former was much lighter than the latter, indicating that the preference was determined by the wave length and not by the brightness of the light; they preferred green to blue under similar conditions, and red to green. They emphatically preferred white light from which the ultra-violet rays had been subtracted to ordinary white light, 6.7 times as many being found in a compartment covered by a screen impervious only to ultra-violet rays (150). The effect of ultra-violet rays on many animals is very deleterious (167). The avoidance of the ultra-violet rays and the seeking of red by negatively phototropic animals is almost universal.

The part of the body of the earthworm affected by the light influences the reaction. Darwin indeed reported that the worms withdrew into their burrows only when light fell on the head end (91), but decapitated worms were found by Graber to show the same light and color "preferences" as normal ones, though in a less marked degree (150), and Yung obtained evidence that sensitiveness to light is distributed over the body (473). According to Hesse the anterior end of the worm is most sensitive, the tail next, and the middle region least (168). Not only the region, but the amount of body surface affected, also makes a difference. When the whole length of the worm was illuminated, the percentage of reactions was to that obtained where the front third only was involved as 26 to 10.2, while the relative occurrence of responses when the middle third and the posterior third alone were stimulated is represented by the figures 2.4 and 1 respectively (312). The effect of colored rays has been found to be proportionate to their intensity; that is, the green and yellow regions of the spectrum are most effective (473).

Although the ordinary response of the earthworm to light is negative, it has been possible to determine experimentally a positive phototropism in *Allolobophora fœtida* for very low intensities, and the emergence of worms from their burrows at nightfall has been referred to this tendency to seek very faint light (1).

No parallel in our own experience can be found for the sensation received by an eyeless animal from light. In many of the marine worms, however, well-developed eyes exist, but not such as are capable of giving clear images. The function of the eyes of marine worms seems to be chiefly that of receiving stimuli from *shadows*. Many tube-dwelling worms will withdraw into their tubes if a shadow is cast upon them, and the term "skioptic" has been suggested for this class of reactions (158, 173, 373). The leech Clepsine shows the same kind of behavior; the slightest shadow cast on the surface of the water in a dish where these animals are resting quietly will cause them to reach up and sway from side to side in apparent search for prey (438).

A curious effect of colors on tube-dwelling worms has been observed. When placed under either blue or red glass, the sensory activities of the worms seemed to be inhibited for a time, the effect being more striking in the case of the red glass. When brought suddenly from under blue glass into ordinary white light, the worms showed intensified reactions; while bringing them from under red glass to white light inhibited their reactions for from two to five minutes (158).

The fact that animals which display positive phototropism show also an "aversion" to red and a tendency to seek colors that contain the ultra-violet rays, while negatively phototropic animals avoid light that has ultra-violet rays, and seek red, which lacks these rays, has pointed to the probability that apparent color discriminations in the lower forms of animals are really reactions to the intensity of the light, and especially to the intensity of the ultra-violet rays. This position, however, has recently been questioned by Minkiewicz. He has succeeded in changing the reactions of a Nemertean worm, *Lineus ruber*, to colored light, while its response to white light remained unaltered. When placed in diluted sea water the animal would, after a day, direct itself toward violet rays, although still negative in response to white light. On the fourth day the ordinary "chromotropism" was restored; that is, the worm sought red rays. After two or three weeks of life in the diluted sea water, on being restored to ordinary sea water the worm's chromotropism was again inverted, becoming positive to the violet rays, while negative phototropism persisted. Moreover, intermediate stages in the passage from the red- to the violet-seeking phase were observed; a stage where, still positive to red, the animal ceases to distinguish red from yellow, and others where it seeks violet, but has

K

become indifferent to green and yellow. These stages last for several hours, but corresponding ones have not been observed in the passage from the violet phase back to the red phase; perhaps they occurred too rapidly to be noted (274).

§ 45. *Vision in Mollusks*

In the phylum Mollusca we find eyes of all grades of development, from mere pigment spots in certain Acephala to the elaborate eye of the squid, with its lens, iris, and contractile pupil. Such an eye is fully capable of forming an image. Among the Acephala there are many instances of reaction to light in the absence of all visual organs. The sensitive parts are commonly the siphons, which are projected from the shell to take in currents of water containing nourishment, and withdrawn in response to sudden darkening in some cases, to sudden illumination in others, and in still other instances to either (102, 290, 373). In *Pecten varius*, which has eyes on the border of its "mantle," Rawitz found that a shadow would cause reaction provided that it fell simultaneously upon a considerable number of the eyes, from which he concludes that they may coöperate in a kind of mosaic vision (360).

In snails, although the eyes are undoubtedly concerned in light reactions, a certain amount of skin sensitiveness has been shown. *Helix aspersa*, a negatively phototropic animal, when blinded, reacted one-half as many times to light as when normal; *H. nemoralis*, positively phototropic, only one-eighth as many times; from which the suggestion was derived that the "dermal light-sense" may be more effective in negative than in positive animals (441). Very interesting observations on periodic changes in the responses of marine gasteropods to light have been made by Bohn (55), but these will be more fully considered in a later chapter. The cephalopods, with their highly developed eyes, offer an interesting field for the study of visual reactions, which is as yet almost untouched.

§ 46. *Vision in Echinoderms*

The starfish and sea urchin, among the echinoderms, depend for their responses to light upon pigment or eye spots on the arms. They are positively phototropic, but lose this tendency if the eye spots are removed; a fact which furnishes some evidence for the existence of a specific visual quality (365, 398). Romanes found the sensitiveness to light so great in the individuals examined by him that they discriminated between ordinary pine boards used to cover the face of the tank containing them, and the same boards painted black, light being in both cases admitted through a narrow slit (365).

Various sea urchins have been found responsive to shadows. One, *Centrostephanus longispinus*, has not even the rudiment of an eye. This animal in diffuse daylight seeks the darkest corner and turns its aboral pole to the light. A sudden shadow falling on it causes it to direct its spines toward the shaded side. The reaction time involved is decidedly longer than that to mechanical stimulation, and moreover, although pieces of the animal will react to the latter, responses to shadows depend on keeping the system of radial nerves intact. Hence von Uexküll, who made the above observations, concluded that a special set of nerve fibres is concerned in photic reactions (410). Dubois had suggested, from studies on the mollusk *Pholas dactylus*, that in such cases the pigment changes which occur, under the influence of light, over the surface of the body, furnish the stimulus[1] (102),

---

[1] The pigment changes, Dubois thinks, cause contraction of a muscular layer lying underneath the pigment, which contraction excites the nerve endings. This arrangement, which he terms a "*système avertisseur*," he believes to be involved in the reactions of low forms of animals to various stimuli.

but von Uexküll thinks this impossible, as the light reactions occur before the pigment changes do. This migratory pigment, he believes, acts merely as a screen; the source of excitation for the optic fibres may lie in another pigment which he has extracted and found very sensitive to light (410).

§ 47. *Vision in Crustacea*

The spatial aspect of vision assumes great importance in the arthropods, both because of the precision of their orientation to light in many cases, and because of the peculiar functions of the compound eye so common in this group. This organ appears to be specially adapted to the vision of moving objects (Fig. 10). It consists essentially of a number of simple eyes so crowded together

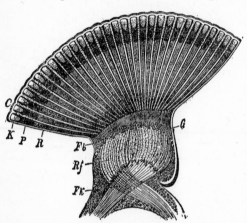

Fig. 10.—Diagrammatic representation of the compound eye of a dragon-fly. *C*, cornea; *K*, crystalline cone; *P*, pigment; *R*, nerve rods of retina; *Fb*, layer of fibres; *G*, layer of ganglion cells; *Rf*, retinal fibres; *Fk*, crossing of fibres. After Claus.

that the common cornea is, as it were, faceted, each facet belonging to an eye. These facets are lens shaped, and back of each lies a refractile crystalline cone. Behind these, in turn, are nervous structures, the rods or retinulæ, each separated from its neighbors by a pigment sheath. Light rays passing through each corneal facet probably produce a single spot of light on the retinula, and the total image is thus a mosaic formed of these spots. Into its characteristics, how-ever, we need not enter. In the present chapter we are concerned only with the evidence that light stimulation in general, and light of different wave lengths in particular, produces specific sensations.

That the visual reactions of Crustacea are accompanied by a special visual sensation, if we suppose these animals to be conscious, is sufficiently evidenced by their dependence on the eyes. To movements and shadows the responses are for the most part given. Bateson, watching shrimps and prawns, noted that they apparently could not see their food when it had been taken from them and lay near at hand, but quickly raised their antennæ when an object was passed between them and the light (11). The little fairy shrimp, Branchipus, will stop swimming as soon as the edge of a shadow falls upon it. "Skioptic" reactions in the family of Cirripedia, to which the barnacles belong, were noted by Pouchet and Joubert in 1875, as well as the fact that those individuals which were attached to rocks, where a sudden shadow might mean danger, reacted, while those attached to floating objects, and therefore exposed normally to light fluctua-tions, did not (348). The problem as to whether light of different colors produces different sensations in the crustacean consciousness was the subject of experiments a number of years ago, in which the Preference Method was used. Sir John Lubbock arranged to have a sunlight spectrum thrown on a long trough containing Daphnias, tiny crustaceans belonging to the lowest sub-class, that of the Entomostraca (Fig. 11). Daphnia is decidedly positive in its phototropism. At the end of ten minutes glass partitions were slipped across the trough at the approxi-mate dividing lines of the spectral colors. The number of animals in each compartment was then counted. The experiment was repeatedly performed, and the greatest number was always found in the yellow-green region (249, 250). Bert obtained similar results with the use of an electric light spectrum; but besides throwing all the colors at once upon the vessel, he allowed each color to act separately through a narrow opening, and noted the speed of the positive response produced. That the "preference" shown for yellow-green light is not a matter of color vision, but of response to the greater intensity of the light in this region of the spectrum, was suggested by Bert (24), and Merejkowsky showed that

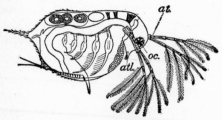

FIG. 11.— Daphnia. *at*, antenna; *atl*, antennule; *oc*, eye. After Yerkes.

the larvæ of Balanus and *Dias longiremis* manifested no color preference when the colors were made of equal intensity (269). Lubbock attempted to prove the existence of qualitative

as distinguished from intensive discrimination by various modifications of the experiment, but without entirely conclusive results (251, pp. 221 ff.). Finally, Yerkes, working on Simocephalus, a form closely related to Daphnia, found that when a gaslight spectrum was used, the animals collected in the red-yellow region, that of greatest intensity for such light; and that if this region had its intensity diminished by a screen of India ink or paraffin paper, the crustacean moved out of it (448). In all probability, then, the reactions of these forms are not accompanied by qualitatively different color sensations corresponding to light of different wave lengths.

That Daphnia seeks a region affected by the ultra-violet rays of the spectrum in preference to darkness, although the two look alike to our eyes, was shown by Lubbock (251, pp. 215 ff.). An effect of physiological condition suggesting the law of general adaptation in human vision is evidenced by the fact that individual Daphnias which have been a long time in darkness will respond to a lower intensity than those which have been long exposed to illumination (94). Many curious results of physiological condition upon orientation to light in Crustacea will be discussed later.

Experiments on the reactions of the crayfish, which is moderately negative in its phototropism, to light coming through colored glasses indicate that the animal seeks red when the light falls vertically, but shows no marked preference when light is passed horizontally through the glass. The tendency to seek red is characteristic of negatively phototropic animals, but in this case it seemed to be stronger even than the tendency to seek black. No definite proof of a specific color reaction is, however, offered (21). The positive reactions to light of Pycnogonids, or sea spiders, a curious group of animals whose classification is uncertain, have been found to depend on the presence of a visual organ (79).

§ 48. *Vision in Spiders*

Spiders do not have the compound eye, but a number of ocelli, or simple eyes; the typical fully developed invertebrate eye with cornea, lens, vitreous humor, rod layer, and pigmented layer in the retina, the latter lying in front of the nerve fibres supplying the retina, instead of behind them as in the vertebrate eye. Experiments have been made on color discrimination in spiders; some by the Preference Method, where the spiders showed an inclination for red when offered a choice of compartments illuminated through red, green, blue, and yellow glass (320); others by attempting to form an association between paper of a certain color and the spider's nest. This latter, containing eggs, was surrounded by colored paper, and when a spider had become accustomed to going in and out over the paper, another color was substituted, and a false nest made in another place, surrounded by the original strips of paper. The spider under these circumstances showed some confusion and tendency to go to the false nest (321). The experiments with Daphnia have, however, suggested a fundamental source of error in experiments on the color vision of animals. A human being who is totally color-blind is nevertheless able to discriminate among objects that to a normal eye have different colors, because such objects take on to the color-blind eye different shades of gray. It is always possible, then, unless special precautions are taken, that an animal's apparent discriminations of color may be really brightness discriminations, in some way analogous to those made by the color-blind person. No such precautions were taken in the experiments just described, and the color sense of spiders remains unproved.

In blind and blinded myriapods, the family to which the centipede belongs, skin sensitiveness to light is shown (329, 335).

§ 49. *Vision in Insects*

The compound eye again occurs in insects, together with ocelli or simple eyes, the latter usually placed in the middle of the head. The respective functions of the two kinds of eyes are not definitely known, though there is a possibility that the ocelli may serve for near vision and for vision in faint light. Plateau, however, finds that insects with the compound eyes blinded and the simple eyes intact are unable to see even in faint light, and has but a poor opinion of the usefulness of the latter. Caterpillars, which have only simple eyes, depend, he thinks, chiefly on their long hairs or on their feelers to warn them of the approach of obstacles (332).

On the color sense of insects there are first the old experiments of Graber by the Preference Method, whose most
definite result was to show that positively phototropic insects
prefer colors containing the ultra-violet rays, while the negatively phototropic ones prefer red, from which these rays are
absent.   No proof that the discriminations were made on the
basis of color proper rather than brightness was forthcoming
(151).   Similar observations were made by Lubbock on ants,
which in their underground life are negatively phototropic,
the eggs and larvæ apparently needing darkness in order to
develop, but on their foraging expeditions are comparatively
indifferent to light.   They showed a preference for red when
tested, and a tendency to avoid the ultra-violet rays, so marked
that they preferred bright daylight from which these rays
had been extracted by chemical screens, to darkness that contained the ultra-violet (248, pp. 207 ff.).   Graber suggested
that the ultra-violet rays produce a skin sensation in the ants;
but Forel agrees with Lubbock that the effect is visual, because he found that varnishing the eyes made the ants indifferent to ultra-violet (130).   Ants of the family Lasius seem
to be normally insensitive to these rays (134).   It is just possible, then, that a visual sensation of quality wholly foreign
to our experience may accompany the action of ultra-violet
rays on insects.   Loeb has noted that the relative effect of
violet and ultra-violet vibrations, as compared with that of the
rest of the spectrum, is greater, the less developed the visual
organ (233).

Lubbock's experiments on the color sense of bees are more
to the point than those on ants, for they were made not by the
Preference Method, but by associating a color with food.   No
precaution, however, was taken against the brightness error.
He found that bees which had eaten honey from blue paper
would pick out the blue pieces from a number of differently

colored papers, whose positions were altered during the experiments (248). Forel got similar results, and reports that
a bumble bee thus trained would select all the blue objects
in the room for special examination (130). Lubbock's
tests with wasps gave negative results.

We have already noted the dispute as to how far visual
sensations in general are involved in the reactions of bees to
flowers, and have seen that Plateau maintains their relative
unimportance in this connection, as compared to smell.
Besides the experiments which we have quoted on pp. 96–
97, he adduces the facts that he could never persuade insects
to alight upon artificial flowers, though these were not distinguishable by human eyes from real ones (336–338); that
bees show no preference for flowers of any particular color
(339); and that they often make errors, in alighting on closed
buds, seed pods, and wilted flowers, which indicate defective
vision (341). But Josephine Wéry and others have noted
that bees do seek artificial flowers (434). Even Plateau
does not deny that an insect may perceive flowers from a
distance, "whether because it sees the color in the same way
that we do, or because it perceives some kind of contrast
between the flowers and their surroundings" (339).

Von Buttel-Reepen gives one or two instances to show
that the color perception of bees is sometimes influential in
helping them to recognize their own hives. He reports a case
where a stock of bees had been driven from their hive and
scattered. The front of the hive was blue. Some of the
bees tried to find their way into other hives, and selected for
their efforts those which had blue doors. This authority
believes, moreover, that the sense of sight has occasionally
something to do with the reception of bees into a foreign hive.
"Robber bees," which steal honey from strange hives, when
they begin their downward career, approach the strange

dwelling with a peculiar hesitating flight; afterwards, says von Buttel-Reepen, they become "frecher." He declares that when attempting to alight before a foreign hive they are often driven off by the rightful occupants before their odor can have been noticed, and ascribes this reaction to the sight of their hesitating method of approach. On the other hand, when a broodless stock joins itself to one that has a brood, the latter is induced to receive them peacefully because of their assured manner (72).

The majority of bee students incline to the belief that bees are guided back to their hives from long flights by visual memory, though the phenomena are not easy to explain. Solitary wasps, it seems highly probable from experiments, find their nests by sight; but this subject will be more fully discussed in Chapter XI.

§ 50. *Vision in Amphioxus and in Fish*

The vertebrate eye differs in origin and in structure from any form of invertebrate eye, the most striking difference in structure being perhaps the situation of the pigmented layer of the retina behind the nerve-fibre layer, which is responsible for the existence of the blind spot where the trunk of the optic nerve breaks through the retinal layer. Another point of unlikeness consists in the fact that the invertebrate optic nerves do not cross on their way to the brain, while in the vertebrates there is either total or partial crossing of the fibres. In both the vertebrate and the simple invertebrate eye the image is formed by means of a lens, although Nagel has suggested that the function of the lens in the lower forms of eye is rather to collect the light than to produce an image (293).

The reactions of Amphioxus to light offer as chief evidence that they are accompanied by a specific sensation quality the fact that they may be fatigued independently of other reactions. The only structures suggesting a visual function are pigment spots on the back near the head, and other pigment cells distributed down the back. Amphioxus makes negative reactions to light, especially when the light, from which heat rays have been excluded by passing it through water, is directed at any point on the back, the most sensitive region lying just back of the eye spot (225, 311). The eye spot itself, and the front end of the animal, are insensitive. Fatiguing the light reactions had no effect on response to other forms of stimulation (311). Attempts to test the "color preferences" of Amphioxus by illuminating different parts of a trough with differently colored lights gave negative results (225). A skin sensibility to light has been observed also in larval lampreys, which will give negative reactions even when the optic nerves are cut (310). Blind fish have been found to react to light, apparently through the skin (107).

Among the many animals whose supposed color preferences Graber tested were two species of fish, but no convincing proof of their powers of color discrimination was obtained (151). Bateson placed food on differently colored tiles, and observed that the fish picked it off most readily from white and pale blue, and least readily off dark red and dark blue; which establishes little save that the bait was probably more conspicuous on the former (12). Professor Bentley and the writer succeeded in getting fairly conclusive evidence that one fish, of the common variety of chub, *Semotilus atromaculatus*, could associate a given pigment with food. Two dissecting forceps were used, alike except that to the legs of one were fastened, with rubber bands, small sticks painted red, while to those of the other similar green sticks were attached. The forceps were fastened to a wooden bar projecting from a wooden screen, which divided the circular tank into two compartments, and hung down into the water. Food was always placed in the red pair of forceps, which were made frequently to change places with the green ones; and the fish was caused to enter the compartment half of the time on one side, and half of the time on the other. This was to prevent identification of the food fork by its position or the direction in which the fish had to turn. The animal quickly learned to single out the red fork as the one important to its welfare, and in forty experiments, mingled with others so that the association might not be weakened, where there was no food in either fork, and where the forceps and rubber bands were changed so that no odor of food could linger, it never failed to bite first at the red. Moreover, the probability that its discrimination was based upon brightness was greatly lessened by using, when we experimented without food, a different red much lighter than that in the food tests. The fish successfully discriminated red from blue paints in the same way, and it was afterwards trained, by putting food in the green fork, to break the earlier association and bite first at the green (421).

§ 51. *Vision in Amphibia*

The fact that the commonest form of color blindness in human beings affects the qualities red and green, and that these colors have the most restricted area of visibility, might tempt one to the belief that ability to distinguish red and green is a late acquisition in the animal kingdom. So far, comparative psychology offers no support for this view. The fish whose behavior has just been described certainly made some sort of distinction between the colors red and green. And the only evidence of color vision in the Amphibia is evidence that frogs discriminate, in some fashion, between red and white, although the difference to the frog may be one of brightness merely. Yerkes, in studying the frog's power to learn by experience, caused it to go through a simple labyrinth leading to a tank of water. At the point where the first choice between two paths occurred, a red card was placed on one side and a white card on the other. When the frog had learned to take the correct path, toward the white, the cards were exchanged, without any other alteration in the conditions; and the decided confusion of the animals indicated that they had discriminated between the red and white cards and had learned to react with reference to this discrimination (454).

Two species of frogs tested by Ellen Torelle showed positive phototropism, associated, as usual, with a tendency to prefer blue to red light (401). The frog's phototropism, moreover, persists even when the animal is blinded, although in the normal animal the eyes are involved in the reaction, since it occurs when the skin is covered and the eyes left intact (224, 308). Skin sensitiveness to light has been noted also in salamanders (103). The nature of the "dermal light sensation" remains a mystery. It can hardly, in frogs, be a painful irritation, since it produces a positive response; and it is not due to heat rays, for it occurs when these are intercepted by passing the light through water. As Parker says, radiant heat and light, "distinct as they seem to our senses, are members of one physical series in that they are both ether vibrations, varying only in wave length" (308). While, then, the nerve endings in human skin are sensitive only to the slowest of these vibrations, the heat rays, those in the skin of the frog may respond to the whole series, with what accompanying sensation qualities we cannot say.

§ 52. *Vision in Other Vertebrates*

In some reptilian eyes, and in those of all birds, a few fishes, and Ornithorhyncus, there are attached to the ends of the cones in the retina transparent, colored globules like little drops of oil. The significance of these colored drops is wholly unknown. If they really transmit to the cones only those colors which they seem to, then the color sensations of the animals possessing them must be wholly different from ours.

No experimental tests on color vision in reptiles have been made, so far as the writer is aware. As for birds, in the palmy days of the doctrine of sexual selection we should have felt quite sure that the bright colored plumage of many species indicated ability to distinguish colors. Some experimental evidence of this power has been obtained. A chick that had learned to pick out bits of the yolk of a hard-boiled egg from the white was given bits of orange peel, which he seized, but seemed to find exceedingly distasteful. Afterwards he was for some time suspicious of the bits of yolk. On the other hand, after having learned to avoid bad-tasting black and yellow caterpillars, he did not transfer his aversion to black and yellow wasps; probably their points of difference from caterpillars were so numerous that the resemblance of color was not attended to (281, pp. 40-41).

Color vision in the English sparrow and the cowbird has been tested by a method previously used on monkeys. A number of glasses of like size and shape were covered inside and out with differently colored papers, including red, yellow, blue, green, dark and light gray. These glasses were placed in a row on a board, and food was put always in the same glass, the position of which, however, was changed in the different experiments. The sparrow and cowbird learned to pick out the right vessel under these conditions (345). Somewhat similar tests were fairly successful with pigeons, which were also experimented on by Graber's method of allowing a choice between compartments illuminated through differently colored glass. Although the pigeons showed no tendency to avoid any particular color, they indicated a preference for green and blue. This result it was attempted to verify by pneumographic tests, and a greater quickening of breathing was recorded under green and blue lights than under other light stimuli (371).

Raccoons have been trained to discriminate cards of different colors and brightnesses in the following pairs: black-white, black-yellow, black-red, black-blue, black-green, blue-yellow, red-green. The two last-named discriminations proved decidedly more difficult, and one of the four raccoons tested never learned to distinguish red from green or blue from yellow (82).

In none of the above described experiments, however, is the brightness error eliminated. Kinnaman's color tests on monkeys did make an attempt in this direction. The monkeys were tested with glass tumblers covered with papers of different colors, and when it had been shown that they were able to identify a vessel of a particular color as associated with food, the possibility that their discriminations might have been based on brightness rather than color was investigated in the following way. First, the animals' power of distinguishing different shades of gray was tested, and it was found that they could barely detect a difference considerably greater than that between the "brightness values" of the colors used; that is, the grays that a color-blind human being would have seen in place of the colors. Secondly, this result was confirmed by covering the glasses with gray papers varying in brightness somewhat more than did the colors used, and finding that the monkeys distinguished these grays decidedly less well than the colors. Thirdly, it was proved that a colored glass could be picked out correctly many times from among three others covered with gray paper of the same brightness as the color (221).

The most elaborate and careful experiments that have yet been made on vision in the lower animals are those of Yerkes on the Japanese dancing mouse. The method consisted in teaching the animals to associate one of two differently illuminated compartments with a disagreeable electric shock. In the perfected experiments on brightness discrimination, the illumination of the compartments was varied in intensity by arranging a light above each. One light could be kept at a constant height and the other raised or lowered. Weber's Law was proved to hold for the one individual tested; the ratio of the difference in brightness to the absolute brightness being about one-tenth, between the limits of 5 and 80 hefners of absolute brightness. For testing color discrimination, after a series of experiments with colored papers, a somewhat similar apparatus was used, the light being filtered through colored screens (Fig. 12). No ability to discriminate green and blue was displayed unless the two were made very different in brightness. Light blue and orange, green and red, violet and red, were discriminated even when their brightnesses were considerably varied. Yet the possibility that these discriminations were made on the basis of brightness rather than color differences is suggested by an interesting kind of evidence. After a mouse had learned to choose, for example, green rather than red, it was offered a choice between light and darkness, and showed a uniform preference for the former, although untrained mice do not. This looks as though the green had been previously chosen as the lighter of the two colors. If such were the case, the brightness values of the colors for the mouse must be quite different from those which they have for a human being. In fact, there are reasons for thinking that the red end of the spectrum is much darker to the mouse's than to the human eye. Even allowing for the possibility

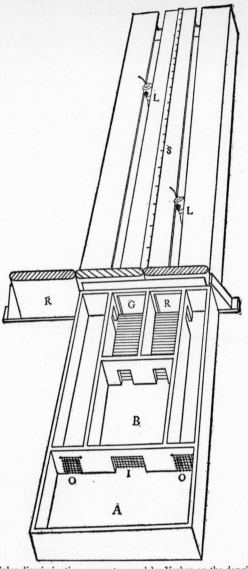

FIG. 12. — Color discrimination apparatus used by Yerkes on the dancing mouse. *A*, nest-box; *B*, entrance chamber; *R*, *R*, red filters; *G*, green filter; *L*, *L*, incandescent lamps in light box; *S*, millimeter scale on light box; *I*, door between *A* and *B*; *O*, *O*, doors between alleys and *A*.

of discriminations based on brightness differences other than those appreciable to human beings, Yerkes concludes that the mice have a certain degree of ability to distinguish red, green, and violet as colors. The mouse retina seems to be lacking in cones (469).

CHAPTER VIII

SPATIALLY DETERMINED REACTIONS AND SPACE PERCEPTION

§ 53. *Classes of Spatially Determined Reactions*

MODIFICATION of the behavior of animals with reference to the spatial characteristics of the forces acting upon them appears at the very beginning of the scale of animal life, and throughout is quite as important as modification with reference to the kind or quality of such forces. It assumes a number of distinct forms. Some of these suggest to us, interpreting them as we must on the basis of our own experience, no conscious aspect at all; they seem rather mechanical effects upon a passive organism. In other cases, it appears possible that the mental process which we know as space perception, involving the simultaneous awareness of a number of sensations consciously referred to different points in space, may accompany the reaction of an animal with reference to the spatial relations of its environment. And sometimes we can only say that differences in the space characteristics of a stimulus may modify the accompanying sensation in some manner which yet apparently does not involve space perception as we know it.

Our task in the following pages will then be to examine the different ways in which animal behavior is adapted to the spatial characteristics of stimuli, and to ask which of these suggest as their conscious accompaniment some form of space perception. A classification of spatially determined responses that is not, indeed, ideally satisfactory, but may serve our purpose, divides them into five groups: —

1. Reactions adapted to the position of a single stimulus acting at a definite point on the body.

2. Reactions to a continuous stimulus, which involve the assumption of a certain position of the whole body with reference to the stimulus: orienting reactions.

3. Reactions to a stimulus that moves, *i.e.* that affects several neighboring points on the body successively.

4. Reactions adapted to the relative position of several stimuli acting simultaneously.

5. Reactions adapted to the distance of an object from the body.

These forms of behavior will be successively discussed.

§ 54. *Class I : Reactions to a Single Localized Stimulus*

Responses to stimulation that are adapted to the point of application of the stimulus are to be found among very simple animals. They may be subdivided into three groups: first, cases where the part of the animal that reacts is the part directly affected by the stimulus; second, cases where the whole animal reacts by a movement in the appropriate direction; and third, cases where a part of the body not directly affected by the stimulus moves toward the point stimulated.

1. Amœba furnishes an example of the first class. Its negative reaction occurs by the checking of protoplasmic flow at the point where a strong mechanical stimulus affects the body; its positive reaction by a flowing forward of the protoplasm at the point where a weak stimulus acts, and its food-taking reaction by an enveloping flow on both sides of the point stimulated. This would seem to be the most primitive way of adapting response to the location of a stimulus: the effect is produced just where the force acts, as it

might be upon a piece of inanimate matter. In no animal with a nervous system, probably, is the process quite so simple. The bell of the jellyfish contracts at the point where a stimulus, mechanical or photic, is applied; yet although these responses are made when the nervous system is thrown out of function, they occur more slowly, and in the normal animal the nervous tissue is probably involved, while, of course, a long conduction pathway is traversed when, to use a familiar illustration, the baby pulls back its hand from the candle flame.

2. Paramecium and other infusoria, planarians, the earthworm, and various other animals give us illustrations of movements of the entire body differing according to the point affected by a single stimulus. If the front half of Paramecium is touched, the animal gives the typical avoiding reaction of darting backward and turning to one side; if the hinder end be touched, it moves forward (211, p. 50). On the other hand, it makes no difference in its reactions to stimuli affecting either side of the body; the turning is always to the aboral side even when the stimulus comes from that direction (211, p. 52). If strong mechanical stimulation be applied to the head end of a planarian, there is a response which seems to belong under type (1): the head is turned away from the stimulus. If the hinder region is touched, strong forward crawling movements of the body are produced. The positive reaction in the planarian, turning the head toward the stimulus, also suggests type (1), but in reality it has been shown by Pearl to be a far more complex affair than the mere flow of protoplasm at the stimulated point, and to involve the contraction of several sets of muscles (316). The earthworm creeps backward if the front half of the body is affected, turns away from a stimulus applied to the side of the anterior end, and creeps

forward if the stimulus affects the posterior half of the body (210). In general, a reaction of type (2) rather than type (1) will occur in proportion to the degree in which an organism's movements are coördinated and it tends to act as a whole.

3. One of the prettiest examples of the most highly coördinated form of response to a single localized stimulus, namely, movement of some other part of the body toward the point affected, is to be found in the swinging over of the jellyfish's manubrium toward the spot on the bell touched by food. "In the typical feeding reaction," says Yerkes, "the manubrium bends toward the food. If during such a movement the piece of food be moved to the opposite side of the bell, the manubrium, too, in a few seconds will bend in the opposite direction, that is, again toward the food " (451). The sea urchin responds to mechanical stimulation by moving the spines toward the place stimulated (410). In the higher animals this form of reaction has largely superseded other methods of adapting behavior to a stimulus acting at a definite point. Where grasping appendages exist, the obvious device is to move them toward the point of stimulation in order either to seize or to remove the object. This involves not merely that the effects of the stimulus shall diffuse so as to involve general locomotor movements, but that the effect shall be exerted very definitely upon a particular set of muscles in a particular way. The "scratch-reflex" of mammals, and the reaction whereby a frog rubs its hind leg on the spot of skin affected by a drop of acid, are further examples.

What can we say regarding the conscious accompaniment of the reactions described under these three heads? When a stimulus applied at point *a* brings about a reaction different from that produced by precisely the same stimulus acting on point *b*, are the accompanying sensations different, supposing the animal concerned to be conscious? If they are, the difference must be what has been called a difference in *local sign*. There is certainly no evidence that *space perception* is concerned. Space perception in our own experience always involves the simultaneous awareness of several stimuli. But where a single stimulus only is operative, the fact that reaction to it is modified by its location cannot mean that the relations of that location to the location of other stimuli are perceived. The truth is that space perception is so constant a factor in our own experience that we cannot imagine how a single sensation can be modified in connection with change of place of the stimulus, where space perception does not exist. A touch at any point on the skin of a human being is referred to a definite point in a constructed space, tactile and visual; it is given its proper place in a complex of sensations. What modification of it would correspond to its location if it stood alone in consciousness we cannot now conceive.

§ 55. *Class II: Orienting Reactions; Possible Modes of Producing Them*

Various forces, such as gravity, light, electricity, centrifugal force, currents of water and air, are all influences causing certain organisms to bring their bodies into a definite position. Such reactions, involving the direction of the whole body with reference to a continuous force acting upon it, are known as reactions of orientation. There are various ways in which they might conceivably take place.

(*a*) They might be due to the "pull" of a force upon the passive body of an animal. In the case of gravity or of a current of wind or water, if one part of the body were heavier or offered more surface to the force, the position assumed could be explained without supposing any activity on the animal's part. In such a case there would be no reason for thinking of the reaction as conscious.

(*b*) The response might be due to the effect of a force acting unevenly upon the two sides of the body, and thereby unevenly affecting the motor apparatus on the two sides, thus causing the animal to turn until the forces acting upon symmetrical points were balanced. This, although involving activity on the animal's part, would not, if the force acted directly on the muscles, suggest any conscious accompaniment.

(*c*) The orientation might take place by a negative reaction on the animal's part to a definite stimulus given when the animal was in any other than the final, oriented position. If gravity were the force in question, the stimulus might be the pressure exerted within the body by particles of different density, or by the fluid or mineral bodies in a statocyst organ. If the stimulus were light, the organism might be oriented by giving the negative reaction when its head entered a region either brighter or darker than the optimum illumination. In such cases, where the ordinary negative reaction is the only one involved, there is no reason to suppose the occurrence of any conscious accompaniment, other than the possible unpleasantness connected with that reaction.

(*d*) Orientation to gravity might occur through a specialized "righting" reaction, given in response either to a stimulus within, say, a statolith organ, or, as in the planarian, to the absence of accustomed contact stimulation on one surface of the body. The reaction in these cases being a specialized one, it is possible that a peculiar sensation quality might be involved.

(*e*) Orientation might take place through a movement occurring when the position of several stimuli perceived simultaneously was disturbed, and tending to restore them to their original position. This is the principle involved, as we shall see, in explaining the rheotropism or current orientation of fishes, and the anemotropism, or orientation to air currents, of insects, as due to an instinct to keep the visual surroundings the same. And this form of orientation alone suggests a true space perception as its conscious accompaniment.

Such being the conceivable ways in which orientation may be brought about, what are the observed facts? They may be considered under the heads of orientation to gravity, to light, and to other forces.

§ 56. *Orientation to Gravity: Protozoa*

To this form of reaction the term "geotropism" or "geotaxis" has been applied. In various Protozoa negative geotropism, or a tendency to rise against the pull of gravity, has been observed: first by Schwartz in two single-celled organisms frequently classified as plants, Euglena and Chlamydomonas (378); and eight years later by Aderhold, who suggested, without accepting it, the theory that the orientation may be due simply to the greater weight of one end of the organism's body (2). This view was maintained by Verworn: the action of gravity, he urged, must be purely passive. It cannot operate as a stimulus to active response on the animal's part, for a stimulus is always a change in environment, and gravity is a constant force (416). This ignores the fact that the animal's relations to gravity may change though gravity does not. According to Verworn's theory, the geotropic orientation of a single-celled organism takes place through a series of "little falls" whereby the heavier end is directed downward. Massart opposed this view on the basis of observations which showed that the actual movements of the organisms did not correspond to it, but were the result of active orientation. If response to gravity is passive, then dead animals should fall through the water in the same position as that assumed by living animals when oriented to gravity. Massart experimented with various Protozoa by killing them and studying their methods of sinking, which he found not always the same as the attitudes assumed in response to gravity (259). There is always the possibility, however, that the methods employed to kill may change the specific gravity of some part of the body. Jensen offered the theory that reaction to gravity may be due to the difference in the water pressure on the two ends of the animal. He asserted that when the air pressure on the water was reduced by exhausting the air above, there was an increase in the geotropism, indicating a relative rather than an absolute sensibility to pressure (215), but Lyon points out that this process may affect the animals in various other ways besides altering the air pressure. Increasing the air pressure, or protecting the surface with oil, has no effect upon geotropism, Lyon finds, and he urges that Jensen's theory requires enormous sensibility to pressure differences on the organism's part, as great as that needed by a human being to note the difference between the air pressure on the head and that on the feet (255). Another suggestion was offered by Davenport, namely, that negatively geotropic organisms swim in the direction where the greatest resistance to their progress is offered. This is like one theory put forward to explain rheotropism, or the tendency of animals to swim against currents, and anemotropism, or the "head against wind" movement of insects; and as Rádl (355) first and Lyon (254) afterward pointed out, it assumes the fact to be explained, for only if an animal actively opposes a force, will that force exert more pressure at one point of its body than at another.

The theory cannot explain why an animal at rest should be oriented. Another argument that tells against it is offered by experiments showing that animals placed in solutions of the same density as their own bodies, in which, therefore, they have no weight, still display negative geotropism, and that the direction of the response is not reversed when the fluid is made heavier than the animals (255). Lyon's own theory, accepted by Jennings, is that the stimulus for geotropism is furnished by the action of gravity within the body of the organism, upon substances of different weight which exert varying pressures and take up different positions according to the position of the body (255).

It has been shown that the reactions of Paramecium to gravity are modified by a variety of conditions. Negative geotropism, in a sense their normal condition, is favored by plentiful food supply and by an increase in temperature within certain limits; positive geotropism, movement downward, may be brought about temporarily by mechanical shock, by salts and alkalies, by temperature changes (278, 388) to which, however, the animals may adapt themselves; with less constancy by increase in the density of the fluid containing them, and with lasting effect by lack of food. It has been suggested that the downward movement under these circumstances is protective, since it shields the animals from surface agitation of the water, from surface ice, and from failure of the surface food supply (278). We shall see that similar conditions often change the direction of an animal's response to light.

§ 57. *Orientation to Gravity: Cœlenterates*

Among the cœlenterates, geotropism is shown by certain hydroids, whose stems have a tendency to curve upward and their " roots " a tendency to grow vertically downward when the animals are placed in a horizontal position (402). The sea-anemone Cerianthus, whose normal position is head upward, will right itself if placed in any other position, though the righting reaction may be inhibited by contact stimulation on the side of the animal. It ordinarily lives with the body enclosed in a tube, and when taken from its proper habitat it seems to "prefer" a position, even horizontal, where the sides of the body are in contact with a solid, to a vertical position with its sides uncovered (237). The righting reaction of Hydra is not determined by gravity at all; the animal will take any position, vertical or horizontal, but "seeks" always to have its foot in contact with a solid (418). Some actinians have shown an interesting modification of gravity reaction through what we may call habit. Six specimens of *Actinia equina* were selected that had been fixed to the rocks in an "upside-down" position, that is, with the mouth end downward; and six others that had been right side up. In the first experiment all were placed upside down; the tendency to right themselves was decidedly stronger in those which had been previously erect. Similarly, when twelve selected in the same way were all placed right side up, the ones that had previously been in the reversed position showed a certain inclination to reassume it (143). On the other hand, the orientation of the polyp *Corymorpha palma* to gravity was entirely unaffected by keeping the animal for a long time in a position where it could not right itself; it assumed the upright position as soon as it was set free (402).

It was noted in the chapter on hearing that the peculiar organs occurring in certain Cœlenterata and in many other animals, which were originally called otocysts because of their supposed auditory function, have had their name changed to that of statocyst since it has appeared that they subserve chiefly orientation to gravity. In jellyfish, removal of these organs does not seem to affect the animal's power of keeping its balance; apparently equilibrium is maintained here by the simple action of gravity, for dead jellyfish float in the right-side-up position (286, 291). It has been suggested that the statocyst organs are for the reception of stimuli produced by shaking, to which medusæ are apparently sensitive (291). Negative geotropism exists in Gonionemus, which swims to the surface of the water when disturbed (470). In ctenophors, the statocyst organ, which is usually at one pole of the body, has been found to function as an organ for the maintenance of equilibrium (415).

§ 58. *Orientation to Gravity: Planarians*

A good example of a specially developed reaction having for its result the "righting" of an animal in an abnormal position is offered by the behavior of a planarian that has been turned over so that its back rests on the surface of support. The reaction consists of a turning of the body, beginning with the head end, about the long axis, so that a spiral form is assumed. The dorsal surface of the animal is convex, the greatest thickness of the body being in the middle line. When the planarian lies on its back, it thus naturally tips to one side, like a keeled boat out of water. This side, being brought into contact with a solid, gives a reaction analogous to the negative one, that is, it extends or stretches. Such a stretching of one side when the planarian is right side up would of course produce a turning in the opposite direction, a negative reaction. In this case, however, the opposite side does not contract to allow of turning, but maintains the same length. The necessary result is that the body is thrown into a spiral: as soon as the ventral surface of the head comes into contact with the solid, in consequence of the turning, the negative reaction of that end ceases. Thus the righting is progressively accomplished (316). The whole response can hardly be classed under the head of geotropism. Like that of Hydra, it is not made as the result of the pull of gravity, but is a reaction to contact stimulation; the animal will crawl in an upside-down position as readily as any other provided that the ventral surface and not the dorsal is in contact with a support.

§ 59. *Orientation to Gravity: Annelids*

Geotropism, in the marine worm *Convoluta roscoffensis,* has been found to fluctuate with the rise and fall of the tides, even when the animal is removed to an aquarium. In normal life the worms burrow in the sands at rising water, and come to the surface when the tide retreats. Prolonged exposure to air, or increase in the intensity of the light, causes them to move down the slope of the shore to moist places. These movements in the normal environment are represented by upward and downward movements of the animal when confined in a glass tube. Keeble and Gamble thought these oscillations in geotropism did not occur in darkness, and that the stimulus bringing them about was photic. When the summation of light stimuli passes a certain amount, they maintained, positive geotropism appears; when the after effect of light stimulation is dissipated, the negative phase recurs (140). Bohn, however, finds that the oscillations do persist in darkness, and that their primary cause is the mechanical shock of the waves, as is further indicated by the observation that shaking the tube will cause the worms to descend (35). The geotropism of Convoluta is dependent on the statocyst (140).

§ 60. *Orientation to Gravity: Mollusks*

Among Mollusks, the slug has had its reactions to gravity carefully observed. When placed in a horizontal position on an inclined glass plate, these animals tend to turn either upward or downward, moving either with or against the force of gravity. Davenport and Perkins found that the same individuals differed at different times in this respect, and concluded that the sense of the geotaxis was determined by obscure conditions. They also found that an inclination of only 7.5° on the part of the glass plate, representing only 13° of the full force of gravity, is sufficient to make the slugs orient themselves with reference to the pull of the earth, though the precision of such orientation increases as the angle increases (95). Frandsen thought it was the weight of the posterior part of the body that determined whether the movement should be up or down: that the natural tendency of all was to go downward, but that in some individuals the posterior part, which is poorly controlled, was heavier than the anterior, and pulled the animal around head upward (135). The statocyst organs in a cephalopod, Eledone, have been shown to function in maintaining equilibrium (137).

§ 61. *Orientation to Gravity: Echinoderms*

Very interesting righting reactions, in the starfish and sea urchin, are described by Romanes. The starfish rights itself by twisting around the tips of two or three of its rays until the suckers in the ventral side have a firm hold of the supporting surface, and then continuing the twisting, always in the same direction on the different rays, until the whole body is turned. The sea urchin, "a rigid, non-muscular and globular mass," with relatively feeble suckers, has a much harder time of it, and does not succeed in pulling itself over unless it is perfectly fresh and vigorous. It occasionally rests for some time when it has reached a position of stability halfway over, before continuing the process (365).

Lyon has observed marked negative geotropism in the larvæ of the sea urchin. He was unable to test Davenport's theory of the nature of the geotropic response by putting the animals in a solution of the same density as their own bodies, for the reason that such a fluid was too dense and sticky (being made of gum arabic and sea water) for them to swim in. That the response was merely a passive one he thinks improbable, because the larvæ from eggs that have been rapidly rotated, or "centrifuged," as it is called, have all the pigment on one side of their bodies and may therefore be supposed to have their ordinary balance disturbed; yet they rise to the surface just like the rest (256).

§ 62. *Orientation to Gravity: Crustacea*

That the statocyst organs in Crustacea are probably connected with equilibrium rather than with hearing we have already seen. Delage in 1887 found that Mysis, Palæmon, and other forms displayed serious disturbance of equilibrium when both eyes and statocysts were destroyed, showing that the eyes also play a part in the maintaining of balance (97). The eyes have been found to coöperate with the statocysts in the fiddler crab, Gelasimus, and also in another decapod, Platyonichus (78). Neither of these has statoliths. *Penæus membraneus*, on the other hand, was found to be permanently disoriented by destruction of the statocysts or even removal of the statoliths, while blinding produced no great disturbance, probably because of the animal's nocturnal habits (19, 138). Young crayfish with the statocysts destroyed will swim upside down as readily as right side up (71).

M

But the prettiest evidence for the static function of the statocysts was obtained when powdered iron was substituted for the mineral bodies in the open statocysts of Palæmon. It was found that when a magnet was brought near, the animal would respond by taking up a position corresponding to the resultant of the pull of the magnet and that of gravity (226).

Specific righting reactions occur in many Crustacea, though in some cases these seem to be merely the incidental effects of their ordinary locomotion. Branchipus, the fairy shrimp, normally swims upside down; if turned right side up when moving along the bottom of the vessel, it continues to move in this position without showing any disturbance until it happens to rise a little from the bottom, when apparently the weight of the body pulls it around into the usual upside-down position. The crayfish has two methods of righting itself: a quick "flop" executed with the tail, and a slow and laborious raising of itself on one side and tipping over (96).

Many Crustacea show marked responses to gravity: for example, Parker found decided negative geotropism in the females of the marine copepods whose depth migrations he studied. It seems to be needed to counteract the tendency of the animals to fall to the bottom by their own weight (304). In certain copepods, light was observed to change the sense of the response to gravity, not by taking its place as a directive stimulus, but apparently by producing some physiological change in the animals. Their normal geotropism was positive, that is, they had a tendency to move downwards. In darkness, however, their geotropism became negative. They were also negatively phototropic to strong light. If, when in the negatively geotropic phase, they were illuminated from below by intense light, from which they would ordinarily have moved away, the change from negative to positive geotropism induced by the light was of sufficient influence to make them move downward toward it (113). Other facts regarding the relation of geotropism and phototropism are mentioned on pp. 182 ff.

§ 63. *Orientation to Gravity: Spiders and Insects*

Spiders and insects have no statolith organs. Bethe thinks that equilibrium is maintained in their case as a natural result of the position of the centre of gravity and the distribution of air in the body. He supports this view by experiments in which dead insects, allowed to fall through the air, assume the normal position, and is inclined to think that all animals without special static organs maintain their balance in this way (27). Negative geotropism in certain insects, as evidenced by a tendency to creep from horizontal planes up vertical ones, was observed by Loeb (234). In light the eyes of insects have probably much to do with maintaining equilibrium. Certain aquatic insects, in experiments where the light was made to strike them only from below, as soon as they left the support on which they were resting, turned themselves upside down (355).

§ 64. *Orientation to Gravity: Vertebrates*

It has long been known that in vertebrates the static function resides in the ear, and especially in the semicircular canals (*e.g.*, 70, 85, 128, 147). Various experimenters have noted that operations on the ears of fishes disturb the equilibrium of these animals. Sewall, indeed, found that section of the semicircular canals in the shark had no effect on its balancing powers, although operations on the vestibule and ampullæ did disturb movement (380); and Steiner got no effect on equilibrium from removing the contents of the labyrinth (391). Errors in method and observation probably influenced these results. Loeb found that severing the auditory nerve or removing the statoliths from the dogfish caused the fish to incline toward the operated side and to roll the eyes in that direction (238). Total extirpation of one labyrinth in the perch was observed by Bethe to make the fish curve toward the affected side. The fish Scardinius showed a tendency to curve toward the opposite side (27). Lee's experiments on the dogfish showed a very definite relation between the position of the canal operated upon and rolling movements of the fish. Cutting the front canals caused the fish to dive forward, cutting the rear canals made it dive backward, and cutting the canal on either side made it roll over toward that side. A natural explanation of this behavior is to suppose that the absence of stimulus from the cut canal produces the same effect that rolling the fish in the opposite direction, and thus diminishing the pressure of the fluid in the canal, would produce. The fish "feels as if" it were being rolled over, and makes movements to regain its equilibrium. When the nerves supplying the ears on both sides were cut, the fish became perfectly indifferent to its position and would float upside down without any effort to right itself. The vestibule and otoliths of the fish ear are thought by Lee to be concerned with statical equilibrium; that is, with the maintenance of position while the fish is at rest, while the canals are concerned with balance during motion (dynamic equilibrium) (230). It may be added that experiments on the sea horse indicate that destruction of the labyrinths in this animal has no effect on equilibrium: the upright attitude is due to the position of the air bladder and is assumed even by dead animals (139).

That vision may materially aid in maintaining equilibrium in vertebrates is indicated by evidence from various sources, among others, the observation of Bigelow that goldfish in which the nerves supplying both ears had been cut recovered after two or three weeks and could swim quite normally except when they were placed in a large body of water and made to swim rapidly, when they showed no power of preserving their balance (33). Their successful performance of slower movements was very likely due to the use of sight.

Sensory impulses from the body muscles themselves undoubtedly coöperate with those from the semicircular canals in the maintenance of balance. They are evidently involved in the peculiar withdrawing movements by which land animals, even puppies, kittens, and young rats whose eyes have not opened, save themselves from falling when they reach the edge of the object on which they have been crawling (271, 384). Water-dwelling animals, accustomed to plunge off solid supports, lack this protective instinct; Yerkes showed that among several species of tortoises, some land-dwelling, some amphibious, and some aquatic, the first mentioned were much more reluctant than the second to crawl off the edge of a board, and the second more reluctant than the third (459).

§ 65. *The Psychic Aspect of Orientation to Gravity*

Glancing back over these examples of the responses made by animals to gravity, we note that while in some cases the earth's attraction appears to act mechanically upon the animal, causing the body passively to assume a certain position, the common method of bringing about orientation seems to be that some structure in the body, placed in an abnormal position, presents a stimulus which brings about a compensatory movement. This structure may be heavier particles of the body substance, as probably is the case in Paramecium; it may be a statolith, or the fluid in the labyrinth; it may be the eyes. In any case, what shall we say about the sensation quality involved? Perhaps the reactions produced are wholly reflex. Perhaps the statolith or the canal fluid produces a specific sensation quality. Or perhaps, as Verworn thinks, the sensation quality is merely that of pressure (415). Whatever its nature, spatial perception, the perception of the spatial relations between several stimuli simultaneously apprehended, plays no part in the orientation of animals to gravity.

§ 66. *Orientation to Light: Photopathy and Phototaxis*

One of the first facts that confronts the student of the ways and means by which animals become oriented to visual stimuli is the distinction which Loeb drew between what he called *heliotropism* and *sensibility to difference* (Unterschieds-empfindlichkeit) (239); and to indicate which the terms "phototaxis" and "photopathy" have also been applied. The phenomena are as follows. Strasburger, working on the swarm spores of certain plants, thought he had evidence that their reactions to light evinced not so much a tendency to seek a certain intensity of illumination, as a susceptibility to the direction from which the light came. He placed over the vessel containing them an India ink screen, thicker at one end so as to cause gradations in the intensity of the light reaching the vessel. When the light fell perpendicularly through this screen, the distribution of the swarm spores through the vessel was nearly uniform; that is, the differences of intensity had no effect. When the screen was removed, and the light fell at an angle, the spores immediately oriented themselves to its direction, and preserved this orientation even when the screen was replaced (392). The word *phototaxis*, instead of being used to designate any reaction to light, has been narrowed to designate the tendency to orient with reference to the direction rather than to the intensity of the light.

Now on the other hand there are some cases where animals apparently seek or avoid light without being oriented at all; that is, without having their bodies placed in a definite position during the movement. Planarians are an example of this. Increased intensity of light stimulates them to activity; they crawl about until they reach a shaded portion, where they come to rest. Their movements are not directed straight away from the light; in other words, it does not negatively orient them, but it excites them and the shadow brings them to rest (239). To cases such as this, where a certain intensity of light stimulates activity while a different intensity may inhibit it, but where no orientation of the body with reference to the direction of the rays occurs, the term "photopathy" may conveniently be applied. Bohn suggests that the tendency of certain animals to come to rest in shaded portions may really be an expression of fatigue produced by the action of the light (55).

A second problem arises in connection with the mechanism of phototaxis. *How* does light orient an animal? Does it exert an effect upon the muscles or locomotor organs of the body that is equivalent to pulling the animal around into the required position? Or does the organism become oriented because in a series of movements those which would bring it out of the oriented position are corrected by negative reactions? Again, if the effect of light upon the body is direct, producing orientation by bringing the animal at once into line with the light rays, is this effect produced by the *direction* of the light rays as they pass through the body, or by the fact that in any other than the oriented position two symmetrical points on opposite sides of the body are illuminated with *unequal intensity*, a theory of phototaxis which would bring it into nearer relation with photopathy?

§ 67. *Instances of Photopathy and Phototaxis*

The phenomena of orientation to light in different groups of animals suggest now one, now another of these questions. In Protozoa, although attempts have been made to show that orientation is produced by the direct effects of light on symmetrical points, according to the observations of Jennings (206) and Mast (261), it seems to be due to negative reactions given when the organism, in its ordinary swimming movements, either passes into a region of greater or less illumination, or swings its anterior end "toward or away from the source of light, so that it is shaded at one moment and strongly lighted at the next." That is, the reactions are caused, not by the direction of the light rays as such, but by differences in the intensity of illumination. Strasburger's results, in which the swarm spores moved toward the light into a region of less intense illumination, Jennings holds were due to the fact that "turning the sensitive anterior end away from the source of the light" would diminish the effective illumination of the animal more than passing into the slightly less illuminated region. That is, the two ways of changing the intensity of the stimulus, moving forward into a darker region, and turning the head end away from the light, are here opposed : the latter effect is stronger than the former, hence the organisms do not turn the head end from the light, or rather they make the negative reaction when it is so turned, and do move toward the shaded region. "If the difference in intensity of light in different parts of the drop were increased till the change in illumination due to progression is greater than the change due to swinging the anterior end away from the source of light, then the positive organisms would gather in the more illuminated regions" (211, p. 148).

In Volvox, also, orientation is held by Oltmanns (298) and Mast (262) to be an affair of intensity differences rather than of light direction. The reaction of a Volvox colony, which in moderate light is positively phototropic, occurs in consequence of a response by each individual in the colony given when, as the colony rotates, that individual passes from a higher to a lower intensity of light.

In Hydra, the effect of light is photopathic rather than phototactic. We have seen that these animals, when subjected to light either above or below a certain "optimum" intensity, wander about until they reach a region of the right degree of illumination; their movements manifest no definite orientation (444). One sea-anemone, *Actinia cereus*, observed by Bohn, does show an oriented response to light. Weak light causes expansion of its tentacles perpendicularly to the light rays. If the light is increased, the tentacles "tend to orient themselves in the direction of the rays, and finally converge in a bundle parallel to that direction," a response which has the effect of protecting them from the intense light (62).

The medusa Gonionemus offers an instance of opposition between photopathy and phototaxis, the former being negative, the latter positive, in daylight. That is, it moves toward the light when swimming, but being less active in darkness than in light, it comes to rest, and hence tends to collect, in darkened regions. Intense light gives a negative phototaxis. Sudden decrease and sudden increase of light intensity have alike the effect of temporarily inhibiting activity. On swimming either from shadow into sunlight, or from sunlight into shadow, the medusa stops, turns over, and sinks to the bottom. But when this effect has been produced by entering shadow, the animal, on again becoming active, may move in any direction; when it has been produced by entering sunlight, the medusa on beginning to move again "usually turns in such a way as to move back into the shaded region." This effect Yerkes, who first observed it, thinks due to the contraction of the bell on the more illuminated side; that is, it is a definite reflex to a localized stimulus. Orientation results from the fact that the greater intensity of stimulus on one side of the bell produces contraction at that point (451, 470, 468).

We have already seen that planarians offer an illustration of photopathy. Light is not, however, wholly without effect on the direction of the animal's movements. It has been found that when planarians are placed with the head toward the source of light, they have a distinct tendency to turn out of the path, while if their heads are directed straight away from the light, their tendency is to keep in the path (313). It is probable that when the animal turns its head toward the light, its movement is checked by a negative reaction. An attempt has been made to show that photopathy, rather than response to the direction of the light rays as such, governs the responses of the land planarian *Bipalium kewense* to photic stimuli. The apparatus was arranged so that a shadow was thrown from above upon an area of light coming horizontally from one side. Although the animal is negatively phototropic to a marked degree, it would crawl toward the source of light in order to get into the shadow (81). The explanation for this may very likely correspond to that offered by Jennings for the reverse behavior of Strasburger's swarm spores. That is, the planarian might have obtained a greater diminution of light intensity by moving into the shadow than by turning aside from the path of the rays. The one possibility excluded is that the negative reaction of planarians is a response to the direction of the light rays as such.

The same evidence for photopathy, as distinct from phototaxis produced by direction of light, has been obtained for the

earthworm *Allolobophora fœtida* (81). Yet the movements
of earthworms are oriented by light; as we have seen, they
tend to move away from a source of light. This orientation
Holmes believes to take place by the checking of random
movements of the head in the direction of the light. In the
crawling movements stimulated when light is thrown upon
the worm, the head is turned from side to side. If it happens
to be turned toward the light, it is withdrawn. Holmes explains the observation of Parker and Arkin that the head of
the worm is much more apt to turn from the light than toward
it (312), by saying that account was probably taken here only
of the first decided turn made. He himself experimented by
lowering a worm, crawling on a wet board, while its body was
in a straight line and contracted, into a beam of light at right
angles to the body, and noting the first movement of the
head. This was found to be twenty-seven times away from
the light and twenty-three times toward the light. A similar
method of orientation by "trial and error" was observed in
the leech and in fly larvæ by Holmes (185).

E. H. Harper, on the other hand, working on the earthworm *Perichæta bermudensis*, declares that if the light is
strong enough there are no random movements of the head at
all, but that the first movement is a direct reflex away from
the light. When the light is only moderate, the appearance
of random movements is due to the fact that the worm is less
sensitive in a contracted than in an expanded state. Locomotion consists in a series of contractions and expansions,
and "as each extension begins in a state of lower sensibility,
the anterior end may be projected toward the light, only to
be checked when its increase of sensibility with extension
makes the stimulus appreciated" (161). A similar suggestion that orientation may occur either by a definite reflex or
as the outcome of random movements, according to the ani-

mal's physiological condition, is to be found as early as the work of Pouchet on fly larvæ. He noted that the courses taken by the larvæ away from the light were either straight, "or they present to right and left indentations due to the wavering movements which the animal makes . . . in a certain number of cases, as if to take at each instant a new direction." These individual differences might have been accounted for, says Pouchet, by differing degrees of hunger in the larvæ (347).

Phototaxis in certain tube-dwelling marine worms was observed by Loeb. *Spirographis spallanzanii* gradually curves its tube until its oral end faces the direction from which the rays of light come; and another marine worm, whose tube is absolutely stiff, adapts itself to a change in the direction of the rays by curving the newly formed portions of the tube as it constructs them (236).

Attempts to show the independence of photopathy and phototaxis by causing a positively phototactic animal to move toward the source of light even when, by an arrangement of screens overhead, such movement brings it into a region of dimmer illumination, have been made with apparent success on the crustacean Daphnia (93). That no increase in the intensity of the light will reverse Daphnia's positive phototaxis is also evidence that photopathy, the seeking of an optimum intensity, is absent in these Crustacea (457). Simocephalus, being made to collect in the brighter regions of a trough and showing no orientation to light rays entering the trough at right angles, seemed to display photopathy independent of phototaxis (448). It is very difficult, however, to be sure in such experiments that the direction of the light rays and the intensity of the illumination are really independently varied, for the diffusion of light by floating particles and its reflection from the sides of the trough offer disturbing factors. The amphipod *Talorchestia longicornis*, which moves toward the light but comes to rest in shaded portions, seems to combine positive phototaxis with negative photopathy (181). Loeb's observations on the larvæ of the arachnid Limulus, the horseshoe crab, and upon insect larvæ, may also be mentioned here. When strongly negative, the former moved away in the line of rays of sunlight falling obliquely from a window upon the vessel containing them; the shadow of the window bar lay across the vessel, and the animals continued to move through it in the same direction, although, on passing out from it, they went into a more brightly lighted region (239). A similar illustration of phototaxis without photopathy was found in the caterpillars of the Porthesia moth, which give a positive response, and in fly larvæ, which are negative (235).

§ 68. *Direction and Intensity Theories of Phototaxis*

The problem as to whether orientation to light is brought about by the influence of the direction of light rays as such, or by the fact that light falling upon an oriented organism from a given direction affects symmetrical points with different degrees of intensity, is one requiring much nicety of discrimination between concepts. Loeb, in his earliest discussion of the subject, expresses himself positively in favor of the former hypothesis. "The orientation of animals to a source of light is, like that of plants, conditioned by the direction in which the light rays traverse the animal tissue, and not by the difference in the light intensity on the different sides of the animal" (233). To this Bohn urges as a "fundamental objection" that "the 'luminous rays' which strike a living body have, save in wholly exceptional cases, various directions, being reflected, diffused and refracted by neighboring bodies" (55). Certainly if definite orientation to light occurred only when an animal's body was traversed by rays in one predominant direction, it would be of little practical service. The other view, that the important factor is the difference in the intensity of stimulation of opposite points on the unoriented animal's body, is that held by Verworn (417). Holmes points out that no crucial test experiment of the two hypotheses has ever been made. Such an experiment would require that a semi-transparent animal should have two symmetrical points on its body, *a* and *b*, stimulated with exactly equal intensity, each by a ray of light coming from a different direction. Under such circumstances, according to the theory of Verworn, the animal ought to move straight forward (181). An attempt to get evidence was made by Davenport and Cannon in a study of Daphnia. They proposed the following question: Do positively phototactic animals move *more rapidly* toward their optimum intensity than toward an intensity below the optimum? If orientation is determined, as the Verworn theory supposes, by the *relative* intensity of light on different points of the organism, then the absolute intensity of the light ought not to affect it. If, on the other hand, the direction of the rays orients the animal, then precision of orientation should increase as the absolute intensity approaches the optimum. Daphnia was found to move somewhat less rapidly toward the light when the intensity of the latter was reduced; this fact was held to be due to diminished precision of orientation and hence to tell for the theory of Loeb [1] (93).

§ 69. *The Eyes in Phototaxis*

The directive theory of phototaxis is of little significance in connection with the reactions to light of organisms whose bodies are opaque and which have eyes. For the eyes seem to be fundamentally concerned in orientation to light. That

[1] A discussion of the intensity and direction theories will be found in Holt and Lee's article on "The Theory of Phototactic Response" (187).

this is the case in Daphnia was shown by Rádl, who placed the animal under a microscope in such a way that only the eyes could be moved. When the light coming from below was diminished, the eyes rolled upward; when the light coming from above was diminished, they rolled downward. The precise positive phototaxis of Daphnia, Rádl thinks, is primarily an eye movement, the body being turned to follow the eyes (354). Indeed, Rádl is of the opinion that in all animals having eyes, the essential feature of phototropism is eye-orientation, wholly analogous to fixation in the case of human vision (356). In amphipods, blackening of one eye of a positively phototropic animal caused a turning toward the blackened side, as if the animal were trying to restore the missing illumination; similar experiments upon negative animals produced turning toward the other side (181). Like phenomena have been observed in other Crustacea, in mollusks, annelids, and insects. Bohn, like Rádl, is inclined to explain the light tropisms of animals with eyes as entirely due to an effect, either tonic or inhibitory, according as the animal is positive or negative, of light acting through the eyes upon the muscles of the same side of the body. If one eye received more light than the other, a positive animal would turn toward the darker side because the muscles on the side toward the light would be more strongly stimulated. A negative animal would turn toward the light because of inhibition of muscular activity on that side. Orientation may then be effected in a normal animal when the eyes are equally illuminated (55).

§ 70. *Influences Affecting the Sense of Light Orientations*

In no class of animal responses to stimulation is the effect more dependent upon the coöperation of a number of conditions than in those involving orientation to light. Many influences have been found to reverse the sense of light reactions, transforming negatively phototropic into positively phototropic animals, and *vice versa*. That such reversal should occur in response to increase or decrease of the *intensity of the light* is what one would naturally expect; if a certain intensity of illumination is favorable to the life processes of an animal, it would seem appropriate for it to seek light of that intensity but avoid light of greater intensity. Many animals, like Gonionemus, are positive to light of moderate intensity and negative to strong light (451). The females of the crustacean Labidocera migrate to the surface of the water at nightfall because, like the earthworm, they react positively to faint light; and move downward at sunrise because they are negative in their response to intenser light (304). On the other hand, Holmes observed that *Orchestia agilis*, an amphipod crustacean, would, if brought from strong to weaker light, become negative for a short time; the meaning of such a change it is difficult to conjecture (181). Sudden reduction of light causes a temporary negative phase also in *Convoluta roscoffensis* (140).

Prolonged action of light may alter phototropism: the "depth migrations," that is, the periodical movements toward and away from the surface of the water, in the free-swimming larvæ of the barnacle, Balanus, are due apparently to the fact that an exposure of several hours to light will make positive animals negative, even though the light at the end of the period of exposure is decidedly fainter than it was at the beginning (153). The positive reactions of the water insect Ranatra increase in violence the longer the light acts; on the other hand, after being kept in darkness for several hours, Ranatra is negative on first being taken out (186). Daphnias kept in darkness for a time become decidedly negative to diffused daylight, whereas if kept in light they would have been

positive. A sudden change in light intensity, either brightening or darkening, has the effect of making positive Daphnias
temporarily negative (302).

Temperature changes influence response to light. The obvious suggestion here would be that since increased temperature often accompanies increased intensity of light, animals
that are positively phototropic only up to a certain degree of
illumination ought to become negative when the temperature
is decidedly raised. This, however, is by no means always
the effect produced by increased temperature. Strasburger's
swarm spores became positive in higher temperatures, negative in lowered ones (392). *Orchestia agilis*, which we have
just seen becomes temporarily negative on being brought from
strong into weak light, may be made positive again if the water
is slightly warmed. When the same animal is dropped into
water, it becomes strongly negative, but it will show a positive
response if the water is heated almost to a fatal point (181).
On the other hand, the copepods and annelid larvæ studied by
Loeb were made negative by increased, positive by lowered,
temperature. Other crustaceans, *e.g.* Daphnia (457), had
their responses to light unaffected by a fairly wide range
of temperature changes.

Increasing or decreasing the density of the water will also
affect phototropism. In some copepods diluting the water
produced negative responses to light, while increasing its density brought about those of the opposite sign (239). Diluting
the water produced negative phototaxis in the larvæ of
Palæmonetes (257). Parker failed to find any such effect in
the case of the copepods studied by him (304). W. Ostwald
has called attention to the possibility that "internal friction"
between the organism and the medium may affect various
tropisms. Freshly caught Daphnias, which are negative
or indifferent, quickly become positive if gelatine or quince

N

emulsion is added to the water. Since they would become so in time anyway, Ostwald thinks the mechanical friction of the sticky liquid simply acts as a " sensibilator " and brings on this positive phase sooner (302).

Change in the purity of the water also sometimes produces change of sign in the response to light. The amphipod Jassa, negative in ordinary sea water, becomes positive in foul sea water (181). The *presence of chemicals* is an influence probably identical with the one just mentioned. Various Crustacea have had the direction of their reactions changed by carbonic or other acids, ammonium salts, ether, chloroform, paraldehyd, and alcohol (244). The ultra-violet rays will make positive Balanus larvæ temporarily negative (245).

The state of hunger or satiety in an animal must be reckoned with: the caterpillars of Porthesia, for example, are decidedly positive when hungry, much less so when fed (236). The slug *Limax maximus*, ordinarily negative to strong light, is positive to light of any intensity when hungry (135).

Mechanical stimulation is most striking in its effect on light reactions. Pouchet in 1872 noted that fly larvæ after having been shaken fail to display their usual orientation to light (347). The copepod *Temora longicornis*, usually negative, can be made positive by shaking it (239). Very curious phenomena of a similar nature have been observed in the case of some Entomostraca. Certain individual specimens of the ostracod Cypridopsis appeared to be decidedly positive, others negative. Careful experimental analysis of the conditions revealed the following as the true state of affairs. The animals are predominantly negative. But contact with a mechanical stimulus has the effect of making them positive; thus a negative animal that is picked up in a pipette, or merely comes in contact with the end of the trough in swimming away from the light, may become positive. In course of time such a positive animal will become negative of its own accord, so to speak, without further mechanical stimulation, but such stimulation, if applied, makes it negative at once (405).

Similar experiments upon Daphnia and Cypris gave results of the same general character. The strong positive tendency of the former may, by several times taking the animal up in a pipette, be made very temporarily negative; the opposite effect could not be well tested because of the difficulty of preserving the negative state long enough to experiment on it. In the case of Cypris, an animal temporarily negative could be made positive by picking it up, but the positive phase could not be similarly reversed. No other sudden stimulus produces the effect which is thus induced by mechanical contact (449). And no possible analogy from our own experience suggests itself; the phenomenon remains a mystery.

The effect of contact was observed by Holmes in the terrestrial amphipod *Orchestia agilis*. The most permanent phase of these animals is positive, although they are at rest under seaweed on the beach by day. But when they are thrown into the water, they become strongly negative, no matter what the intensity of the light; and to a considerable extent this effect is independent of the temperature (181). In the case of the copepod *Labidocera æstiva*, being picked up in a pipette will make the females, ordinarily positive, negative for a time. The males are normally slightly negative, but picking them up, instead of reversing this tendency, increases it (304). The strong positive phototropism of the "water scorpion" Ranatra, an hemipterous insect, may be made negative by handling, and especially by dipping in water (186).

Periodical changes in the sense of response to light have been observed in animals subjected to periodical changes in environment. The gasteropod mollusk Littorina lives on the rocks of the seacoast in regions where it is covered with water at high tide and exposed to the air at low tide. According to the height at which they are found, some of these animals undergo the alternations of wetness and dryness at the ordinary tidal periods, twice a day, while others are reached by the water only at the special high tides occurring every fourteen days. Mitsukuri showed that when the waves of a rising tide cover these mollusks, they display negative phototropism and seek shelter in rock cavities; while as soon as they are again exposed to the air, their phototropism becomes positive and they emerge in search of food. Further, he found that a Littorina whose phototaxis was negative could be made positive by being subjected to the action of a stream of water for a time (275). Bohn later studied the effects of placing black or white screens near the animals at various angles to their crawling movements, and found that the black screens exerted an attractive influence at certain times, the white screens at others. These changes in the "sense" of the phototropism correspond in time to the oscillations of the tide, even though the animals are studied in the laboratory; they tend gradually to grow less pronounced, however, under such circumstances. Further, the level from which the Littorinas are taken influences the nature of their response to light. Those from high levels, "which undergo prolonged and intense desiccation, habitually move following the direction of the luminous field in the negative sense; the Littorinas from low levels, which undergo only short and slight desiccation, move, habitually, following the direction of the luminous field in the positive sense." The former become positively phototropic at the time of highest water, the latter negatively phototropic at the time of low water. In all cases, the tendency is for the animals to become negative at low-water time. The attraction of the dark screens represents that of the dark surface of the rocks (55). Similar oscillations corresponding to the periodicity of the tides were observed in the annelid *Hedista diversicolor* (55) and in the sea-anemone *Actinia equina* (65).

A further influence upon light reactions which is doubtless involved in the formation of the rhythms just described, has been emphasized by Bohn; namely, the "hydratation" or desiccation — the *wetness* or *dryness* — of the tissues. The oscillations of Hedista just mentioned may be explained by supposing that when the annelid is dry, light has the power of exciting muscular movements. This means that when the worms have accidentally crept into the shade, they stop, giving the effect of negative photopathy. If one eye has its illumination diminished, there is an inhibition of muscular activity on that side, and consequently a turning in that direction. At the period of high tide, when the muscles are wet, the action of light on the animal is inhibitory and the above phenomena are reversed. When the Littorinas observed by Bohn are decidedly moist or decidedly dry, black and white screens exert an influence that is proportional to their area; the attractions and repulsions seem irresistible, "the mollusk in the neighborhood of shelter or food continues on its way toward the screen as if drawn by a fatal force, as if it saw and felt nothing." But when the tissues of its body are in an intermediate stage between "hydratation" and desiccation, large screens have no effect upon it; it reacts to small objects in its neighborhood. "The animal seems, as it were, to disengage itself from the influence of external forces, seems no longer to behave like a pure machine: it goes to the stones and seaweed where it may find shelter and nourishment, as if it saw and was conscious of them" (55).

The *state of rest or movement* is still another factor. The "mourning cloak" butterfly, *Vanessa antiopa*, on coming to rest in bright sunlight, orients itself with the head away from the light. When it moves, on the other hand, it flies toward light of any intensity (307). Bohn also has noted that certain butterflies orient themselves when alighted in such a way that the posterior part of the eyes is toward the light. When in this position there is a tendency for the wings to be spread apart, while when the insect is facing the light the wings are closely folded (55). The effect on the wings was noted in Vanessa also, and, it is suggested, may have some function in bringing the sexes together (307). The pomace fly when at rest is not oriented at all. Light exerts upon it merely the effect of stimulating it to movement, a "kinetic," not a directive, effect. When the movement has been started, however, it is directed toward the light: positive phototaxis appears. But owing to the kinetic influence of the light, when the insects have been long exposed to sunlight they tend to come to rest in the more shaded portions, with their heads away from the light, for this is the position in which they are least stimulated to movement. The kinetic effect increases with the intensity of the light, but its "directive effect," through which orientation is secured after the movement is started, was at least in one case lost under intense light (74).

The *background*, finally, sometimes determines the sense of the reaction. Keeble and Gamble found that while the crustacean *Hippolyte varians* would move toward the light whether it was on a white or black background, *Macromysis inermis* was negative on a white ground and positive on a black ground (218).

§ 71. *Mutual Influence of Light and Gravity Orientations*

Orientation to light and orientation to gravity are not without mutual influence in determining the behavior of an animal. Supposed instances of this have been noted in the case of the periodically changing geotropism of *Convoluta roscoffensis* (140) and in the copepods observed by Esterly (113). The relations of gravity and light responses in the larvæ of the squid, a cephalopod mollusk, seem to be as follows. The larvæ have a tendency to rise to the surface of the water both in darkness and in light, suggesting negative geotropism. Two test tubes were arranged by Loeb, one lying horizontally and at right angles to a window, the other inclined at an angle of 45 degrees from the upright position, and with the upper end directed away from the window. Larvæ were placed in both tubes; those in the former showed positive phototaxis by collecting at the end nearest the window, but those in the latter gave evidence that their negative geotropism was stronger than their positive phototaxis by rising to the upper end, although it was farthest from the source of light (239). It is not usual for geotropism thus to come off victorious in a contest with other tendencies. Jennings says, "As a general rule the reaction to gravity is easily masked by reactions to other stimuli" (211, p. 150). In the mollusks observed by Bohn, the tendency in ascending or descending the rocks is to orient the body in the line of the greatest slope. When light and gravity are acting together upon the animal, its movement seems to be a resultant of the two, but if the mollusk is made to move on a vertical plane, gravity thus exerting its maximal force, the influence of the light disappears altogether; and if the animal is put in an upside-down position by further tipping of the surface, the sense of its phototropism is reversed; that is, it may be repelled instead of attracted by a dark screen (55).

A curious tendency has been noted by many observers in insects with both eyes blinded; namely, to fly straight up into the air. Forel thought they did so because in no other direction could they escape obstacles (130); but this fact they would have to learn by experience, for which, in some cases at least, they do not take time. Plateau believed the rising into the air was due to sensations produced by the action of the light on the surface of the body, leading the insects in the direction of the strongest light, which usually comes from above. He supported this view by showing experimentally that a blinded insect would not rise if set free at night, while on the other hand, if liberated in a lighted room, it would, in spite of the blinding, fly toward the light or the lightest part of the ceiling (332, 334). In the butterfly Vanessa, Parker thinks the rising due to negative geotropism, as the insect flew upward in a darkened room (307). Axenfeld suggested that it might be caused by light penetrating the integument of the head (7).

§ 72. *The Psychic Aspect of Orientation to Light*

What shall be said of the psychic aspect of all this complex mass of facts regarding the orientation of animals to light? If such orientation occurs in some animals by the immediate action of light on the body tissues, either by virtue of the direction of its course through them, or by the relative effects on the motor apparatus, at symmetrical points, of stimulations differing in intensity, there is no analogy for this in our own experience. We are not pulled about into line by the direct action of light on our bodies, and we cannot imagine what the conscious accompaniment of such a process would be. If orientation occurs through the giving of a negative reaction whenever the body chances to move out of the oriented position, we may conjecture that the negative reaction is, here as elsewhere, accompanied by unpleasant consciousness; whether also by a specific visual sensation will be evidenced by the existence of a sense organ or by any other of the arguments

mentioned in Chapter IV. If the effect of light is merely
"kinetic," causing no orientation, but movement about until
the animal chances to come into the shadow, vague restlessness or uneasiness is the human experience most closely
resembling its possible conscious accompaniment. In none
of these cases does spatial perception appear to be concerned.
Where, however, the response to light depends upon the eyes,
the accompanying psychic process may have a spatial character. Even though the eyes do not give clear images, if the
reaction is determined by the greater intensity of illumination
on one eye than on the other, it is possible that the visual field
present to the animal's consciousness may contain gradations
of intensity arranged side by side in a spatial pattern. An
important advance from mere phototropism to visual space
perception is made, according to Rádl, when an animal's eyes
are oriented by "a dark point in light space" rather than by
"a bright point in dark space," but the conditions that render
such orientation possible he does not attempt to define, other
than by suggesting that they are connected with the structure
of the eye itself (358).

§ 73. *Orientation to Other Forces*

One force, which, as was noted in Chapter III, produces
orientation, namely, the electric current, we shall leave out
of account. It is not a stimulus to which animals are normally subject, and though its action on living matter is of
great interest to the physiologist, the comparative psychologist's difficulty in finding a psychic interpretation for the facts
may justify setting them aside. Similar considerations apply
to orientation to centrifugal force. There remain the orientations that have been termed respectively " rheotropism "
and " anemotropism," responses to currents of water and to
currents of air.

The tendency shown by many aquatic animals to orient themselves with head up-stream, and to swim against the current, was formerly thought to be a response to the pressure exerted by the current — a reaction leading the animal to resist pressure. Lyon, however, pointed out that this explanation assumes rheotropism on the animal's part. It is because the animal opposes the current that the current exerts any pressure. If it merely allowed itself to be carried passively along, and if the current surrounding the animal flowed with uniform velocity in all its parts, no stimulus whatever could be exerted by the water pressure (254). It seems probable that eyeless animals do not, as a matter of fact, orient themselves against a current of this sort, and that rheotropism in their case occurs when a current of unequal velocity disarranges their movements, or when they are in contact with a solid body. Thus Jennings has suggested that in Paramecium the reaction is due to the fact that unless the animal has its head to the current, the flow of the latter will interfere with the normal backward stroke of the cilia, causing negative reactions until the disturbance is removed by proper orientation (211, p. 74). In animals with eyes, however, there is reason to think that apparent rheotropism is largely an affair of vision. Lyon's theory of rheotropism in fishes is that the fish orients itself and swims in such a way that its surroundings, the bottom of the stream, for example, shall appear to the sense of sight to be at rest, an hypothesis which, as we shall see, was adopted by Rádl to explain the "hovering" of insects in one place (355). Lyon supports it by experiments where the bottom or sides of the aquarium were caused to move in the absence of any current in the water, and the fish was found to follow them. When the fish was placed in a revolving glass cylinder, it followed the revolutions, although there was a slow current, of course, in the same direction, against which, on the pressure theory, the fish should have moved. Still more decisive was the experiment where young fish were placed in a corked bottle full of water which was submerged and put near a wall covered with algæ. When the bottle was moved in one direction, all the fish went to the opposite end, although no current could have been produced. Again, a wooden box with ends of wire netting, the bottom covered with gravel and the sides with seaweed, was used; fish (Fundulus) were placed in it, and the box was held lengthwise in a strong current. The fish oriented themselves, but as soon as the box was released and allowed to float away, they lost their orientation, though their relation to the current was in no way altered. Blind fish, Lyon found, oriented themselves by touch, sinking to the bottom. There does, however, appear to be, in some cases, a genuine pressure reaction to current, for when water is rushing through a small hole into a tank containing blind fish, they keep their heads to the current without touching anything. Here the different parts of the stream have different velocity, and pressure stimuli are actually applied to the skin. There must be pressure reaction, also, when fish actually swim up-stream instead of merely maintaining their places against a current (155). Such a reaction was displayed, probably, by some shrimps which, being in the water with the fish in the revolving tank experiment, did swim against the current instead of with it (254).

Some very interesting behavior touching on this same point was observed by Garrey in a school of the little fish called sticklebacks. He noted that if any object was moved along the side of the aquarium containing them, the whole school would move along a parallel line *in the opposite direction*. If an individual fish happened to be heading directly toward the object, it would turn in the opposite direction from the

one in which the object was moved; if it was heading somewhat in the opposite direction already, it would turn farther
in that direction until parallel with the object's line of motion;
if it was heading somewhat in the same direction as the object,
it would "back off hesitatingly," and reverse itself by a turn
in either direction, usually taking the way around toward
which it was already partially headed, if the object was rapidly
moved, but the other way around if the object's motion was
slow. At first sight this behavior seems to display an instinct
precisely opposite to that of keeping the visual field constant.
Yet the sticklebacks, when placed in a cylindrical glass tank
inside of a black and white striped vessel, moved with the
latter when it moved, proving that they possessed the usual
tendency shown by Lyon to be involved in rheotropism.
Garrey points out that movement in the opposite direction is
produced not when the whole visual field moves, but when it
is at rest, and one object in it moves. Can it be, he asks, that
the moving object "fixes the attention" of the fish and produces an apparent motion of the background in the opposite
direction, which motion the fish follows? (141.)

Rheotropism in water arthropods may be similarly accounted for, and in the opinion of Rádl, this same tendency
explains the habit swarms of insects have of hovering over the
same place, a phenomenon which Wheeler thought might be
due to odors emanating from the soil (435). Insects will often
be found to follow an object over or under which they are
grouped in the air, if it be moved (355). Swarms of insects
may be noted in the air over a country road, following its
windings and apparently oriented by the contrast between
the road and the dark banks on either side. When, however,
resting insects turn so as to keep their heads to the wind, the
reaction is evidently really due to the wind and not to their
visual surroundings (370). Probably the disturbance to their

wings produced by any other position causes them to rest only in the "head-on" orientation.

The responses of animals to different intensities of *heat* seem not to involve a definite orientation of the body. A temperature above the optimum produces wandering movements, which cease when the animal happens to reach the proper temperature (265, 268, 457). If we were to adopt the terminology applied to light reactions, we should say that thermopathy rather than thermotaxis is the rule.

CHAPTER IX

Spatially Determined Reactions and Space Perception
(*continued*)

§ 74. *Class III: Reactions to a Moving Stimulus*

Specialized response to a stimulus in motion, that is, one which successively affects several neighboring points on a sensitive surface, is also frequently met with in animal behavior. Its usefulness is obvious: a stimulus in motion is very commonly a living creature, hence either an enemy or food. In any case it must be reacted to with extreme promptness. Reactions of this class may be distinguished as tactile or visual according as the moving stimulus is mechanical or photic.

We find good examples of specialized reactions to *motile touch* in the cœlenterates. The sea-anemone, Aiptasia, gives its most violent reaction, involving all the tentacles at once, when touched by a moving object (291). The medusa Gonionemus makes, in the case of a moving mechanical stimulus, its single exception to the rule of responding by the feeding reaction to edible substances only. The tentacles will be wound corkscrew fashion about a glass rod drawn across them, they bend in toward the mouth, and the bell margin bearing them contracts; the feeding reaction goes no further, however. But the response is differentiated from that to any other form of stimulation by its greater speed: the reaction time is from .3 to .35 of a second, compared with .4 to .5 of a second for other stimuli (451). Special vigor and speed generally characterize reactions to contact with moving objects. In eliciting the scratch-reflex of dogs, an object drawn along the skin is decidedly more effective than one pressed against the skin for the same length of time (382, p. 184). The physiological effect is probably, Sherrington says, the same as that involved in the "summation" of successive slight stimuli applied at the same point. As is well known, the latter will bring about a response of considerable violence, though each one acting alone would apparently be without effect.

Is it likely that these responses to moving stimuli in contact with the skin involve the perception of movement as a form of space perception; that is, a perception of the successive positions occupied by the stimulus and their relative direction? I think we may say that they probably do not, in the lower animal forms at least. And a chief reason for saying so lies in the fact that the reactions are so rapid. To perceive the spatial relations of stimuli, or any other relations, is a process not favored by great speed of response. The quicker the reaction, the less clear the perception of its cause: such seems to be the general law. The sensation accompanying contact with a moving object may differ in intensity from that accompanying a resting stimulus; it may, in the lower forms, differ qualitatively in some way not represented in our own experience, but it can hardly be connected with the more complex psychic processes involved in any form of space perception.

In vision, also, there are special arrangements for reacting to moving stimulation. The sensitiveness of many animals to changes of light intensity, although not a direct adaptation to the spatial characteristics of a stimulus, serves the same purpose, for changes in light intensity are oftenest brought about by objects in motion. In the mollusk *Pecten varius*, a transition from shadow vision to movement vision is illustrated : the animal closes its shell when a shadow is moved so as to fall on its eye spots in rapid succession (360). Generally speaking, the simple invertebrate eye, however, is adapted to respond to changes in light intensity rather than to moving objects. Plateau found that caterpillars, which have only simple eyes, could see moving objects no better than those at rest (333), and Willem was inclined to think snails saw resting objects better than moving ones (441). On the other hand, the compound eye is specially formed to be affected by moving stimuli. The crayfish will react to anything of fairly good size in motion, but is apparently unable to avoid stationary objects in its path (21). The poor vision of the compound eye for resting objects is shown by the ease with which insects may be captured if the movements of the captor are very slow. They may be readily approached, also, if the movements are all in the line of sight, that is, directly toward the insect, so that successive facets of the compound eye are not affected, as would be the case in lateral movements. Let the reader try bringing the hand slowly straight down over a fly, and see how much closer he can come before the fly is disturbed than he can if the hand is moved from side to side. Plateau, from experiments on different orders of insects, concludes that "visual perception of movement" is best developed in the Lepidoptera (moths and butterflies), Hymenoptera (ants, bees, and wasps), Diptera (flies), and Odonata (dragon-flies); that the distance at which movements can be seen does not exceed two metres, and averages 1.5 metres for diurnal Lepidoptera, 58 cm. for Hymenoptera, and 68 cm. for Diptera (335).

It is possible that response to a moving stimulus received through the eye may be accompanied by spatial perception of movement, although if the eye is compound, the experience must differ from our own visual movement perception.

§ 75. *Class IV: Reaction to an Image*

By an image is meant the perception of simultaneously oc-curring but differently located stimuli as having certain spa-tial relations to each other. Through its means, or that of the nervous processes underlying it, there arises the possi-bility of adapting reaction not merely to the location of a single stimulus, but to the relative location of several stimuli. Responses may thus be adjusted not only to the direction of an object but to its form. On the basis of such adjustments a whole new field of possible discriminations is opened up.

The commonest arrangement for the production of a visual image is the double convex lens, which collects the rays of light diverging in their reflection from an object and brings them together again upon the sensitive retina. The lenses found in many simple invertebrate eyes seem, however, very ill adapted to the image-producing function. It is probable that they serve rather to intensify the effect of the light rays by bringing them together, than to give a clear-cut image (293). In the eye of certain invertebrates, such as the Nauti-lus, a gasteropod mollusk, while there is no lens, the opening admitting the light rays is so small that an inverted image might be formed through it, such as may be obtained through a pinhole. It is unlikely, however, that this eye is really an image-producing organ. Hesse includes under image-form-ing eyes only the camera or convex-lens eye, the mosaic eye, and the superposition eye. The last is a peculiar form of com-pound eye where light can pass from one section to another, and where the image is formed by the coöperation of various refracting bodies (176).

The simplest and vaguest conceivable visual image would be that of a visual field whose different parts should differ in brightness. An eye capable of furnishing indications

o

merely of the direction from which the greatest illumination comes might produce this kind of an image, which would of course not allow the perception of objects, only that of brightness distribution. We have already seen that the orientations of certain animals to light seem to be produced through a tendency to take such a position that the two eyes shall be equally illuminated. If the two visual fields are combined in the case of such animals, as they are in our own binocular vision, under ordinary conditions the oriented position would give a visual field whose brightness is equal throughout, while any other position would give greater brightness at one side of the field. If they are not combined, if there is no binocular vision, we cannot imagine what the resulting perception is. That the direction from which the light comes influences ants in finding their way is, we have seen, the opinion of Lubbock (248) and of Turner (408). It was found not to be important to white rats in learning a labyrinth path (431).

§ 76. *Methods of investigating the Visual Image: the Size Test*

The presence of a visual image that is something more than a visual field of graded brightnesses has been tested by methods which may be divided into two groups: those which investigate the effect of stimuli differing in area but of the same intensity, and those which test discrimination of the form of objects.

Bohn's observations on the mollusk Littorina show that its reactions are influenced by the size of the illuminated or darkened surface, as well as by the intensity of the light. When neither very wet nor very dry, Littorina will react to small objects in its neighborhood, whereas in an extreme state of "hydratation" or desiccation it responds to the attraction or repulsion of the larger screens with fatal uniformity (55).

Plateau attempted to test the responses of certain Diptera to the size of an opening admitting light, by placing them in a dark room, into which light entered from two sources. One was a single orifice large enough to let the insects out; the other was covered with a net whose meshes were too fine to allow them to pass. The amount of light from the two sources could be made equal. When this was done, the insects, which were positively phototropic, sought the two equally often; if the light from either was made more intense, they went to that one. Plateau concluded both that the flies could not see the netting and that the area of the light source did not affect them (328). On the other hand, Parker found that the mourning-cloak butterfly did discriminate areas, flying to the larger of two sources of equally intense light (307).

This method of testing the image-forming power of an animal's eyes has recently been elaborated by L. J. Cole. He subjected animals with decided positive or negative phototropism to the influence of two lights made equally intense but differing in area, one coming through a piece of ground glass 41 cm. square, the other a mere point. Eyeless animals, the earthworm, for example, reacted equally often to each light. Animals whose eyes from their structure have been judged capable of perceiving merely the direction of light rays, such as the planarian Bipalium, confirmed the argument from structure by showing little more discrimination than the eyeless ones. On the other hand, animals with well-developed compound or camera eyes, for example certain insects and frogs, did distinguish between the lights, going, if positively phototropic, toward the one of larger area; if negatively phototropic, away from it (80).

Discrimination of boxes differing in size, but alike in form, placed in a row along a board, food having been put in one, was imperfectly learned by two Macacus monkeys; the errors leaned in the direction of taking the larger vessel (221). Raccoons were taught to distinguish perfectly between two cards, one $6\frac{1}{2} \times 6\frac{1}{2}$ inches square and the other $4\frac{1}{2} \times 4\frac{1}{2}$, shown successively. The animals were to climb on a box for food when the larger card was shown and to stay down when the smaller one appeared. As we shall see later, L. W. Cole, the experimenter, thinks the learning gave evidence not only of a spatial image, but of a memory image (82).

One apparent effect of size upon visual perception relates to the distance at which an object produces a reaction. Caterpillars, for example, are described as giving evidence of seeing a slender rod extended toward them at a distance of about a centimeter; large masses they reacted to at somewhat greater distance (333). It is highly doubtful whether this means that the simple eye of the caterpillar could give a perception of two objects as differing in size if they were equally distant. Myriapods, which make very little use of sight and do not perceive their prey until they touch it, give evidence of seeing an obstacle having a rather broad surface, the size of a visiting card, at a distance of about 10 cm., if it is white and reflects much light, or if it is blue; but not if it is red, — another indication of the relation between white and blue light, red light and darkness, noted on p. 123 (329).

§ 77. *Methods of investigating the Visual Image: the Form Test*

The second method of studying visual images, that of testing an animal's power to discriminate *forms*, has been applied chiefly to the higher vertebrates. Bumblebees, to be sure, were thought by Forel to evince a capacity to distinguish a blue circle from a blue strip of paper when they had previously found honey on a blue circle, even though the two had been made to exchange places. They flew first to the place where the blue circle had been, but did not alight upon the strip. Wasps, also, according to Forel, distinguished among a disk, a cross, and a band of white paper, going first to the form on which they had last found honey (130). Various species of birds were experimented on by the method of placing cards carrying simple designs over glasses covered with gray paper, food being placed always under the same card. The English sparrow and the cowbird both learned to distinguish a card bearing three horizontal bars and one bearing a black diamond from each other and from plain gray cards. On the other hand, the sparrow, curiously enough, did not succeed in discriminating vessels of different form; the cowbird was not fully tested with these, but gave some evidence that it was learning (344, 345). Pigeons were only moderately successful in a similar test (371).

Many dogs have been taught to distinguish printed letters on cards; Sir John Lubbock's poodle "Van" is a familiar example. Van learned to pick out cards marked "Food," "Bone," "Out," "Water," and the like, and to present each on its appropriate occasion. It took him ten days to begin to make the first step of distinguishing between a printed card and a plain one; in a month this was perfected and in twelve more days, when he wanted food or tea, he brought the right card one hundred and eleven times and the wrong one twice. The second mistake consisted in bringing the word "door" instead of "food," indicating that it was really the look of the words that he distinguished (251, p. 277 f.).

The dancing mouse could not learn to distinguish two equal illuminated areas of different forms (469). Raccoons learned to discriminate a round card from a square one (82). Thorndike taught the two Cebus monkeys under his observation to come down to the bottom of the cage for food when a card bearing the word "Yes" printed on it was exposed, and to stay up when one bearing the letter "N" was shown. The conditions seem to have been complicated, however, by the fact that the two cards were not placed in quite the same position. Further tests with cards carrying various designs showed varying degrees of capacity to distinguish them on the part of the monkeys (397). Kinnaman got negative results with his two Macacus monkeys in attempting to train them to distinguish cards such as those used in the later experiments of Porter on birds. His monkeys, however, proved able to distinguish vessels of different forms, "a wide-mouthed bottle, a small cylindrical glass, an elliptical tin box, a triangular paper box, a rectangular paper box, and a tall cylindrical can." These vessels differed in size as well as in form (221).

Special evidence of the comparative development of the visual image in different genera of ants is suggested by Wasmann to be furnished by the facts of mimicry. Certain insects belonging to orders other than the Hymenoptera inhabit ants' nests, and have in many cases become more or less modified to resemble their hosts. Wasmann thinks that these resemblances, which have been established on account of their protective value, are in insects living among ants of well-developed visual powers, such as would deceive especially the sense of sight, while in the "guests" of ants whose vision is poor, the mimicry is adapted to produce tactile illusions (426).

§ 78. *Class V : Reactions adapted to the Distance of Objects*

The factors that make possible the perception of the third dimension, depth, or distance outward from the body, in invertebrate animals are little known. Certain invertebrates do give evidence of the power to judge distance. The hunting spiders, for example, which do not make webs, but pursue their prey in the open, leap on it from a distance of several inches. Dahl thinks distinct vision is limited to two centimeters (88), and Plateau says capture is not attempted until the prey is within this distance (332). The Peckhams, however, tested a hunting spider by putting it at one end of a narrow glass case sixteen inches long, at the other end of which a grasshopper was placed. When eight inches from its victim, the spider's movements changed, and at four inches the leap was made[1] (321).

Reactions of this character, where the animal makes a single movement adapted to the distance of an object from it, are almost the sole evidence we can get of accurate perception of the third dimension. The alleged performance of the jaculator fish, which, as described by Romanes, "shoots its prey by means of a drop of water projected from the mouth with considerable force and unerring aim," the prey being "some small object, such as a fly, at rest above the surface of the water, so that when suddenly hit it falls into the water," would involve distance perception (364, p. 248). The catching of insects on the wing by various amphibians, reptiles, and birds has the same significance. A salamander cautiously stalking a small fly will not strike until it gets within a certain distance. In Necturus and in other animals the pause just before snapping at food has been suggested to be for the purpose of proper fixation (438).

Yerkes's tests of the so-called "sense of support" in tortoises indicate some power of estimating distance by vision

[1] Porter observed that the distance at which spiders of the genera Argiope and Epeira could apparently see objects was increased six or eight times if the spider was previously disturbed by shaking her web (346). This, of course, does not refer to the power to *judge* distance.

in these animals. He experimented, it will be remembered, with individuals belonging to three classes: land-dwelling, water-dwelling, and amphibious. The first mentioned would crawl off the edge of a board 30 centimeters above a net of black cloth only with much reluctance when their eyes were uncovered; when blindfolded they would not move at all. The water tortoises plunged off without hesitation from a height of 30 centimeters, but hesitated slightly at 90 centimeters, although some individuals would take the plunge at once even from a height of 180 centimeters. When blindfolded, all of the water tortoises rushed off at any height. The land-and-water-dwelling tortoises hesitated at 30 centimeters and at 90 centimeters showed a conflict of impulses, trying to catch themselves before launching off. When blindfolded they would not leave the board at all, though they moved about upon it freely (459).

Some of the most important conditions of distance perception in our own experience are lacking in the lower vertebrates and in invertebrates. Stereoscopic vision, the appearance of solidity given to objects by the fact that the visual fields of the two eyes combine, thus producing blending of two slightly different views of the object looked at, has been held to be dependent on the partial crossing of the optic nerves on their way to the brain, whereby each retina sends nerve fibres to both hemispheres of the brain. This arrangement does not appear in the animal kingdom below the birds; whatever function it plays in space perception is, then, absent from reptiles, amphibians, fish, and invertebrates. Certainly stereoscopic vision cannot exist in animals whose eyes are so placed that the same object cannot be seen by both, as is the case with most fishes. In birds, whose eyes are situated too far toward the sides of the head for the same object to cast its images on the foveas or centres of the two retinas, there appears to be a secondary fovea in each eye, so placed as to suggest that it serves binocular vision, while the primary fovea is used for monocular vision. Convergence, the turning of the eyes toward each other to bring the two images of an object on the central part of the retinas, which is an important aid to human estimations of distance, is also necessarily lacking in animals without binocular vision. A third factor in our own perceptions of distance, the accommodation of the crystalline lens, that is, the alteration of its convexity through the pull of the accommodation muscle to enable it to focus objects at different distances, has been carefully studied in connection with the lower animals by Beer. Through experiments on the refractive powers of eyes dissected from the dead animal, he reached the conclusion that no invertebrates but cephalopods have the power of accommodation. It is rudimentary or lacking also in some members of the fish, lizard, crocodile, snake, and mammal families. In cephalopods, fishes, amphibians, and most reptiles, the process of accommodation does not involve a change in the form of the lens, but an alteration in the distance between the lens and the retina. The device of increasing the curvature of the lens for vision of near objects appears first in certain snakes, and is found throughout the higher vertebrates (18).

Where accommodation does not exist, as in most invertebrates, it is possible to trace other arrangements for adapting vision to the distance of the object seen. Thus in compound eyes, part of the eye may be adapted to near vision and part to far vision. This is suggested by the fact that some of the little tubes, or ommatidea, of which the compound eye is composed, diverge from each other by a less angle than others, indicating that they are suited to the reception of more nearly parallel rays. In insects with both simple and compound eyes one form may be used for near and one for far vision. Spiders appear to have the principal eyes adapted for far vision and the auxiliary eyes for near vision, while one spider, Epeira, has part of the hinder median eye adapted to each (176).

§ 79. *Some Theoretical Considerations*

The temptation is strong to speculate upon the essential nature of the conditions which make possible true space perception, the simultaneous experiencing of sensations that are referred to different points in space. Such speculation must be of the most tentative description, yet the following suggestions seem not wholly unwarranted by the facts. For one thing, it looks probable that the ability to suspend immediate reaction is essential to space perception. Can a spatial complex of sensations occur in the experience of an organism unless that organism is capable of receiving a number of stimuli on a sensitive surface and of suspending, for a brief period at least, all reaction? Let us take as an example of such a complex a visual field, within which different color and brightness qualities are arranged in definite order, some above, some below, some to the right, others to the left. Could such a balance of tendencies to move the eye as is involved in the simultaneous perception of a number of elements preserving regular space relations to each other have been brought about unless no single one of the tendencies were irresistible? One can readily imagine an eye functioning in such a way that every stimulation of it, though occasioned by rays from several different directions acting simultaneously, should issue at once in a resultant movement. Would not the accompanying consciousness be a single resultant sensation, rather than a complex of spatially ordered elements? It is a good deal easier, of course, to ask than to answer such questions.

Again, the power of getting true spatial images seems to be bound up closely with the power of moving the sensitive surface. We get our best tactile space perceptions through active touch, involving movement of the hands and fingers; our visual space perceptions are profoundly influenced by eye movements. Where the movements of an animal's body as a whole are very rapid, as in the case of winged insects, this fact may compensate for the immovability of its eyes. Forel, as we have seen, thinks that insects which can explore objects by moving the antennæ, bearing the organs of smell, over them, may have smell space perceptions, such as are unknown to our experience; they may perceive the shape and size of odorous patches as we could do if our organs of smell were on our hands (132). Now, movement of a sense organ brings about the same result that movement of a stimulus across a resting sense organ does; that is, the stimulus affects different points of the sensitive surface in succession. But the vital significance of the two is quite different; movement of an object across a resting sense organ means very likely that the object is alive; it must be instantly reacted to, and the speed of the reaction is unfavorable to the formation of a true space perception. Movement of the sense organ, however, gives a series of impressions on successive points of the sensitive surface, from a resting object. While the sense organ is being moved, it is probable that other reactions of the animal will be suspended. Whether any part in the formation of that complex conscious content which we call a spatial image, consisting of different sensations simultaneously apprehended, is played by the "lasting over" of the impressions on one sensitive point after the stimulus has passed on to the next, a phenomenon which we find both in touch and in sight sensations, it is impossible to say. We are, however, apparently justified in the statements that the essence of space perception, as distinct from other conscious processes that may accompany spatially determined reactions, is the presence of an image in the sense above defined, and that a movable sense organ is an important condition for the production of such an image.

CHAPTER X

THE MODIFICATION OF CONSCIOUS PROCESSES BY INDIVIDUAL EXPERIENCE

THE reactions of animals to stimulation show, as we review the various animal forms from the lowest to the highest, increasing adaptation to the qualitative differences and to the spatial characteristics of the stimuli acting upon them. It is therefore possible to suppose that the animal mind shows increasing variety in its sensation contents, and increasing complexity in its spatial perceptions. But besides this advance in the methods of responding to present stimulation, the higher animals show in a growing degree the influence of past stimulation. While a low animal may apparently react to each stimulus as if no other had affected it in the past, one somewhat higher may have its reaction modified by the stimulation which it has just received. An animal still more highly developed may give evidence of being affected by stimuli whose action occurred some time before; and finally, in certain of the vertebrates, perhaps, as in man, conduct may be determined by the presence in consciousness of a memory idea representing a past stimulus. "Learning by experience," or "associative memory," as we saw in Chapter II, has been regarded as the evidence *par excellence* of the existence of mind in an animal. That it does not serve this purpose to entire satisfaction was also pointed out in that earlier chapter, and will be more clearly apparent as we survey in the following pages the various ways in which an organism's past experience may modify its behavior, asking each time what the possible conscious aspect of the modification may be.

§ 80. *Absence of Modification*

In the first place there presents itself for consideration the case of animals that meet a situation by *repeating the same reaction over and over again*. For example, Paramecium encounters an obstacle in its path. It performs the only reaction in its power, the avoiding reaction; it darts backward, rolls to one side, and proceeds forward at an acute angle to its former course. Suppose that the obstacle is so large that the animal strikes it again. The negative reaction is repeated and again repeated if need be until the course is sufficiently altered to carry the Paramecium clear of the obstacle. To behavior of this sort Jennings has extended the term "trial and error" (206, p. 237). The expression was first used by Lloyd Morgan to distinguish between the human method of solving a problem and the dog's method, the latter being called "trial and error" (282, p. 139). Morgan meant that the dog does not attempt to reason the matter out beforehand, making use of his previously acquired knowledge before beginning to act; but that he attacks it at once in some manner derived from individual experience or racial inheritance. If this method fails, he tries another similarly derived, and so on until one method proves successful. Paramecium also tries over and over again, although what it tries is always the same thing. Whether Paramecium's behavior is really shown to be akin to the dog's, by calling both "trial and error," is questionable, however; the resemblances between the performances of an animal that invariably responds with the same reaction until it chances to be carried beyond the reach of the stimulus, and those of a human being who successively "thinks of," that is, recalls the ideas of various devices until the right one is obtained, is but super-ficial. Certainly the behavior of the Paramecium, "trial and error" though it may be, is not learning, and gives no evidence either for or against consciousness as its accompani-ment. If it has a subjective side, the unpleasantness that is most naturally regarded as the accompaniment of a negative reaction would seem to be modified in no way by the repeated performance of the reaction.

§ 81. *Heightened Reaction as the Result of Previous Stimulation*

But even in the lowest animals the effect of a stimulus is often, as we have seen, altered by the "physiological con-dition" of the animal, and this condition is commonly the result of the stimulation previously received. Sometimes the influence is in the direction of increasing the violence of the response. Thus in the earthworm Jennings points out that various stages of excitability may exist, due to the action of previous stimulation and varying all the way from a state of rest, where a slight stimulus produces no effect, to a condi-tion of violent excitement, where moderate stimulation will cause the animal to "whip around" into a reversed position or wave its head frantically in the air (210). This increased excitability suggests the "nervous irritation" produced in a human being by an accumulation of disagreeable stimuli; but an increased unpleasantness is the only obvious interpre-tation of its psychic aspect.

§ 82. *Cessation of Reaction to a Repeated Stimulus*

While response to a given stimulus may thus be altered by reason of the fact that other stimuli have been acting upon the animal just previously, certain interesting modifications of reaction occur when the same stimulus is repeatedly given.

One form of such modification is found where the stimulus is of moderate intensity and not harmful to the animal. The Ciliata Vorticella and Stentor, which spend a part of their time attached to solids by a contractile stem, contract at the first application of a moderately intense mechanical stimulus, but fail to react at all when the stimulus is several times repeated (203). Hydra responds to mechanical stimulation by contraction, but gets used to the process when repeated and gives no further reaction (418). The sea-anemone Aiptasia reacts by a sharp contraction to a drop of water falling on it; later it ceases its response to this stimulus. If exposed to light, it contracts and remains in this state for some hours, but afterwards expands again (207). The annelid *Bispira voluticornis* was found by Hesse to give no further response to sudden shadows when the stimulus was frequently repeated (173). Von Uexküll reports that the sea urchin *Centrostephanus longispinus* ceased to respond to shadows after three successive stimulations (410). Nagel observed that certain eyeless mollusks which react to sudden darkening very quickly get used to the stimulus and cease to respond; often after one reaction they decline to react for several hours.[1] The mollusks that responded to sudden brightening rather than to shadows, that were in Nagel's phrase photoptic rather than skioptic, took longer to become accustomed to repeated stimulation, but did so by gradually weakening their reaction (290). A web-making spider that was found by the Peckhams to drop from its web at the sound of a large tuning fork declined to disturb itself after the stimulus had been

---

[1] The opposite phenomenon is reported by Rawitz of the mollusk Pecten, whose response to a shadow was the shutting of its shell. Repeated or long-continued shadowing, instead of doing away with the reaction, caused the animal to remain with closed shell for a long time; an intensification of the reaction which suggests the effect of summation of stimuli (360). We may infer that the stimulus in such a case is injurious.

repeated from five to seven times (320). Ants "become used" to the ultra-violet rays which they ordinarily avoid (119).

If learning by experience be extended to cover every case where an animal reacts to a stimulus differently because of earlier stimulation, then this is learning by experience. An interesting point suggests itself in regard to the permanency of such learning. In case the animal the next day responds with less vigor to the excitant which it got used to the day before, there would seem some plausibility about the interpretation of Nagel, who says with that inclination in favor of the psychic which always characterizes him, that the behavior of his mollusks "makes the assumption of a certain power of judgment in these animals unavoidable. The animal recognizes that the repeated shadow is not due to the presence of an enemy or other danger" (290). On the other hand, of course, it is perfectly conceivable that an animal might go through such a process of judgment and still be unable to remember it the next day. However, if we find that only very recent stimulation has any effect, the suggestion that this effect is due to some purely physiological alteration in the organism lies near at hand.

As a matter of fact, the higher the animal the more lasting appears to be the result of "getting used" to a stimulus. For instance Hydra, if it is allowed to reach full expansion after having contracted at a touch, will respond to the second touch just as it did to the first; the stimuli, to influence each other, must come in quick succession. The relation of loss of reactive power to the interval between the stimuli was prettily shown by Hargitt for a tube-dwelling marine worm, *Hydroides dianthus*. Shadows were thrown from a pendulum whose rate could be varied, and it was found that if a full second intervened between the stimuli, the reaction

P

would always be given; if the interval was half a second, after the first few stimuli many of the worms failed to react, while if the interval was only a quarter of a second, almost all of them became indifferent (158). Mrs. Yerkes observed that the same annelid would often fail to respond to shadows repeated at intervals of from 5 to 10 seconds, and that 95 out of 200 responded when the interval was from one to two minutes (447). On the other hand, the spider experimented on by the Peckhams for some time reacted each day to the sound of the fork by dropping from its web until the sound had been repeated some half dozen times; but *after the fifteenth day it would not drop at all* (320). There is an adaptive aspect to this difference between Hydroides and the spider. An animal that has little power to discriminate among stimuli could not afford to suspend its negative re- action for any length of time, for another stimulus, indis- tinguishable from the one to which it had become accustomed, might happen along and end its career. But a creature with greater capacity for qualitative discrimination can safely suspend reaction for a considerable period to one out of the many stimuli which it is capable of discriminating.

Where the effect is temporary, the most obvious suggestion as to its cause is *fatigue*. In our own experience this word is used chiefly with reference to motor processes; we perceive a certain signal, but are too fatigued to respond. On the sensory side, when a repeated stimulus is no longer perceived, we call the phenomenon one of *adaptation*. That the failure of Stentor to respond to successive stimuli is not due to motor fatigue appears quite certain to Jennings, since under favor- able conditions he has obtained reactions from the animal for a far longer period than that occupied by the process of getting used to slight mechanical stimulation (203). And in most of the cases cited, the acclimatizing process seems to occur too rapidly to make fatigue of the motor apparatus probable. The most natural analogy to the phenomenon in our own experience is sensory adaptation, such as we find, for instance, in the fact that a moderate weight laid on the skin ceases after a time to be felt. The psychic accompaniment of such modification of behavior is probably, if it exists, merely the gradual disappearance of all sensation.

Another case of the cessation of reaction to a repeated stimulus is reported by Wasmann of ants in an artificial nest, which assumed the fighting attitude in response to the movement of a finger outside the nest, but after two or three repetitions of the motion were no longer disturbed (426). Where animals as high in the scale as the ant and spider are concerned, it is possible that this process of getting used to a stimulus may involve rather a dulling of emotion than a disappearance of sensation.

That adaptation is itself adaptive hardly needs to be emphasized. As Jennings suggests, if the sea-anemone that contracts at the first ray of light were to remain contracted in steady illumination, it would lose all chance of getting food under the new conditions (207). The negative reactions ordinarily involve interruption of the food-taking process, and it is important that they should not be continued in response to stimulation that is relatively permanent. Hargitt thinks that the loss of reaction to repeated shadows which he observed in marine worms may be an adaptation to the varying illumination caused by ripples at the surface of the water (158).

Does such loss of reactive power ever occur in connection with a positive or food-taking reaction? One would expect that a single condition would bring it about under such circumstances; namely, loss of hunger. And, as a matter of fact, observers of the feeding processes in many lower forms

have found that these cease or turn into negative responses
when the animal is satiated; although Piéron indeed reports
that while the responses of *Actinia equina* and *A. rubra* to
mechanical stimulation cease on repetition of the stimulus,
those to food stimulation continue indefinitely (327). If the
change from food-taking to negative reaction has a conscious
accompaniment, this might naturally be thought of as a
change from pleasant to unpleasant affective tone. One
very interesting case of such a change in the feeding reaction
occurs in the sea-anemone. Nagel observed that if a ball of
filter paper soaked in fish juice were placed upon one of the
tentacles of Adamsia, it was seized as eagerly as a ball of fish
meat, but that when this deception had been several times
repeated, the ball was held for a shorter period each time, and
was finally rejected as soon as offered. Nagel is inclined to
think that this is learning by experience, and points out that
the psychic life of Adamsia must possess little unity, for the
"experience" of one tentacle does not lead other tentacles to
reject the paper balls at once (291). Parker finds similar
behavior in Metridium, and explains it by saying that the
filter paper offers but a weak food stimulus, and that "the successive application of a very weak stimulus is accompanied by
. . . a gradual decline in the effects, till finally the response
fails entirely"; in other words, that we have adaptation to a
food stimulus (303). Jennings fed Aiptasia alternately with
pieces of crab meat and with filter paper soaked with meat
juice, the result being that the fifth piece of filter paper was
rejected — but so was the crab meat thereafter. Jennings
came to the conclusion that the phenomenon is due simply
to loss of hunger on the animal's part, and that where Parker
found that the crab meat would be taken after the filter paper
was refused, it was because the latter was a weaker stimulus
and naturally was the first to call forth the effects of

satiety. The objection to the hunger hypothesis is that other tentacles of the same animal will react after one tentacle has stopped; satiety ought surely to affect the entire organism (207). Allabach, in the light of these researches, made a careful study of Metridium. She disposes of the psychic learning by experience theory of Nagel by saying that the only experience upon which the animal could reject the filter paper must be experience that it is not good for food. This could be learned only by swallowing it; but the failure of the reaction occurs just as well when the animal is prevented from swallowing the filter paper. That the phenomenon is not one of adaptation to weak stimuli is shown by the fact that it may be brought about by successive feedings with meat which is not allowed to be swallowed. It cannot be due to loss of hunger, for this is experimentally shown to affect all the tentacles at once. Allabach concludes that it is simply a case of local fatigue of the tentacles. The taking of food by a tentacle involves the production of a considerable quantity of mucus, the immediate supply of which is probably exhausted after a few reactions, and a short period of rest is required (3).

This explanation seems, however, not precisely adapted to the most recently published experimental results bearing upon the point; those of Fleure and Walton. They tested Actinia with a scrap of filter paper once every twenty-four hours, placing it on the same tentacles, which usually carried it to the mouth, where it was swallowed and later ejected. After from two to five days the mouth would no longer swallow the fragment, and in two more days the tentacles refused to take hold of it. Other tentacles could be "deceived" at least once or twice after this, but very soon manifested the inhibition, indicating that a nervous connection and not merely local fatigue was involved. All traces of the "learning" were lost after from six to ten days' interval. Another anemone, Tealia, "learned" more quickly than Actinia (127).

Modification of behavior closely analogous to this was observed in fishes by Herrick. Catfish, when the barbels were touched with a bit of meat, immediately seized it. If a piece of cotton wool were used instead of the meat, they made the same reaction, but after this experience had been repeated a certain number of times they ceased to respond to the cotton, although they still took meat eagerly, showing that neither hunger nor fatigue was involved. Moreover, the "learning" would persist for a day or two. "I rarely," says Herrick, " after the first trials, got a prompt 'gustatory' reflex with the cotton" (165). In these cases it looks very much as though we had to deal with a real discrimination between stimuli, a type of behavior which will be considered under a later heading.

§ 83. *Varied Negative Reactions to a Repeated Stimulus*

Another way in which reaction to a repetition of the same stimulus becomes modified is as follows: *the animal under a strong stimulus tries, one after another, different forms of negative reaction until one of them is successful in getting rid of the stimulus.* Here is a genuine case of trial and error, where, however, different reactions are tried. The Stentor furnishes us with a typical example of this: when attached by its stem and stimulated strongly a number of times in succession, it first tries the ordinary negative reaction, bending over and to one side. Next, it reverses momentarily the direction in which its cilia are whirling. If this, several times repeated, does not succeed in getting rid of the stimulus, the animal contracts strongly upon its stem. This also is continued for some time, but if the stimulus is kept up, too, the Stentor finally breaks away and swims off (203).

There are many examples of similar behavior in other animals. Hydra, which sometimes displays the phenomenon of adaptation by refusing to react at all to repeated stimulation, in other cases tries first the ordinary negative response of contraction, and later moves away from the region it has been occupying (418). Frandsen found that if the slug *Limax maximus* has a tentacle touched several times in succession, it at first withdraws the tentacle and turns away from the stimulus. Later, it may move toward and push against the stimulus, and do the same if the touch is on the side of its body, resisting and curving around the obstacle — another way, of course, of getting rid of it (135). Preyer, again, observed a very pretty instance of this sort of behavior in the starfish. He slipped a piece of rubber tubing over the middle part of one of the arms of a starfish belonging to a species in which those members are very slender, and found that the animal tried successively various devices to get rid of the foreign body, to wit, the following: rubbing it off against the ground, shaking it off by holding the arm aloft and waving it pendulum-wise in the air, holding the tube against the ground with a neighboring arm and pulling the afflicted arm out, pressing other arms against the tube and pushing it off, and, finally, as a last resort, amputating the arm. This, says Preyer, is intelligence, for the emergency is not one normal to the animal, and it is adapting itself to new conditions (350). It would, however, be demanding too much even from intelligence to suppose that the starfish's behavior is entirely new. A human being, capable of ideas, could only, in a similar predicament, "think of," that is, call up, ideas of the behavior which on former occasions somewhat resembling the present had proved effective. Do such cases of the trial of different devices indicate that the animal concerned calls up any kind of idea or image of each device before putting it into practice? Decided evidence in favor of such a supposition might be furnished if the "trial and error" needed to be gone through with only once. A human being brought into such conditions and guiding his conduct by ideas would, if placed in a similar emergency soon afterwards, immediately recall the idea of the successful action and waste no time over the unsuccessful ones. But we have no reason to think that such is the fact with our primitive animals. Preyer's starfish, when confined by large flat-headed pins driven into the board on which it lay, close up in the angles between its arms, managed to escape by trying a large variety of movements, and gradually diminished, Preyer says, the number of useless movements made in successive experiments (350). O. C. Glaser, on the other hand, has recently found that the echinoderm *Ophiura brevispina* does not improve at all with practice in removing obstructions from its arms. The very versatility of the starfish, this writer thinks, tells against its perfecting any one movement through experience (145). Stentor and Hydra go through the same series of reactions each time, without apparently being influenced by their previous behavior. And again we must remind ourselves that there is no reason why their conduct, adaptively regarded, should be otherwise. An animal with so little power of distinguishing qualitative differences among stimuli cannot be in any way aware that the stimulus which affects it a second time is going, as in the previous case, to be so persistent that the ordinary negative reaction will not get rid of it. Further, each reaction of the series performed by the animal is more disturbing to its ordinary course of life than the preceding one. The Stentor can bend to one side and still continue the food-taking process; if it reverses its ciliary action, feeding must be momentarily interrupted; while contraction on the stem and breaking loose from its moorings are still more serious infractions of the normal routine. It would be decidedly disadvantageous to take the last step while there was any chance that milder measures might prevail.

In all probability, since the behavior just described has no permanent effect upon the animal, it is physiologically due, as Jennings suggests (208), to the overflow of the nervous energy set free by the stimulus into first one channel and then another. In most cases the movements resulting are all adapted to getting rid of the stimulus, though only one of them is successful in so doing; but we have on record one case where, in a supreme emergency, the stimulus being not only repeated but increased in intensity, every possible outlet is tried, whether it has any fitness to the situation or not. This was observed by Mast, testing the effect of increased temperature on the reactions of planarians. The first influence of such increase from 23 degrees to 26 degrees C., is to produce heightened activity and positive reactions. Then, from 26 degrees to 38 degrees, the reactions are negative. From 38 degrees to 39 degrees, violent crawling movements set in, and then, curiously enough, the righting reaction is given, perfectly irrelevant, of course, to the conditions. Finally, the anterior and posterior ends are turned under, the central part is arched upward, and the animal falls over forward on its back (260).

In all these cases where repetition of the same stimulus produces successively different forms of the negative reaction increasing in violence, it is most natural to think of the psychic accompaniment as an increasing degree of unpleasantness. In our own experience, repeating a stimulus does not alter the quality of the resulting sensation, except where the structure of a special sense organ is a modifying factor, as in the case of visual after-images. Repetition of the stimulus does with us human beings diminish the intensity of the accompanying sensation; but this process is the natural accompaniment, as we have seen, of diminishing reaction, not of varied and increasingly violent reaction. A decidedly disagreeable stimulus acting repeatedly on a human being may produce unpleasantness that grows more and more intense until it is unbearable; the behavior of a human being under such circumstances is much like the animal behavior we have just been describing. Various movements calculated to get rid of the stimulus are tried, each more energetic than the last. Hence, if the lower animals behaving thus are conscious, we may plausibly assert that their consciousness under these circumstances is increasingly unpleasant. But the human experience in such a case would be, or might be, further characterized by the presence of ideas. That is, the human being would *think* of the different ways to get rid of the stimulus one after another. This many, at least, of the animals that try different negative reactions are apparently incapable of doing. We judge that they are so by the simple fact that on being subjected after an interval to the same presumably disagreeable stimulus, they do not at once make the reaction that was previously successful in getting rid of it. A human being, recalling that reaction in idea, would be able to do so. We shall see in the next chapter that many animals, while they do not learn the successful reaction from a single experience, do gradually diminish the number of unsuccessful ones made in a series of experiences. It may be that as more experimental evidence is accumulated, this will be found to be the case throughout the whole animal kingdom, but at present it looks as though the lowest forms may, when an injurious stimulus is repeatedly given, pass through their whole repertoire of negative reactions in one experience after another, without any shortening of the process. Trial and error this may be called: learning it is not.

§ 84. *Dropping off Useless Movements: the Labyrinth Method*

The next form of modification of behavior by individual experience which we shall consider occurs when an animal, under the influence of some stimulus which it strives either to get rid of or to get more of, goes through a series of reactions until one proves successful; *on being after an interval of time placed in the same situation, the unsuccessful movements are fewer, and further repetition causes them to be dropped off entirely.* This is the mode of behavior which was first brought into clear relief by the experiments of Thorndike on chicks, dogs, and cats. Since then an increasing number of investigators have shown its existence in a large number of forms. One of the simplest methods for the testing of this sort of learning is the *labyrinth method.* In its developed form it was first used, I believe, by Small in his work on white rats, and was suggested by the natural habits of the animal, which is, of course, accustomed to run about through narrow passages. The plan consists in placing food, or something else attractive to the animal, at the end of a series of passages containing a number of false turns. The labyrinth used for the rats was very complicated, being in fact a replica in wire netting of the Hampton Court maze, but much simpler ones have since been employed for other animals. One advantage of the labyrinth method is that it requires nothing of the animal except what is perfectly natural to it, namely, *locomotion.*

The lowest forms which have been thus far tested by this means are certain Crustacea. The crab *Carcinus granulatus* was placed in a very simple labyrinth with only two points where a choice between the right and wrong paths was possible. At the end of the labyrinth was the aquarium, and the crab's discomfort out of the water served as the occasion stirring it to activity. In fifty experiments the path had not been perfectly learned, although the time was greatly reduced. A still simpler path was then offered the animal by placing a wire screen partition in the middle of the aquarium, with an opening in the centre and food on the other side; and in ten trials the time occupied by the crab in finding the food was much lessened. Still neither of the two animals tested had learned to go straight to the opening, but each followed a habit of its own, one moving directly toward the food, hunt-

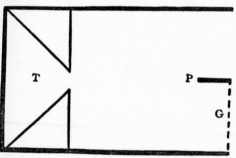

ing for an opening near it, and then going to the middle where the opening was; the other always following the edge of the screen all the way around until it came upon the opening (453).

FIG. 13. — Labyrinth used by Yerkes and Huggins in experiments on the crayfish. *T*, compartment from which animal was started; *P*, partition at exit; *G*, glass plate closing one exit.

A labyrinth offering only a single choice of passages was used in testing the crayfish; again one end of the box communicated with the aquarium (Fig. 13). About halfway down the length of the box a partition put in longitudinally divided it into two passages, one of which was closed at the end by a glass plate. In sixty trials the animals, which had originally chosen the correct passage 50 per cent of the time, came to choose it 90 per cent of the time. A second series, with a single animal upon which more tests a day were made, resulted in the formation of a perfect habit in two hundred and fifty experiments. The glass plate was then shifted to the other passage, and the crayfish was naturally

completely baffled for a time, but succeeded in learning the
new habit (471). Ants of the species *Stenamma fulvum piceum*
have been tested in a labyrinth by Fielde. The observations
indicated that this ant's tendency to be guided by the chemical
traces of its own footsteps militated to a certain extent against
shortening the path by dropping off useless turnings. Each
ant followed her own previous trail through the labyrinth to
the nest. Yet some tendency for the movements to become

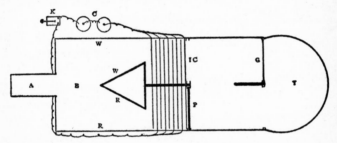

Fig. 14. — Labyrinth used by Yerkes in experiments on the frog. *A*, box opening into maze; *E*, entrance; *T*, tank; *G*, glass plate; *P*, partition; *IC*,
electric circuit whereby animal could be given shock on entering wrong
passage; *C*, *K*, cells and key; *R*, *R*, red cardboard; *W*, *W*, white cardboard.

automatic and independent of the smell clew was shown by
the fact that when an ant had gone over the path many times,
a portion of the track might be obliterated without inter-
rupting her course [1] (118).

A simple form of the labyrinth method has been used on
fish (Fundulus), which were kept by a screen in the sunny end
of an aquarium, the darkened end being also the place where
they were fed. One upper corner of the screen was cut out.
In a couple of days, allowing six or eight trials a day, the fish
learned to swim straight up to this corner (394). A more
complicated labyrinth was also used, but the time required

---

[1] Cf. the observations of Piéron referred to on p. 94.

to learn it is not stated. The greater speed and ease of locomotion in the fish as compared with the crustaceans may have been one factor concerned in the former's greater rapidity of learning.

With the green frog, the labyrinth pictured in Figure 14 was used. After one hundred trials, practically no errors were made (454). Another animal whose learning powers have

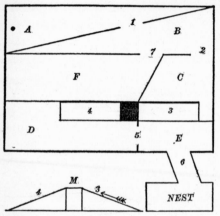

been tested by this method is the turtle.

The labyrinth was distinctly more complex than that used for the frog. It involved four blind passages, and led to the turtle's comfortable, darkened nest.

During the first four trips the time was reduced from thirty-five minutes to three minutes and

FIG. 15. — Labyrinth used by Yerkes with turtles. *A*, starting point; *F*, blind alley; 3, 4, 6, inclined planes.

thirty seconds; in the fourth trip the animal took two wrong turns. The time of the fiftieth trip was thirty-five seconds. In a second labyrinth (Fig. 15), two inclined planes were introduced, up and down which the turtles had to crawl. This labyrinth took them longer to traverse, and the time curve shows greater irregularity, rising, for instance, to seven minutes on the forty-fifth trial, after having been as low as two minutes and forty-five seconds at the thirty-fifth. The process of shortening the path was observed very prettily in connection with the inclined planes. The turtles had to turn about as soon as they had reached the bottom of the descending plane. They soon began to make the turn before they got to the bottom, and finally to throw themselves over the edge as soon as they reached the top (450).

Some of Thorndike's experiments on chicks involve the labyrinth method, others what we shall call the puzzle-box method. The chicks were confined in small pens, with food outside. In some cases they could get out by running to a particular spot, or up an inclined plane; in other cases by pecking or pulling at something. Both sorts of action were learned; obviously the former, involving simple locomotion on the animal's part, are the ones which concern us at present (393). Porter found that the English sparrow quickly learned the Hampton Court maze (344), and that the vesper sparrow and cowbird learned a simpler form in twenty or thirty trials (345). Pigeons tested by Rouse acquired the ability to traverse four different labyrinths, and it was noted that their experience with the earlier ones seemed to help them in the later ones (371).

White rats observed by Small learned the Hampton Court maze, in nine experiments made at intervals of two days, so well that they committed only two errors in the ninth test, but the significance of this time is obscured by the fact that the rats were allowed to run freely about the labyrinth every night (385). Watson's earlier work with the white rat was designed to compare the learning processes of the young with those of the adult animal. The rat is born unable to care for itself, and before those observed by Watson had reached the age of twelve days, they were unable to find their way by a simple labyrinth path back to the mother. At twenty-three days of age they learned a labyrinth more quickly than adults, probably because of their greater activity, although for the same reason they made more useless movements. The object of the research was to test Flechsig's theory that learning depends upon the presence of medullated fibres in the central nervous system; this was found to be unconfirmed, since at twenty-four days, when the rat is psychically mature, the medullation of its fibres is highly imperfect (430).

In his later experiments on white rats Watson's aim was to investigate the nature of the sensations which guide them through a labyrinth. The results will be discussed a few pages farther on (431).

Allen's work on the guinea pig was intended for comparison with Watson's study of the white rat, because the young guinea pig comes into the world, not helpless like the baby rat, but well equipped on both the sensory and motor sides. In the labyrinth, here, the mother was put at the end of the maze, and the sight and smell of her were supposed to serve as the stimulus to activity. Before the young animals had reached the age of two days, they did not succeed in learning a comparatively simple path, but at that age they did learn it, and proved the fact when the wire netting box in which they were placed was turned about, by pushing at the place where the opening had formerly been. At three days, they learned a more complex labyrinth, and appeared to possess the learning capacity of adults (4).

In Yerkes's study of the Japanese dancing mouse, the reactions to irregular and to regular labyrinths were compared, and it was found that a maze of the latter type, that is, one where left and right turns alternated, was more quickly learned and more perfectly mastered than an irregular one. Yerkes urges the importance of keeping account of the errors made by an animal as well as the times occupied in traversing a maze (469). Watson's later work on the white rat gives only the turns (431). In many cases, especially with animals not naturally active, the time values have little significance;

an animal in a sluggish mood may traverse a path very slowly and yet make no errors.

Kinnaman taught two *Macacus rhesus* monkeys the Hampton Court maze. That they had an anticipatory idea of the pleasure in store for them at the centre he thinks evidenced by the fact that they would begin to smack their lips audibly on reaching the latter part of their course. Yet for them, as for the rats, one of the most persistent errors lay in taking the wrong turning at the outset (221).

What is the mental aspect of the process of learning a labyrinth? Does it involve that form of memory which consists in the revival of images of past experience? Or is it simply the gradual formation of a habit of movement, at no stage of which a memory image functions? In the first place, we may note that no method less calculated to involve images could well be devised. A human being in such a labyrinth as that at Hampton Court, with all his wealth of image-forming and controlling power, is at a loss to make use of it for his guidance. Secondly, there are various phenomena displayed in the experiments which tell against the image theory. For one thing, the *slowness* of the learning process in the simple labyrinths indicates that memory in this sense is not concerned. When an animal has the choice between two passages only, if it possessed the power of recalling, in any terms whatever, a memory image of its previous experience, surely thirty or forty trials would not be required before the right path was taken at once. Again, the *nature of the errors* made in some cases suggests that memory images are not present. For instance, when Small's two rats had learned the complicated labyrinth almost perfectly, the one error in which they both persisted lay in taking the wrong turn at the entrance. Now this, it is safe to say, would be the very first error that a being which guided itself by images would eliminate. It might be

Q

difficult to remember, in the image-forming sense, the later turns, but surely "turn to the right" or "turn to the left" would present itself in some sort of terms at the entrance, if the animal could have memory ideas at all. Furthermore, it is very difficult to interpret the learning process here as a case of association of ideas. In Small's labyrinth, two kinds of errors could be made: the one would land the animal in a *cul-de-sac*, the other simply meant taking a longer passage when a shorter one would suffice. If the former came to be avoided as the result of the calling up of a memory idea, this idea might be that of being brought up short and compelled to retrace one's steps, but how are we to imagine the idea of a shorter path as balanced against that of a longer path? Small says they must be "distance or temporal ideas in tactual-motor terms," and urges that our own lack of experience of such ideas should not make us doubt their existence in the rat mind; but Thorndike's position, that no ideas are involved at all, that the rat merely comes gradually to "feel like" taking one turn rather than the other, seems more probable.[1] In other words, we have the formation of a habit of movement rather than an association of ideas.

But though ideas may not be involved, the further question remains as to what kind of peripherally excited sensations are influential in the learning process. This question really resolves itself into two. First, by what "clews" does the animal guide itself in learning the labyrinth path? Second, do these clews continue necessary to its guidance when the habit is formed? The two parts of the problem have not always been kept distinct by those who have used the method.

As regards the first part, Small obtained evidence that his white rats were not guided merely by the *smell* of their own tracks in finding their way to the centre of the maze, from

[1] See his review of Small's work, Psych. Rev., vol. 8, p. 643.

various observations, among others the fact that they ran all over the passages in their earlier trials, so that smell might have guided them wrong as well as right (385). This conclusion was confirmed by the experiments of Watson, who found that rats with the olfactory lobes removed learned the labyrinth as readily as normal rats (431). Yerkes, in his labyrinth tests upon the crawfish and the frog, excluded smell as a means of guidance by washing the labyrinth out between trials (454, 471). For certain species·of ants, as we know, smell is the dominant factor. *Visual* clews seem to be used by different animals to different degrees. The frog displayed a disturbance of its habit when red and white cards placed on either side of the passage were interchanged (454). The crawfish seemed to recognize and draw back from the screens in the blind passage before running against them (471). The pigeons tested by Rouse, when required to go through the labyrinth in darkness, were obliged to relearn it, although they made the first turn correctly. Perhaps, Rouse suggests, the stimulus to the first turn was the sound of the door lifted to admit them, or the touch of the narrow entrance (371). On the other hand, Small found that altering the direction of the light had little effect on the performances of his white rats. He also placed wooden pegs painted red, at each division of the paths, in the middle of the correct path, and caused the labyrinth thus arranged to be learned by hitherto untrained rats. They did not learn it any faster through the presence of these visual hints, nor, when it had been learned, were they at all discomposed by the removal of the pegs (385). Allen's guinea pigs did not alter their behavior with alteration of the position of colored cards placed as guiding marks (4). And Watson's blinded rats learned the labyrinth as readily as normal ones (431).

Rouse found that the pigeon could make use of *auditory*

stimuli as clews. He arranged to have an ordinary electric
bell rung whenever the birds entered a wrong alley, and a
wooden bell sounded when they emerged and took the right
course. After they had learned the path under these conditions, the two kinds of sound stimuli were interchanged, and
the result was a certain amount of confusion on the part of
the birds. Another device consisted of a board with electric
wires, laid on the floor of the labyrinth. A bell was rung
whenever a pigeon stepped on the board, and the bird was
given an electric shock; when the experience had been
repeated a number of times, the pigeons would show uneasiness at the sound of the bell, wherever they happened to be in
the labyrinth (371). In white rats, Watson found that partial deafness, produced by throwing the middle ear out of
function, had no effect on the ability of the rats to learn the
path (431).

Various stimuli may, then, serve as clews in the process of
learning the labyrinth. But in certain cases, neither visual,
olfactory, nor auditory stimuli seem to be at all concerned.
This was true of Watson's white rats, and probably of Allen's
guinea pigs. Special tests were made to investigate the rôle
of tactile sensations in the labyrinth performances of these
animals. With the guinea pigs, a cardboard labyrinth was
substituted for that of wire netting, and a black cloth placed
on the floor (4). Watson's white rats, when the vibrissæ
(long whiskers) were removed, learned the maze as well as
normal rats. Those which had already learned it manifested
some disturbance on having the vibrissæ removed, showing
a tendency to bump into the partitions and hug the walls.
Watson does not report whether this same disturbance failed
to appear in the rats without vibrissæ that were learning the
labyrinth for the first time; he merely gives the times occupied in traversing the course to show that the learning process

was normal. It would be very strange and quite out of accord with the general behavior of animals in labyrinths if a prac- tised rat should be more disturbed by the removal of an accus- tomed stimulus than an unpractised one. No effect on the learning power of the rats was produced by making their paws anæsthetic (431). Yerkes has shown, although with- out operating on his subjects, that the Japanese dancing mouse does not necessarily depend on sight, smell, or touch for guidance in the labyrinth (469). It should be noted that proof of an animal's ability to learn a maze when deprived of a certain class of sensations does not show that it normally makes no use of those sensations in the learning process.

As a matter of fact, the stimuli which originally give the "clews" in the case of the white rats must be the rats' own movements. "Muscular sensations dependent on the direc- tion of turning," "kinæsthetic sensations," are the only elements in our own experience that suggest themselves as possibilities where an animal *learns* the maze equally well when blinded, anosmic, deaf, and partially deprived of touch (431). But this is not the same as saying that when an ani- mal has learned the labyrinth, it is "guided by kinæsthetic sensations." Nor can we show that an animal was not guided by some other stimuli, say visual ones, in learning the laby- rinth, when we prove that having once learned it, the animal is not disturbed by the removal of these stimuli. For when the labyrinth path has been learned, the habit may be in a sense quite independent of the very stimuli that served to form it, precisely as the pianist becomes independent of the notes in playing a familiar piece. The fact that Yerkes's frogs *were* disturbed, after the habit had been formed, by the inter- change of the cards, indicates that visual stimuli were still important to them; but if they had not been disturbed by such interchange, when they were fully practised, it would not have proved that the cards had played no part in forming the habit.

In the same way, it is not likely that a thoroughly practised animal needs to have in consciousness even kinæsthetic sensations. Watson attempts to describe the processes in the mind of a practised rat as follows: " What leads up to the act of turning? The 'feeling' (probably only vaguely 'sensed') which may be expressed anthropomorphically in these terms: 'I have gone so far, I ought to be turning about now!'" "If the turn is made at the proper stage . . . the animal may be supposed thereby to get a 'reassuring feeling,' which is exactly comparable from the standpoint of control to the experience which we get when we touch a familiar object in the dark " (431, pp. 95–6). I do not think these before and after 'feelings' are necessarily present at all in the consciousness of an animal whose labyrinth habit is fully formed. Such an animal has become a little machine which takes so many steps along a straight path, turns to the right, takes so many more steps, and so on until the performance is complete. If, indeed, it makes an error in this process, then the kinæsthetic sensations may come into play, but otherwise there would seem to be no reason for assuming in the fully practised animal consciousness of any stimulus except the initial one which starts it on its path.

Very curious are the results obtained by Watson when the entire labyrinth was turned through an angle of 90 degrees. Although no turn which the animals had to take was in any way altered by this proceeding, the rats showed decided confusion, the blind rats as much as the others. This latter fact would indicate that alteration in the direction of the light was not the source of the confusion; but when the maze was rotated through 180 degrees, the blind rats were not disturbed, while the others were. More investigation, decidedly, is needed before we can decide, as Watson does, "either that static sensations have a rôle, or . . that the rat has some non-human modality of sensation which, whatever it may be, is thrown out of gear temporarily by altering the customary relations to the cardinal points of the compass."

One or two incidental observations regarding the behavior of animals in labyrinths are strongly suggestive of the automatic character of the movements involved. An animal that has gone astray on the path will often find the way back to the starting-point, and from there traverse the whole road rapidly and unerringly (*e.g.* 450, 431), apparently in the same way that a piano player who has a piece "at his fingers' ends," but has stumbled in a passage, can go through with entire success if he starts over again. As piano players know, in such a case it is much better not to attend to stimuli at all, but to think of something else; the movements will take care of themselves better if consciousness intervenes as little as possible.

Again, in the process of learning a labyrinth, habits of movement are often formed that are of no use whatever; that do not lead to success, and hence cannot be guided in any sense by the animal's experience of their pleasant consequences. Rouse and Small both report this tendency to form useless habits, and in the case of some salamanders observed by the writer, which never finally mastered the labyrinth they were placed in, habits of going elaborately wrong would make their appearance and persist for several days, each animal remaining true to its individually acquired tendency. The mere fact that the movements were accidentally performed two or three times in succession created a persistence in doing them, although they led to no pleasurable consequences whatever.

§ 85. *Dropping off Useless Movements: the Puzzle-box Method*

The dropping off of useless movements is further illustrated in those experiments where animals are required to work some kind of mechanism. This may be called briefly the *puzzle-box method.* It is obviously an advance in difficulty over the labyrinth method in that it requires *the formation of a new*

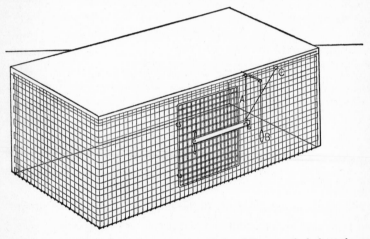

FIG. 16. — Puzzle box used in Porter's work on birds. *A B*, one method of attaching string to latch; *C*, a second method. In the first, the loop at *B* had to be pulled; in the second, the string had to be pushed in.

impulse rather than the mere guidance of an old one; it does not merely direct the animal in the performance of something that he would do anyway, but causes him to do something that he otherwise would not do. Yet the distinction is not so fundamental as it seems.

The puzzle-box method has been tried with birds, rats, cats, dogs, raccoons, and monkeys. Thorndike, its originator, made some experiments of this type on chicks; the animals were confined in pens, from which they could be released by pecking at a string or some such object. In other cases, as we have seen, these tests should be classed rather with the labyrinth method, as requiring merely that the chick should run out at a given definite place (393). Porter tested English sparrows with boxes containing food, which could be entered by pulling a string fastened to a latch, or by pushing the string into the wire netting with which one side of the box was covered (Fig. 16). The sparrows learned very quickly; one of them by the tenth test had left out all unnecessary movements (344). In later experiments a cowbird and a pigeon also learned to open a similar box. Before beginning the test the birds were accustomed to being fed in the box with the door open. Their first success in opening the door lay in accidentally clawing or pecking at the proper point, and in later trials the action was simplified; thus the birds learned not to attack other parts of the box, to use the bill instead of the claws, and to stand on the floor beside the box instead of hopping upon it. A point of some interest arises in connection with the fact that one or two of the birds, for instance the male pigeon, opened the door in the simplest possible way, although not very quickly, the first time they tried it, and that these birds showed very little improvement in speed through subsequent trials; whereas the ones that had the most difficulty about the first execution of the act ultimately reduced their speed much below that of the others. It is possible, as Porter suggests, that "greater difficulty and therefore more vigorous activity on the part of the animal in the initial trials of any series may naturally be expected to lead to more rapid progress in the later ones" (345). In Rouse's test of the pigeon by the puzzle-box method, it showed less aptitude than that displayed by the English sparrow (371).

Small tested his white rats with two boxes containing food. One could be entered by digging away the sawdust which was banked around the lower end of the box, if the digging was done in a particular place; the other, by tearing off strips of paper which held shut a spring door. The result of the earlier series of experiments with the first-mentioned box was that after an hour and a half on the first day one rat happened to dig in the right place and entered. The second day this rat took only eight minutes, and the thirteenth day only thirty seconds, to enter. With the second box there was always a tendency to begin by digging, and even in the thirteenth experiment, where the rat got in by biting off the papers in fifteen seconds, she began by two strokes of digging. In a later test with this box the rat chanced to be extremely hungry, and dug violently for several seconds, indicating a blunting of the discriminative powers by hunger, analogous to that which we have found in very low animals. Like Porter subsequently, Small found that "if a rat happens to succeed by several methods, as, *e.g.*, biting, clawing, butting, there is a strongly marked tendency to select the most expeditious and effective method. This apparent selection, however, is rather a matter of inertia than of prevision." The rats were later trained to discriminate between the two boxes, being sometimes presented with one and sometimes with the other. Such experiments, however, may properly be classed under the head of another method which we shall presently discuss. Great individual differences were found among the rats: two of the four tested never learned to get into the boxes so long as they were with their more energetic companions, but merely profited by the activity of the latter (386). Watson's puzzle-box experiments on the white rat were designed, like his labyrinth tests, to compare the powers of the adult with those of the young. The results were practically the same as those of the labyrinth tests, except that in the box experiments, where mere activity counts for less than in a labyrinth, the adult rats solved the problems in less time than that occupied by the young ones (430).

In Thorndike's work on cats and dogs, the investigator placed the animals themselves in the boxes, and food on the outside, so that the problem was not how to get in but how to get out. The getting out could be accomplished in various

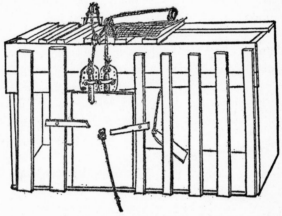

Fig. 17. — Puzzle box used in Thorndike's experiments on cats.

ways, such as pulling a wire loop, clawing a button around, pulling a string at the top of the box, poking a paw out and clawing a string outside, raising a thumb latch and pushing against the door, and so on (Fig. 17). The animals, on being first put into the box, made all sorts of movements in their struggles to get out; the right movement was hit upon by accident. Only very gradually, as the experiment was repeated again and again, were the useless movements omitted, until finally the right one was performed at once (393). Wesley Mills has criticised these pioneer experiments of Thorndike's on the ground that the animals were under such unnatural conditions and in such an extreme state of hunger that they profited by experience more slowly than might otherwise have been the case (273); and this may have been to a certain extent true. In testing monkeys with puzzle boxes Thorndike placed the food on the inside and the monkeys on the outside. He found a marked difference between the speed of their learning and that shown by the cats and dogs. " Whereas the latter were practically unanimous, save in the cases of the very easiest performances, in showing a process of gradual learning by a gradual elimination of unsuccessful movements and a gradual reënforcement of the successful one, these are unanimous, save in the very hardest, in showing a process of sudden acquisition by a rapid, often apparently instantaneous abandonment of the unsuccessful movements and selection of the appropriate one, which rivals in suddenness the selections made by human beings in similar performances " (397). Kinnaman further complicated the box tests with his Macacus monkeys by constructing "combination" fastenings, which required the performance of a set of actions in a certain order, and found that these were mastered by the animals (221) (Fig. 18).

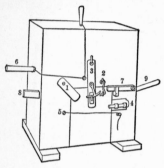

Fig. 18.—Combination fastening used in Kinnaman's work on monkeys. The figures indicate the order in which the parts of the combination had to be dealt with.

Cole's work on the raccoon, finally, indicates that in speed of learning this animal stands "almost midway between the monkey and the cat," while "in the complexity of the associations it is able to form it stands nearer the monkey." The raccoons, like the monkeys, learned combination locks, although they did not learn to perform the various movements involved in a definite order. They showed an interesting tendency to skip at once to the movement that immediately preceded the opening of the door (82).

The question arises, as in the case of the labyrinth experiments, whether, when the animal has learned the proper movements to open a box, he opens it by "remembering" the movement; that is, by having some kind of an idea or image of it in his consciousness, or whether we have to do with the formation of a habit by a process in which ideas are at no time involved. Here, again, the gradual character of the learning process, where it is gradual, points to the absence of ideas; a human being who had once hit by accident upon the right way to open a lock could hardly fail on being confronted with it a second time, at not too great an interval, to recall an idea of the successful movement and perform it at once, without any unnecessary accompanying movements. We have seen an approach to this state of things in the monkeys; accordingly it is possible that they may learn by means of ideas. On the other hand, rapid learning, where the action is very simple and closely connected with the animal's instincts, does not necessarily mean the presence of ideas; in certain cases there may exist arrangements for the rapid modification of an instinctive mechanism which do not involve the production of images at all. The most we can say is that slow learning, by gradual elimination of the useless movements, indicates, so far as we can judge, the absence of any guiding idea of the action. Other evidence against the idea hypothesis was derived by Thorndike from various facts. In the first place he found in the animals observed by him an entire lack of what has been termed inferential imitation.

Imitation in animals has by some writers, notably Wasmann, been classed as a special method of learning by experience (426), and from one point of view it is. But imitation may be, as various authors have pointed out, of at least two different types. The first may be called *instinctive imitation*, and is widespread throughout the animal kingdom. It occurs when the sight or sound of one animal's performing a certain act operates as a direct stimulus, apparently through an inborn nervous connection, to the performance of a similar act by another animal. "If," says Lloyd Morgan, "one of a group of chicks learns by casual experience to drink from a tin of water, others will run up and peck at the water and will themselves drink. A hen teaches her little ones to pick up grain or other food by pecking on the ground and dropping suitable materials before them, the chicks seeming to imitate her actions. . . . Instinctive actions, such as scratching the ground, are performed earlier if imitation be not excluded " (281, pp. 166–167). Imitation in this sense is hardly so much a method of learning by experience as a method of supplying experience. An animal may perform an act the first time because, through inherited nervous connections, the sight of another animal's performing it acts as a stimulus. But it will continue to perform the act, in the absence of any copy to imitate, only if the act is itself an instinctive one, like drinking in birds, or becomes permanent by reason of its consequences, just as would be the case if its first performance had been accidental rather than imitative. As a matter of fact, instinctive imitation seems usually to be concerned with actions themselves instinctive.

Inferential imitation, or what Morgan calls *reflective imitation*, is a different affair. It is the case where an animal, watching another one go through an action and observing the consequences, is led to perform a similar act from a desire to bring about the same result. The most natural description of the subjective side of this process in a human being would be to say that the sight of the other individual's behavior "suggests the idea" of similar behavior on one's own part. Inferential imitation would then not differ fundamentally from any other case of learning by ideas. Now Thorndike, in his experiments on cats and dogs, found, as we have said, no evidence of this type of imitation. A cat put in a puzzle box did not learn the way out any sooner for watching, even repeatedly, the performances of a cat that knew how to get out. With monkeys, Thorndike's most extensive tests were made to find whether the animal would learn to open a box from seeing the experimenter himself do it, and his results were again, on the whole, negative (393). Small's white rats also showed no ability to profit by each other's experience in this way. One of each of the pairs first experimented on solved the problems presented; the other, instead of either attacking them for itself or learning by watching the successful one, contented itself with stealing the food secured by the latter (386). Imitation, according to Yerkes, plays no considerable rôle in the learning processes of the dancing mouse (469).

On the other hand, Kinnaman's monkeys did give some indications of learning by inferential imitation. In one case, the box had to be opened by pulling out a plug. One monkey failed to work the mechanism, and gave up in despair. Another one then came out of the cage, the first one following. Number two went to the box, seized the end of the plug with its teeth and pulled it out. The box was set again, and monkey number one rushed to it, seized the plug as number two had done, and got the food. She immediately repeated the act eight times. A second and similar observation was made where the mechanism was a lever (221). Hobhouse found that cats, dogs, elephants, and monkeys were aided in their learning processes if he "showed" them how to do the thing (177). Whether this was inferential imitation in the sense that they got the idea of the action and of its result by watching him, or whether they were merely aided in focussing their attention on the important object, the string, hook, or lever, it is difficult to be sure.

Berry found that the white rats he experimented on manifested a type of imitative behavior which he is inclined to regard as intermediate between instinctive and fully inferential imitation. "When two rats were put into the box together," he says, "one rat being trained to get out of the box and the other untrained, at first they were indifferent to each other's presence, but as the untrained rat observed that the other one was able to get out while he was not, a gradual change took place. The untrained rat began to watch the other's movements closely; he followed him all about the cage, standing up on his hind legs beside him at the string and pulling it after he had pulled it, etc. We also saw that when he was put back, the immediate vicinity of the loop was the point of greatest interest for him, and that he tried to get out by working at the spot where he had seen the trained rat try " (26).

Now, so far as the light cast by this evidence for and against inferential imitation or the presence of ideas in the animal mind is concerned, the matter seems to stand as follows. We cannot be sure that Kinnaman's monkeys really had an idea of the proper action suggested to them by seeing their companions perform it; the case might have been one of instinctive imitation, taking here a form more elaborate than was seen in cats and dogs because more complicated movements are natural to the monkey than to the lower mammals. If it is certain that Berry's uneducated rat began to watch the actions of the educated one more closely *as a result* of its observation that the latter succeeded where it failed, then, although the imitation was confined merely to investigating the same general locality as that attacked by the trained rat, and not extended to an actual performance of the movement, it would seem to be inferential in type. But precisely this certainty is apparently rather hard to attain. Again, when an animal is assisted in learning by watching a human being who undertakes to show him how, is he given an idea of the act and its results, or does he merely have his attention called to the important part of the mechanism to be worked? True inferential imitation is hard to prove. On the other hand, the failure of an animal to show inferential imitation does not mean that the animal cannot have ideas. We cannot conclude that an animal is incapable of ideas because it does not have them suggested to it under circumstances that would suggest them to our minds.

Again, Thorndike noticed that while after a time the cats that had been caused to go into the box and let themselves out before being fed would go into the box of their own accord, cats that had been from the first dropped into the box at the top did not learn to go into it of themselves. He argues that if the cat had been able to have the *idea* of being in the box, as a necessary prelude to food, it would have been able to pass from the idea of being dropped in to that of going in itself. Further, he found that he could not train the animals to do a certain act by forcibly putting them through it, and concludes that if they had been capable of having the idea of the act, it would have been suggested to them by this process (393). But in each of these cases, the experience which is supposed to give the animal the idea of the act is one that has some points of likeness with the act and other points of decided difference. The experience of seeing another animal perform a movement is very different

R

from that of performing it oneself; the experience of being picked up and dropped into a box is very different from that of walking in through the door, and the experience of being forcibly held and put through a movement differs from doing it without restraint. To the human mind, accustomed to more analysis of its own experiences, one of these would suggest the other, but we cannot argue that because such an association is not made in the animal's mind, therefore the latter is incapable of ideas, any more than we could conclude a total absence of ideas in the consciousness of a man to whom a primrose by the river's brim does not suggest thoughts of the moral government of the Universe.

Moreover, the raccoon, according to Cole, presents some of these very indications of ideas in its learning processes. In the first place, the raccoons, unlike Thorndike's cats, did "run back into boxes into which they had hitherto been lifted." They were picked up by the nape of the neck and dropped into the boxes. On the thirty-third trial in the case of one raccoon, "she turned . . . and went quickly back into the box. She opened the door in six seconds, came out, was fed for a moment from the bottle, and then immediately re-entered the box." It is, then, at least possible that the idea of being in the box was suggested to them from the experience of being dropped in. In the second place, unlike Thorndike's subjects, the raccoon learned to work a fastening by being put through it. For example, raccoon number two had failed to learn to raise a horizontal hook. "To make it a certain failure, I waited thirty-two minutes while he worked steadily. I put him through five times by raising the hook with his nose. He then succeeded in three and four-tenths seconds, then in seven and two-tenths, and so on." Other examples are not quite so clear-cut as this, but there is ample evidence that putting the raccoon through the proper movement greatly facilitated the learning process. Further evidence of the presence of ideas in the raccoon's mind will be considered later (82). Yerkes has found that the dancing mouse is aided in learning by being put through the act (469). Hobhouse thinks that his cats, dogs, elephants, and monkeys showed that their actions were guided by an idea of the result, instead of being merely ac-quired reactions to stimuli, because they varied the means to the end. "In opening the sideboard drawer, Jack [a dog] not merely pulls, but learns for himself how to get his head into the drawer without shutting it again, altering the method when he once hurts himself, and finding another. So again, I have seen him, when standing up to pull open the door of his box by means of a wire, accidentally pushing it with his paws again as he let go. At a second trial he was careful to avoid this, dropping the wire and pushing his nose in as soon as there was room. Similarly, I have seen the elephant shift the box that she was opening when she had found that in a certain position the door would slam to again before she could get her trunk in." These bits of behavior, in Hobhouse's opinion, indicate that the animals have ideas of the changes they wish to bring about (177).

While it may be rash to assert of any particular higher animal that its consciousness never contains ideas, yet the slow acquisition observed in many of these experimental tests certainly gives evidence of a process of learning whose essence consists simply in the *gradual dropping off of un-necessary movements*. Upon the nature of this process, psychology can throw little light. Thorndike declares that the successful movement is "stamped in" because pleasure results from it, while the unsuccessful movements are "stamped out" because no pleasure results. The terms "stamping in" and "out" must refer to some effect upon the nervous system, and of this effect we know no more than that it exists. Jennings says that the disturbance set up in the organism by the stimulus, by hunger or confinement, as the case may be, not finding an outlet by one path of discharge, seeks others in succession until one is found which relieves the disturbed condition. This, we have seen, he and others have found to be the case in very low forms of animal life. But the crucial part of the phenomena we are now considering is described in the following sentence: "After repetition of this course of events, the change which leads to relief is reached more directly, as a result of the law of the readier resolution of physiological states after repetition" (208). And that is all we know of the matter. But we may well note the probability that a habit, in the sense of a fixed way of action not innate in the individual, may originate in two ways: first, by the loss of conscious control in the case of a set of actions originally voluntary and guided by ideas; and second, by the gradual increase of speed and accuracy in the performance of a series of actions, never at any time guided by anything but external stimuli. In our own experience, the first kind of habit formation has been of so much interest that it has diverted attention from the second. Yet the latter is shown constantly in the growth of skill that comes through the *mere repetition* of a series of movements, apart from the "knowing how," which means conscious control.

§ 86. *The Psychic Aspect of dropping off Useless Movements*

The *conscious aspect* of learning by dropping off useless movements must consist largely in the mere *shortening of a period of unpleasantness and unrest*. The useless movements are unpleasant, the successful one brings pleasure;

when the latter comes to be performed at once, the consciousness accompanying must be wholly pleasant. Further, the puzzle-box experiments differ from the labyrinth experiments in that the successful movement is not merely turning in one direction rather than another, a habit which might ultimately become perfectly independent of external stimuli; but a reaction upon a particular object. It is evident that in the course of learning, this object, at the outset unnoticed, must come to stand in the centre of the animal's consciousness, the focus of its attention, as soon as it is perceived at all. Such a change would constitute another feature of the consciousness accompanying this form of learning, in addition to the diminishing unpleasantness which goes along with the dropping off of unnecessary movements. A special aspect of experiments on imitation is connected with this process of learning to *focus attention on the proper object.* Can an animal have his attention "called" to the object by watching some one else operating on it, or must the object gain its power to determine reaction solely by the animal's own experience of the consequences connected with it? Hobhouse's experiments on dogs, cats, and other animal subjects led him to the conclusion that watching his performance did materially assist the animal in this respect. His method was to perform the action of pulling a lever or string repeatedly while the animal was watching; and that this process facilitated learning he thinks evident from the fact that after it had been several times repeated, the behavior of the animal changed in a marked degree; instead of being random, it was definitely directed at the proper object. The suddenness of the transition from random to definite behavior indicates, in Hobhouse's opinion, the effect of being shown. Thus, for example, his dog Jack "after being once shown, . . . learnt to pull a stopper out of a jar with his teeth. The stopper fitted into a large round glass jar, and could be lifted with the teeth by a projecting peg. I lifted it out for him once, and left him to deal with the jar, which he did by knocking it over and rolling it all about the room until the meat was jerked out. At the second trial he pulled at the stopper himself with his teeth; and he repeated this many times " (177). A cat with which the writer is acquainted stands on his hind legs and touches a door handle with his paw when he wishes to be let out. He has never succeeded in letting himself out by any such method. It is possible that the habit may have been acquired from the fact that the door is sometimes opened for him after he has done so; but this is by no means always the case. He is often left to mew for some time after he has pawed the handle. There is, then, the possibility that observing human beings open doors may have caused the handle to occupy the focus of his attention; but one's attitude toward this hypothesis should be extremely cautious.

CHAPTER XI

THE MODIFICATION OF CONSCIOUS PROCESSES BY INDIVIDUAL EXPERIENCE (*continued*)

§ 87. *The Inhibition of Instinct*

IN still another form of experiment that has been devised to study the ways in which animals learn by experience, the object has been to secure the *complete inhibition of an instinctive action*. Obviously two factors will come into play here,—the strength of the instinct and the force of the modifying experience. The latter factor we might suppose to be strongest when the performance of an instinctive action could be made attended with pain, and less strong when the performance of some action opposed to instinct has been found to be accompanied by pleasure.

The first case we find apparently illustrated by Morgan's chick in his dealings with a bee; he needed but one experience with that insect to inhibit entirely, the next day, his instinct to peck at it (281, p. 53). On the other hand, Bethe denied consciousness to the crab because, although every time it went into the darkest corner of the aquarium it was seized by a cephalopod lurking there, it did not in six experiences learn to inhibit its negative phototropism; nor did the crabs learn not to snap at meat, though several times when they did so they were seized by the experimenter (28). The case of the crabs is not, however, fairly comparable with that of the chick, for the latter was not really obliged to inhibit his pecking instinct altogether, but only to direct it away from a certain object, while the crabs had no outlet at all for their photic and nutritive instincts. Very likely a longer course of training than that employed by Bethe might have succeeded in suppressing the instincts. The chick's case really belongs to a form of learning which we shall consider later on; that where the inhibition depends on the discrimination of different stimuli. The purest instance of the kind of modification of behavior by experience at present concerning us is furnished by Möbius's experiments with the pike (276), afterward repeated by Triplett with perch (407). The pike was kept in one half of an aquarium, separated by a glass screen from the other half, in which minnows were swimming about. The pike naturally dashed at them, and received a bump on its nose whenever it did so. After a considerable period of this sort of experience, the glass screen was removed, and the minnows were allowed to swim freely around the pike, when it was found that the latter's instinct to seize them had been wholly inhibited by the disagreeable consequences of such action. Triplett's description of the occasional struggles of the instinct to assert itself is extremely interesting. An analogous case is offered by Goldsmith's account of the shell-inhabiting fish, Gobius, which, when a glass partition was placed between it and its shell domicile, dashed against the glass for a time, but after three and a half hours went around it, and the next day did so after only a quarter of an hour's unsuccessful attempting to get through the partition (146).

The second kind of training in the inhibition of an instinct, where the performance of an action opposed to instinct is made to produce pleasure, is illustrated by Spaulding's work on "Association in Hermit Crabs." He found that these animals, which are positively phototropic, could be trained to go into the darkened part of the aquarium to get food, and finally to do so even if no food was there (389). Especially striking as an example of this kind of learning is the behavior of the insect called the water scorpion in the experiments of Holmes mentioned on page 179. With its head directly away from the light, and the right eye blackened, the natural tendency of this positively phototropic insect was to turn to the left. Yet after a sufficient amount of training in a position where the natural tendency was to turn toward the right, the animal, on being replaced with its back to the light, turned toward the right, an action directly contrary to instinct having been thus brought about by experience, as Holmes thinks, and as we may certainly conjecture, of its pleasurable consequences (186). When the "flight-reflex" comes gradually to be inhibited in animals that are being tamed, we have another instance of this type of learning (*e.g.*, 106).

The chief psychological question involved in the consideration of that form of learning by experience which involves the inhibition or reversal of an instinct is whether there is in the animal's mind an actual representation of the effects of the actions which constitute the animal's training. Does the pike, confronted with the minnow, recall the bump on its nose? Where the learning is very rapid, this always remains possible. Where the process is slower, however, the simpler hypothesis would be that the pleasure and pain of the results operate directly on the animal's tendencies to move, without the intervention of images. In the experiments where the results are painful, the stimulus at first produces, through the animal's inherited nervous connections, a movement toward it. This movement, under the peculiar circumstances of the case, occasions pain, and pain brings about a negative reaction of withdrawal.

It is possible that, as a consequence of the general tendency of the nervous system to establish short-cuts, after repetition of this experience, the appearance of the stimulus may stir up the negative reaction soon enough to inhibit the positive one altogether; through the operation of the same law whereby in learning a foreign language we first pass to the meaning of a word by way of the sound of the English word, but later make the association without any intervening link. On the psychic side, the object which was at first agreeable has simply become disagreeable. As for the cases where the instinct has been reversed by means of pleasurable consequences, the training of the hermit crab was accomplished by pitting a stronger against a weaker instinct. Nothing but the natural victory of the stronger innate tendency to move was required to make the crab go into the dark part of the aquarium to be fed, when the food was actually there; but what made it continue to do so when the food was removed? The representation of the resulting pleasure, Spaulding says; shall we admit this, or confine ourselves to physiological terms, and say that the nervous energy involved in the sight of the dark corner has come to find its natural outlet in movements toward that corner, through the repetition of these movements as a result of the operation of the stronger food instinct? The case of the water scorpion certainly suggests rather the operation of a blind habit than the effect of any *representation* of pleasure. Here the light-seeking instinct is, as it were, pitted against itself; shall we say that the animal, guided by a representation of the pleasure it has previously derived from turning to the left, does so now, when the slightest turn to the right would actually give it that pleasure? Possibly, but the behavior looks more like the working of a mechanical habit of turning.

§ 88. *Inhibition involving Discrimination of Successive Stimuli*

In other experiments requiring the inhibition of an instinct, the animal is caused to discriminate between two nearly similar stimuli, to execute the action when one is presented and to inhibit it when the other one appears. Such tests, as we have seen, are very commonly adopted to investigate sensory discrimination. The principle is the same whether the action to be inhibited is an instinct or an acquired habit. The experiments may be divided into two classes: in the first *only one stimulus is given at a time,* and the animal in consequence is sometimes required to inhibit its response entirely; in the second, *two or more stimuli are given simultaneously,* and the animal simply has to choose among them on the basis of its past experiences. Experiments belonging in the former class were successfully performed by Thorndike with Cebus monkeys. Both of his subjects learned to come down to the bottom of the cage to be fed when the experimenter took a piece of food in his left hand, and to stay up when he took it with his right hand, by being fed in the first case and not in the second. One of the monkeys learned to discriminate in like manner between cards carrying different figures; the other one failed with the cards and learned to react or inhibit reaction only in connection with different movements of Thorndike's hands (397). Professor Bentley and the writer made some experiments on the chub by this method, which gave wholly negative results. The red and green forceps, each containing food, were plunged one at a time into the water; the fish was allowed to get the food from the red forceps, but the green ones were withdrawn before it had a chance to bite. The time which the fish took to rise and snap at the forceps was measured by a stop-watch, and in the course of 131 experiments the animal was not found to rise to the green any less promptly than to the red. In other words, no tendency to inhibit reaction to the green was shown, although our later experiments proved that the fish could distinguish the two (421). Apart from the difference in intellectual level between the fish and the monkey, it is probable that the food-taking instinct was stronger in the former, which came directly from the wild state, where it could afford to lose no chances of nourishment. Dahl's observation that the spider *Attus arcuatus* refused to take house flies after having been presented with one smeared with oil of turpentine, although it seized a gnat, is also a case of inhibition involving discrimination of successively offered stimuli (88). Cole, in his very interesting experiments on the raccoon, raises the question whether discriminations of this type do not involve memory images, and answers it in the affirmative. He used the method to test discrimination of colors, tones, forms, and sizes; the results have been noted in earlier chapters. The cards used were placed on levers so that by a touch they could be pushed up and down. The animals learned to climb up for food when one of two differently colored cards was shown, and to stay down when the other one appeared; to distinguish in a similar way between a high and a low tone, between a round and a square card, and between a card $6\frac{1}{2} \times 6\frac{1}{2}$ inches and one $4\frac{1}{2} \times 4\frac{1}{2}$ inches square. Of course the action of climbing up was not itself purely instinctive, but had become associated with the food instinct. The raccoons also hit upon the trick of clawing up the cards themselves, and if the one that appeared was the "no-food" card, they would either claw it down again and pull up the other, or proceed at once to pull up the other, leaving the "no-food"

one also up. Since the cards were shown successively, Cole
concludes that "remembrance of the card just shown was
required for a successful response." "Why," he asks,
"should the animal put the red card down if it did not fail
to correspond with some image he had in mind, and why
when he put the green up should he leave it up and go up on
the high box for food if the green did not correspond with
some image he had in mind?" (82). It seems to the writer
that the supposition of an image is unnecessary, except
possibly in the experiments requiring discrimination of
sizes. It is perfectly possible, as we know from our own
experience, to react to one stimulus and not to another without going through a comparison of the two, unless the difference between them is merely one of degree. It might have
been possible for a human being to discriminate between
the larger and the smaller cards only by calling up a memory
image of the card not shown and comparing it with the one
before him; it surely would not have been necessary for him
to use images in the reactions to colors, forms, and tones.
And if a human being, accustomed to much dependence on
memory ideas, could get on without them here, surely a
raccoon could. Even in judgments of degree, all laboratory
psychologists know that human beings have a strong tendency
to make absolute rather than comparative judgments, and
use memory ideas but little. Better evidence of the use of
images is furnished by the following method: "Three
levers were placed on the displayer. One, on being raised,
displayed white, another orange, another blue. The plan
was to display white, orange, and blue consecutively, then
to display the same blue three times. I fed the animal if
he climbed upon the high box on being shown the series
white, orange, blue, and did not feed him after the series
blue, blue, blue." That is, the stimulus immediately pre-

ceding the reaction was the same in both cases. The difference lay in the foregoing stimuli. The series "white, blue, red, food, and red, red, red, no food" was also used. The raccoons learned to respond properly, "though," Cole continues, "I never *completely* inhibited the animals' tendency to start up on seeing white or blue, which were precursors of the red which meant food. Thus the animals all anticipated red on seeing its precursors, which in itself seems good evidence of ideation. Many times, however, they turned back after starting at blue or white and looked for the red, then climbed up once more, thus showing that the red was not a neglected element of the situation, but an expected color which they generally waited to see, but sometimes were too eager to wait for." Two of the raccoons had been previously trained in two-color series, while one had experienced only the three-color series. The former showed a decided tendency to go up at the second color when there were three. The latter had been trained first on the series "white, orange, blue, food; blue, blue, blue, no food;" then on the series "white, blue, red, food; red, red, red, no food." "Although blue, his former food signal, was," in the second series, "placed second as a no-food color, he made the mistake of reacting to it only ten times in the first fifty, *because it was not third*, while he did go up to the final 'no-food' red twenty-seven times *because it was third*. It seems certain, therefore, that raccoons are able to learn to distinguish one object or movement from two and two from three, a species of counting not different from that which anthropologists ascribe to primitive man." Certain details of the behavior of the raccoons in these tests are significant. "Each one, on seeing the first red, would drop down from a position with both front paws on the front board to stand on all fours in front of it and merely glance up at the succeeding reds. As soon as the white appeared, however, the animal would lean up against the front board, claw down the white and blue, but *never the final red.*"

Now Cole thinks that the learning of this trick by the raccoons proved that "the animal *retains* an image of the cards which just preceded red." The only alternate supposition seems to him to be that they always reacted to the number of the card in the series, which, if the series were irregularly given, would not have been the same in successive trials. To suggest one's own interpretation of animal behavior that one has not seen, in the place of the experimenter's interpretation, requires some temerity, but to the present writer the most natural way of accounting for the raccoon's performances would be the supposition that in the series white, blue, red, for instance, at the end of which they were fed, the occurrence of white threw them into a state of expectancy, of readiness to climb up on the box; this was heightened by the blue, and finally "discharged" into action by the red. During this process they may have had an *anticipatory* image of the blue and of the red. But when the red came they did not stop to call up *memory* images of the preceding colors, and decline to act until they had assured themselves that those were blue and white instead of red. Preparedness to act was probably already secured by the actual occurrence of the white card at the beginning of the series. In other words, while images may have been present, they were images with a future, not a past reference. A human being reacting to a series of stimuli in this fashion would but rarely, in case his attention had wandered during the giving of the first two stimuli, have to recall them as memory images before reaction, but he might very likely have anticipatory images of the stimuli to come while waiting for them. For reasons that will be later mentioned, it seems probable that anticipation rather than retrospection is the primitive function of ideas.

"It may still be objected," continues Cole, "that retaining an image while you raise three, or even six, colors is hardly retention at all, so short is the time. Of course the fact that the animals made steady and rather uniform progress for six days would show that the impression was not effaced in twenty-four hours. Number one, however, was given a review of his first three-color work after an interval of eighteen days. He did not respond to the three blue cards at all, and made but one mistake in twenty trials to the series white, orange, blue, though he did *start* up at orange six times. The visual images of the colors must therefore have been retained for eighteen days with sufficient clearness to permit successful responses." A certain confusion of thought is evident in this paragraph. The *visual images* of course were not *retained* for eighteen days; what was retained was, possibly, the capacity to have the visual image of the third color in the series suggested by the actual occurrence of the second. The length of time this capacity persisted is quite irrelevant to the question as to whether visual ideas were really present. An animal incapable of having ideas might retain the effect of previous stimulation for a long period, and an animal that had ideas might lose the power of having a particular one suggested to it by a given stimulation after a few hours. What we should really like to know is whether the raccoons could think of color number three if color number two were not actually shown them a few seconds earlier; whether they could "think over" the whole performance when the apparatus was not there; in short, how free and unhampered by the control of present sense stimulation their use of ideas can be. Cole concludes, "We are . . . forced to believe that the raccoon retains visual images." We are, at least, shown some reason for thinking that memory ideas connected with immediately preceding peripheral stimulation may occur in the raccoon's mind.

§ 89. *Inhibition involving Discrimination of Simultaneous Stimuli*

Experiments of the second class, where the different stimuli are simultaneously presented, have been made by Kinnaman on monkeys, by Cole on raccoons, by Porter and Rouse on birds, and by Yerkes on the dancing mouse. Kinnaman's Macacus monkeys entirely failed to discriminate cards with different figures on them when one card was placed on a box with food and the other on an empty box (221). The English sparrow and the cowbird, on the other hand, both learned to do this. Monkeys and birds alike learned to discriminate glasses covered with differently colored papers, and the position or number of a vessel in a series (221, 345, 371). Cole's raccoons learned to discriminate a black from a white glass, and, with more difficulty, a red from a green one (82). The monkeys were able to distinguish fairly well differences in size, and in the form of the vessel. The birds were not tested with size differences, and Porter's birds failed to discriminate the vessel forms; Porter suggests that the monkeys may have been helped by the fact that the vessels Kinnaman used differed in size as well as in form. Rouse found that his pigeons did tolerably well in learning form differences (371). Our own experiments with the chub, where the red and green forks were presented together and the fish learned rather quickly to bite at the red rather than the green even when both were empty (421), also illustrate this method, as does the case of the chick stung by the bee, who, on the basis of this experience, pecks at other insects but avoids bees (281). Similarly, Forel's bees and wasps, which were trained to pick out pieces of paper of particular colors

s

and forms because they have been previously fed from them, exhibit behavior which belongs to this class (130). The method was used also by Yerkes in the experiments to test brightness, color, and form discrimination in the dancing mouse, described on pp. 145 and 197. Yerkes prefers to establish discrimination by associating disagreeable rather than agreeable experiences with one of the alternatives, finding that the motive thus constituted works with greater uniformity. Hence his mice were given slight electric shocks when they made the "wrong" choice, instead of being fed when they made the "right" one. He describes three different types of behavior on the part of the mice in making the choices, which he calls choice by affirmation, choice by negation, and choice by comparison. The first is illustrated when the mouse enters the right compartment at once, the second when it goes to the wrong compartment and turns away from it, the third when it vacillates for some time between the two (469).

§ 90. *Comparison of Methods*

The methods just described have something in common with, and something different from, the puzzle-box method. In both cases a particular object, offering certain peculiarities to the senses, and distinguished from other objects, ultimately comes to occupy the focus of consciousness; but in this method of choice, the other objects are themselves connected, either by instinct or acquired impulses, with a particular reaction which has to be checked. No *definite* tendency has to be inhibited in the puzzle-box method; it is only necessary for random movements to be dropped off. On the other hand, these experiments where inhibition becomes dependent on the presentation of a particular stimulus, differ from tests like those on the hermit crabs or the water scorpion, in that the

latter require the inhibition of an entire instinct. The case
of the hermit crab, that of the chub presented with one pair
of forceps at a time, and that of the chub required to choose
between two differently colored forceps, may represent three
lessening degrees of the amount of inhibitory influence exerted
by experience. The hermit crab entirely abandoned its
ordinary method of reacting to light. The whole instinct
vanished. The chub, if it had refused as a result of experience to rise to the green fork when it was presented alone,
would have suspended an instinctive action so far as that
particular stimulus was concerned, and would have been
condemned to inactivity simply because no other stimulus
appealing to the nutritive instinct presented itself. The chub
offered a choice between two forks is not required to suspend
action at all, save for the brief interval necessary to discriminate between them. We should naturally expect that this
third state of affairs would be the easiest to bring about, and
such seems to be the case. It would probably be effected most
quickly when one of the stimuli was associated with positive
pain, instead of with mere absence of pleasure; hence, very
likely, the extremely rapid learning of Morgan's chick.
Obviously the difference between the first and second of the
two cases just cited is at bottom one of degree, not of kind.
"A whole instinct" means, of course, a reaction to a whole
class of stimuli; but the process by which light, for instance,
is discriminated from other forms of stimulation cannot be
ultimately different from the process by which one kind of
light stimulation is distinguished from another kind.

As we survey the processes of learning involved in all these
methods, the labyrinth method, the puzzle-box method, the
method of inhibition, and the method of inhibition with choice,
we find that they are all cases of the checking of movements
which do not involve positively pleasurable results. Their

psychological aspect in every case means, while the learning is going on, the diminution of unpleasantness and the increase of pleasantness; apart from this, when the learning is completed, it differs in the different cases as regards the part played by the consciousness of certain more or less accurately discriminated objects. As the learning process proceeds, such objects, as we have seen, come to stand in the focus of attention, so that to the cat put in the puzzle-box the string that opens the door is instantly attended to; the chick, half automatically pecking at various objects on the ground, becomes vividly conscious of the appearance of a bee among them; the monkey becomes aware of the difference in color between two vessels otherwise quite similar.

§ 91. *Visual Memory in Homing*

Doubtless all the phenomena which animals exhibit in these various experimental tests are displayed also in their ordinary and normal life. There is one mode of behavior, however, the existence of which has been established by careful observation of an animal in its proper environment, that does not easily find an analogue among the facts we have been describing. I refer to the exercise of visual memory by bees and wasps. The case of the bee, indeed, finding its way from repeated excursions back to a hive which remains in the same place, may ultimately involve the formation of a habit of movement like that displayed in experiments by the labyrinth method. We have already noted on pp. 138, 139 some of the evidence that bees are, at least in their earlier flights from the hive, guided back by visual memory. Lubbock found that bees from a hive near the seashore, when taken out on the water and liberated, were unable to find their way home, although the distance was less than their usual range of flight on land; and he ascribes their failure to the lack of visual landmarks to guide them (248). Bethe, who thinks bees are guided home neither by vision nor by smell, but by an unknown force to which they respond reflexly, also liberated some bees at sea about 1700–2000 metres from their hive, which was near the foot of Vesuvius and beside some very tall and conspicuous trees. The bees failed to return, yet Bethe thinks, if they were guided by vision, the mountain and the trees should have aided them to do so (32). It may well be, of course, that bees cannot see objects at such a distance. Besides his observation that changing the appearance of a hive did not disturb the bees in their homing flight, Bethe urges against the visual memory hypothesis an observation on a hive which had on one side of it a garden, and on the other side a town, which he thinks the bees never visited, as food was to be had in abundance in the garden. Yet when liberated in the town they flew back to the hive with an accuracy certainly not born of their acquaintance with the locality (30). Von Buttel-Reepen, however, doubts whether the bees really never visited the town. Bethe's most striking illustration of his unknown force, however, is derived from his "box-experiments." If a number of bees are carried in a box some distance from the hive, on being liberated they fly straight up in the air. Some of them will return to the hive, but if the distance is great enough, many will drop back upon the box. Now if the box has moved only a few centimeters away during the flight of the bees, they will drop back to the precise spot where it was, and take no notice of its new location. If they were guided by vision, Bethe urges, they could easily see the box (30, 32). This, says von Buttel-Reepen, is arguing that their visual memory must be like ours if it exists at all; it may be a memory, not of the appearance of the box, but of its locality. He himself, repeating Bethe's experiments, observed the bees on dropping back after their upward flight, hunting not at the place where the box had been, but at a height which was about that of their home-hive entrance. He thinks that an important feature of the bee's visual memory consists in a power of accurately estimating height above the ground. If the entrance to the hive be raised or lowered 30 cm., all the returning bees will go to the old place, and it will be hours and sometimes days before they find the new one. Moreover, the same bees tend to return to the same corner of the opening each time. When a row of hives had been arranged, some with openings in front and others with openings at the side, bees which had been driven home in haste by a storm would sometimes try to enter the wrong hive, but if their home hive opened on the side, they would attempt to enter the foreign hive on the corresponding side (72).

It may be granted that there is much evidence in favor of the use of visual memory by bees, although the differences which must exist between the visual perceptions gained by the compound eye and those of our own experience necessarily complicate the phenomena and make them hard to interpret. In the solitary wasps, although Fabre is inclined to assume a "special faculty" of homing, independent of visual memory, basing his assumption on experiments where the wasps returned to their nests, from which they had been transported in a box to a distance of three kilometers (115, Series I); yet the evidence obtained by the Peckhams seems fairly conclusive in favor of memory for visual landmarks. The solitary wasps have been shown by the observations of the Peckhams to depend upon sight for the return to the nest (322, 323), and the same conclusion is indicated for the social wasps by Enteman (112). The Peckhams' belief in the visual memory of solitary wasps rests first upon the fact that the wasp, upon completing her nest, always spends some time in circling about the locality, in and out among the plants, as if she were making a careful study of the region. On leaving the nest a second time she omits this process and flies straight away. A similar "locality survey" is made by hive bees and by social wasps. Secondly, the Peckhams argue that if the wasp does not remember her nest by landmarks, it ought to make no difference to her when the surroundings are altered in any way. They found, however, that a wasp of one species could not discover her nest when a leaf that covered it was broken off, but found it again without trouble when the leaf was replaced. Another wasp abandoned the nest she had made for herself with much labor, because the Peckhams, to identify the spot themselves, drew radiating lines from it in the dust. A third argument against the existence of a special sense of direction is the fact that wasps sometimes are unable to find their nests. In one case the Peckhams dug up the nest of a wasp and she made another five inches away. After an absence of three hours the wasp returned, and seemed to be puzzled as to whether the old spot or the new one were the place of her nest. "At first she alighted upon the first site and scratched away a little earth, and then explored several other places, working about for twelve minutes, when she at last found the right spot." Similarly, when a wasp that was carrying her prey left it for a few moments to go to the nest, as many of them do, apparently to see that all is right there, if any of the surrounding objects were altered she often had great difficulty in finding the prey again. On one occasion a wasp of another species dug its nest in the midst of a group of nests of the Bembex wasp. These latter are usually dug in a wide bare space of earth which has no vegetable growth to serve as a landmark. When the intruder had finished her nest, it looked just like the Bembex holes. She went away, secured a spider, and when she returned she could not find her nest. "She flew, she ran, she scurried here and there, but she had utterly lost track of it. She approached it several times, but there are no landmarks on the B. field. After five minutes our wasp flew back to look at her spider," which she had dropped about three feet away, "and then returned to her search. She now began to run into the B. holes, but soon came out again, even when not chased out by the proprietor. Suddenly it seemed to strike her that this was going to be a prolonged affair, and that her treasure was exposed to danger, and hurrying back she dragged it into the grass at the edge of the field, where it was hidden. Again she resumed the hunt, flying wildly now all over the field, running into wrong holes and even kicking out earth as though she thought of appropriating them, but soon passing on. Once more she became anxious about the spider, and, carrying it up on to a plant, suspended it there. Now she seemed determined to take possession of every hole that she went into, digging quite persistently in each, but then giving it up. One in particular that was close by the spider seemed to attract her, and she worked at it so long that we thought she had adopted it, for it seemed to be unoccupied. At last, however, she made up her mind that all further search was hopeless, and that she had better begin *de novo;* and forty minutes from the time that we saw her first she started a new nest close to the spider, as though she would run no more risks" (322). An occurrence of this kind certainly lends color to the 'recognition of land-marks' theory. On the other hand, the Bembex wasps themselves find their nests with unerring accuracy, though there is no landmark in the field. Fabre noted that Bembex wasps could not be led astray by any modification of either the look or the smell of their nests, and thought a peculiar form of space memory, unparalleled in our own experience, must be involved in the nest-finding of this species (115, Series I). A similar kind of memory for pure locality, if one may so term it, is maintained by Goldsmith to exist in a fish, Gobius, which lives in a shell. If its shell habitation is moved during its absence, the fish seeks it in the place where it previously was (146). Bouvier, repeating Fabre's experiments on Bembex, obtained a different result. When a stone, for example, that had been at the mouth of a Bembex nest was moved a distance of 2 dm., the wasp, returning, went to the stone. Bouvier accordingly maintains the visual landmark hypothesis (68). Ferton holds the same view with regard to a species of wasp that makes its nest in shells. If during successive absences on the wasp's part the shell is moved from position A to position B, and later from B to C and from C to D, the wasp, returning, goes in turn to each of the positions that the shell has occupied. "In time, she omits to go to A, then to B. Little by little, the image of the previous locations of her nest is effaced in the insect's memory." When she has found it, after each displacement, she makes a new "locality survey," before starting off again (116).

The performances of carrier pigeons in finding their way home have been the subject of a considerable literature, and many theories which it would take a disproportionate amount of time to discuss.[1] While the facts are not easy to explain, careful observations on young pigeons indicate that their powers are acquired, not innate, and that they are influenced by visual landmarks (375). What guides the flight of migrating birds over vast stretches of water, or the young migrants in those species where young and old fly by different routes, remains a mystery.

If we take the case of the solitary wasp as typical of guidance by visual landmarks, it is to be noted that no gradual

[1] For an account of them see Claparède, "La faculté d'orientation lointaine (Sens de direction, sens de retour)" (76).

elimination of useless movements occurs, as in many species the nest is revisited but once. Nor is there any opportunity for the elimination of errors through their unpleasant consequences. Doubtless the wasp does not choose the best possible route for her return to the nest, and doubtless she would improve upon it if she made repeated journeys; but at least she performs at the first trial definite, not random, responses to stimuli that are new to her; responses that are not wholly due to inherited nervous mechanism. We have here a kind of behavior that is not in any sense "trial and error."

Without undertaking the difficult task of explaining it fully, one or two aspects of this form of profiting by experience may be noted. The wasp, when she has finished digging her nest, makes a "locality survey"; that is, she circles about the neighborhood in flight for a few minutes. This conduct on her part is doubtless instinctive. During the process she receives a number of specific visual stimuli. On her flight in search of prey, several visual landmarks probably impress her. When she has secured her spider or caterpillar, she begins the return flight. We cannot attempt to explain all the mysteries connected with this, but at least we can say that the flight back to the nest, and the alighting and burying the prey, are instinctive actions which are carried out only under the influences of the *same* visual stimuli that the animal received on its locality survey and its outward flight. It is essential to their performance that the wasp's nervous system should receive stimulation like that which it has received a short time previously. The case differs from the formation of a habit, such as we saw illustrated in the labyrinth experiments; for while in a habit the action becomes dependent on a certain kind of stimulus repeatedly received, here it is not the *frequent* previous experience of the stimulus that renders it and it alone effective, — for the features of the locality may have been quite new to the wasp when she dug her nest there, — but its *recent* previous experience.

The great thing to be desired with regard to the effect of individual experience upon behavior is that it shall be rapid. One might at first thought say also, "that it shall be permanent." But it is probable that permanence of impression, though valuable, is less so than speed of modification; for too great permanence of one impression would interfere with the formation of new ones. We have been often told of the value that attaches to the capacity for forgetting. Judged by the standard of rapidity, the guidance of action by a stimulus that has been experienced only once before, though recently, is a form of modification through experience distinctly superior to the guidance of action by repeated stimulation. It has been noted already that if the effect of a stimulus is very painful, the stimulus does not need to be repeated; but obviously it is better for an animal to modify its behavior rapidly without undergoing pain, which must tell upon its vital energies.

Furthermore, we may notice that while recency of experience is more valuable than frequency of experience as regards the rapidity with which behavior is modified, nothing can take the place of frequency where permanence is concerned. It is not to be desired that the wasp should remain permanently subject to the influence of these particular landmarks. On the contrary, their influence must be effaced, in order that she may dig and stock other nests in other localities. The lasting character of the effect produced on the animals in the labyrinth and box experiments has, on the other hand, been proved by nearly all experimenters. One of Small's rats opened a puzzle box with speed and accuracy after an interval of forty days, during which time she had had no tests whatever. The birds tested by Porter remembered the maze well after an interval of thirty days, and one of Thorndike's monkeys opened a puzzle box at once, eight months after his last previous experience with it.

Most rapid of all the ways in which conduct may be modified by experience is the method of the memory idea. The wasp, finding her way back to her nest, is guided by the actual recurrence of certain stimuli which she has experienced on her outward flight. As she has needed no frequent experience of those stimuli to make them effective, her behavior is far superior to that of the frog in the labyrinth. But if she possessed the power to direct her course by the memory image of a stimulus rather than by its actual recurrence, still more time would be saved. Suppose, for instance, that on the devious flight in search of prey three landmarks, A, B, and C, had impressed themselves upon the wasp's consciousness. Suppose that the distance in a straight line from A to C is less than the distance via B. Now if, on the return trip, the wasp can have in mind not only C, which is actually before her, but the memory of B and A and of their relative position, she can greatly shorten her course by flying straight from C to A. Not only is it unnecessary for an animal capable of memory images to wait for the repetition of stimuli many times, before its behavior is modified; it does not need to wait for the complete repetition of a series of stimuli even once, for the earlier members of the series being given, the later ones are suggested in idea.

Yet here, too, frequency of repetition is the condition of permanence. I think it may be said that if an animal is capable of having a memory image at all, a single *recent* experience of two stimuli, fully attended to, is enough to make one of them call up the image of the other. But if the association is to be permanent, nothing but frequent repetition will serve. It is customary to say that a single very vivid ex-

perience may suffice as well as a repeated experience to produce long retention. But the fact is that a single vivid experience amounts to a repeated experience, because it is
usually recalled so often in idea. If we could imagine a
person's having a very forcible impression, which he did not
once recall for a long period of years, it is doubtful whether
he could recall it at the end of that time with anything like
the success which attends his recollection of the familiar surroundings of his childhood.

CHAPTER XII

THE MEMORY IDEA

§ 92. *Evidence for and against Ideas in Animals*

IN the last chapter we have seen that the behavior of the lower forms of animal life, at least, can be fully explained without supposing that the animals concerned ever consciously recall the effects of a previously experienced stimulus in the entire absence of the stimulus itself. We must admit that it is not easy to prove the possession by any animal of memory in the sense of *having ideas of absent objects*, rather than in the sense of *behaving differently to present objects because of past experience with them.* The dog shows clearly that he remembers his master in the latter sense by displaying joy at the sight of him. Can we be sure that he has remembered him in the former sense during his absence; that is, that he has had a memory image of him? Certain pieces of negative evidence have been noted. Where an animal learns to work a mechanism by gradually dropping off unnecessary movements, it looks as if its conduct were not guided by an idea of the right movements, for the association of ideas as we know it is so rapid a process that a single experience of two stimuli together is enough to enable one to revive the other in the form of a memory idea, provided that the experience was recent. When an animal has learned to run through a complicated labyrinth almost without error, but still persists in taking the wrong turning at the outset, we are surely justified in saying that if it has ideas, it does not use them as a human being would, for some kind of idea of the right way to start the labyrinth course would certainly be formed in a human mind after a very few experiences. Thorndike's attempts to make cats and dogs learn by inferential imitation, and by putting them through the movements required, while they do not show absence of ideas in the animals' minds, indicate that ideas were not suggested to his subjects under circumstances which would have suggested them to human beings. Cole's opposite results, however, weaken Thorndike's conclusions. Further, the way in which instinctive actions are often performed by animals indicates that ideas are not present as they would be to a human being's consciousness. Human beings do some things from instinct, but the doing of them may be accompanied by ideas; a mother's care for her child involves ideas of the child's happiness or suffering, and of its future. Enteman's account of the worker wasp which, lacking other food to present to a larva, bit off a portion of one end of the larva's body and offered it to the other end to be eaten, suggests a peculiar limitation of ideas in the wasp's mind, at least while this particular function was being performed (112). The cow, which had lamented at being deprived of her calf, and on having the stuffed skin of her offspring given to her, licked it with maternal devotion until the hay stuffing protruded, when she calmly devoured the hay (279, p. 334), had perhaps experienced some dim ideas connected with her loss, but certainly her consciousness was more absorbed by the effects of present stimulation and less occupied with ideas than a human mother's would have been.

On the other hand, certain features of animal behavior are held by most people to be indications that the creatures thus acting have ideas of absent objects. Dogs and cats are supposed to dream because they snarl and twitch their muscles in sleep; but, as Thorndike has pointed out, such movements may be purely reflex and unaccompanied by any consciousness whatever. A dog shows depression during his master's absence, but his state of mind may be merely vague discomfort at the lack of an accustomed set of stimuli, not an idea of what he wants. A cat, indeed, once observed by the writer, did behave as a human being would do to whom an idea had occurred, when, on coming into the house for the first time after she had moved her kittens from an upper story to the ground floor, she started upstairs to the old nest, stopped half way up, turned and ran down to the new one. But errors of interpretation are possible at every turn of such observations. An attempt was made by Thorndike to test experimentally the presence of ideas in the minds of the cats he was studying by the puzzle-box method. He sat near the cage where the cats were kept, and having made sure that the cats were looking at him, he would clap his hands and say, "I must feed those cats." Aften ten seconds he would take a piece of fish, go to the cage and hold it through the wire netting; the cat, of course, would climb up and get the food. After from thirty to sixty trials the cat learned to climb up when it heard him clap his hands and speak, without waiting for him to get the fish. But it is not certain that the hand-clapping came thus to suggest to the cat an idea of the experimenter's taking the food and coming to the cage; rather, in the course of so many repetitions, the clapping of the hands may have become a direct stimulus to the act of climbing up, although Thorndike thinks that the ten seconds' interval rendered this improbable (393). Cole, as we have seen, has observed behavior in the raccoon that might well be regarded as involving ideas (82).

Despite the difficulty of proving that animals have memory ideas, it is not likely that any such gulf separates the human mind from that of the higher animals as would be involved in the absence from the latter of all images of past experiences.

That ideas occur in far less profusion and with far less freedom of play in the animal mind that possesses them at all than in the human mind; that even the highest animal below man lives far more completely absorbed in present stimulations than does the average man, seems also practically certain. In the lack of more definite knowledge on the subject, we may discuss a few related questions that suggest themselves with regard to, first, the primitive function of ideas; secondly, the relation of ideas to qualitative differences in sensation; and thirdly, the nature and possible origin of "movement ideas."

§ 93. *The Primitive Function of Ideas*

(1) What would be the most obvious and fundamental *use* of ideas to an animal? In our own experience, ideas of absent objects have, among the various functions they subserve, two that are rather definitely contrasted, which may be termed the backward and the forward reference of ideas. On the one hand, we recall past experiences purely as such; we indulge in "the pleasures of memory," letting the attention wander over trains of ideas recognized as belonging to the past. On the other hand, we form ideas of experiences we expect to have in the future, ideas which are derived, it is true, from what has happened in the past, but which involve a very different attitude on our part from that required by mere retrospection, — the attitude, namely, of anticipation, of preparing to act appropriately to the situation present in idea. Now if we ask which of these two functions of the idea is practically the more important, we cannot hesitate to say that the second is. To recall the past, except for the purpose of anticipating the future, is an intellectual luxury. As Bentley remarks, "The primary use of the image, we surmise, was to carry the organism beyond the limits of the immediate

T

environment, and to assist it in foreseeing and providing for 'the future.' Its function seems, then, to have been a prophetic one; it was a means to what we may term *remote adaptation*. . . . The past, being less important than the future, must have been known as such later " (23).

It is in making possible the anticipation of a coming stimulus, thus preparing the way for reaction, that the memory image is most fundamentally useful. Can we form any conception of the conditions under which it would most naturally make its appearance, in its simplest, most rudimentary form? Let us suppose that an animal's behavior in a certain case requires a definite series of stimulations for its guidance. The acts concerned have been performed several times, so that when the reaction to number one in the series has occurred, the motor apparatus concerned in the reaction to number two is slightly innervated, although the actual giving of the second stimulus is necessary to produce the movement. Now if the stimuli follow each other in quick succession, this tendency for one movement to help, as it were, in starting the next, would result finally in the performance of the whole set of reactions "automatically," with lapsing consciousness. But suppose the sequence is slow, or that one stimulus in the series is delayed. It is important, perhaps, that the series of movements shall not go on until the delayed stimulus acts. During this time of waiting, it may well be that the nervous energy prepared for the next reaction, besides innervating to some degree the motor mechanism that will be needed, overflows into the sensory centres which the anticipated stimulus is to stir to full activity. The result for consciousness is an idea, an image, though perhaps rather vague, of the stimulus waited for. Why, it may be asked, have we made the process by which *motor* centres become "associated," so that habits are formed, and the innervation of one centre in a series involved in successive reactions produces innervation of the next, fundamental, and suggested that the process of "association" whereby *ideas* are brought into consciousness is secondary and derived? Simply because we find the formation of motor habits far down in the animal kingdom, long before there is any evidence of the existence of ideas. It is interesting to note that Judd has recently advanced the theory that the physiological process underlying the "association of ideas" may involve the motor pathways (217). In any case, we may be pretty sure *a priori* that the primary function of the memory idea or image is to anticipate and prepare the way for reaction to a coming stimulus.

§ 94. *The Significance of Stimuli from a Distance*

(2) Another question that arises in connection with the origin of the memory idea bears on the possible significance of that increase in ability to react to stimuli from a distance which we find characterizing the higher animals. An important difference must exist between the stimuli from objects directly in contact with an organism's body, such as give rise to touch, temperature, taste, and pain sensations in our own experience, and those which proceed from objects at a distance, such as forms of vibratory energy and odors. This difference consists in the fact that the former have a more direct and instant effect upon the organism's welfare, and in consequence demand more rapid reaction, than the latter. A stimulus in immediate contact with an animal's body may have a harmful or a beneficial influence at the moment of its impact; it may be food to be seized or an enemy to be escaped, and the seizing or escaping must be done on the instant. On the other hand, if an animal possesses the power, belonging in increasing degree to the higher animals, of reacting to

an influence proceeding from an object still at a distance, it becomes safe for it to delay the reaction after the stimulus is given. The danger is not so imminent, the food is not yet within reach; the full motor response to stimulation may be suspended for a short interval without imperilling the life interests of the animal. Now what is the import of this delay between stimulus and reaction for the memory idea?

It seems probable that the reproduction of a sensory image by central excitation demands that its original stimulus shall have left upon the nervous system a relatively permanent effect. We may distinguish three grades of animal behavior in response to stimulation. First, there is the condition where, so far as we can see, the animal does not learn by individual experience. A stimulus entering such an organism, and sending its energy out again through whatever motor paths are available, leaves so little effect upon the substance through which it passes that the animal behaves toward a second stimulus of the same kind precisely as it did toward the first. In the next place, we have the grade where the animal learns by experience, without having the power to recall an image of its experience. The chick stung by a bee very likely cannot have later the image of a bee suggested to him, but he can and does refrain from picking up the next bee he sees. Here the stimulus has modified the behavior of the animal, and has left a relatively permanent effect of some sort upon the nervous substance; but renewed stimulation from without is necessary before this modification makes itself apparent. Finally, when we have the possibility of an image, purely centrally excited, and not leading immediately to movement; when a process similar to the original may be set up, not by an influx of energy from without, but by the weaker nervous current coming from some other central sensory region, it is evident that the nervous substance must have been far more profoundly affected by the original stimulus than it was in either of the before-mentioned cases. What characteristics of a stimulus would determine how strongly and deeply it would affect the nervous substance through which its energy passed? Its intensity, the quantity of that energy, of course; but still more emphatically the length of time the energy remained in the centres concerned, without being drained off into motor paths and transformed into bodily movement. Not merely the strength, but the duration of the current determines how deep a path it shall dig out for itself.

Now, as we have seen, stimuli that are in a position to help or harm an organism at the instant of their contact with its body are stimuli demanding immediate motor reaction. In such cases, the energy of the stimulus is deflected at once into the appropriate motor path; it is not delayed long enough in the sensory regions to produce any permanent change there. But where the animal possesses a capacity to be affected by light and sound, which cannot help or harm at the moment of their action upon its body, then reaction may be postponed; then the current of energy sent by the stimulus into the nervous substance is not at once drained off, but may linger sufficiently long to produce whatever alteration, whatever impress upon sensory centres, is needful to insure their subsequent functioning as the basis of a memory image. The delay between stimulus and reaction, made possible by sensitiveness of the organism to stimuli only indirectly affecting its welfare, may then supply time for the nervous modification to be produced that is later to underlie the memory image, as the delay occupied in waiting for an expected stimulus offers a chance to bring this modification into play and call the image to consciousness. The same principle also helps to explain why the human mind gets its clearest and most controllable memory images from the senses whose stimuli do not indicate direct contact of a beneficial or harmful object with the body; while the closer and more direct the stimulation, as for instance in touch and organic sensations, the obscurer the image.[1]

Many of the foregoing sentences are taken from an article by the writer which appeared in 1904 (420). A very interesting discussion of the significance from the neurological standpoint of reaction to stimulation from a distance is to be found in Sherrington's recently published book on "The Integrative Action of the Nervous System" (382, pp. 324 ff.). Sherrington proposes the term "distance receptors" for those receptive organs "which react to objects at a distance," and declares that "the distance receptors contribute most to the uprearing of the cerebrum." The most important significance of the power to act in response to distant objects Sherrington finds to be that it allows an interval for preparatory adjustment, "for preparatory reactive steps which can go far to influence the success of attempt either to obtain actual contact or to avoid actual contact with the object." That these preparatory steps may also involve the germ of the memory image is clearly suggested by Sherrington. "We may suppose," he says, "that in the time run through by a course of action focussed upon a final consummatory event, opportunity is given for instinct, with its germ of memory, however rudimentary, and its germ of anticipation, however slight, to evolve under selection that mental extension of the present backward into the past and forward into the future which in the highest animals forms the prerogative of more developed mind. Nothing, it would seem, could better

---

[1] An exception may be taken to this statement so far as smells are concerned. Some people seem to have difficulty in getting memory images of odors. For the writer, such images are among the most vivid and most readily controlled in her experience.

insure the course of action taken in that interval being the right one than memory and anticipatory forecast." The present writer's views regarding the significance of the delay made possible by reaction through "distance receptors," while independently formed, find thus most valuable support.

§ 95. *Ideas of Movement*

(3) A very striking difference between man and most of the lower animals lies in the immensely greater number of different movements, each adapted to some feature of the environment, that man is able to perform. When we think of the enormous variety of muscular adjustments of which the human race as a whole is capable, and compare it with the limited power of an earthworm to react upon its surroundings, the small extent of its motor repertoire, the gulf that separates them is highly impressive. And the conscious experience of an animal must be profoundly modified by the number and variety of the motor coördinations it has under its control; not only because sensory discriminations in general involve differentiation of motor reaction, but because that breaking up of the crude mass of sense impressions into smaller masses which we call the perception of external objects depends so largely on what the animal is able to do with objects. Think, for example, of a creature able to move in response to its environment, but not able to alter the relative position of different features of that environment; not able, in plain words, to pick up a single object and move it about. "Objects" for such an animal simply would not exist. There would be a vague background of sensation qualities, but no sharply defined groups of such qualities. An object to the human mind is essentially a bit of experience with which things can be done; which can be moved about independently of its surroundings, "handled," used

for one purpose or another. The perception of objects as distinct entities increases with the power of making definitely coördinated and adjusted motor responses to them. That one important condition to the production of such responses lies in the possession of a grasping organ, a highly movable member that can seize objects firmly and thus move them about, is self-evident. The elephant and the monkey, which possess such organs, must have far more definite perceptions of objects, as individual entities to be separated from their backgrounds and used, than any other lower animals. But to the acquisition of the most complicated and perfect systems of motor reactions another factor contributes.

This factor is the *movement idea*. A movement idea is the revival, through central excitation, of the sensations, visual, tactile, kinæsthetic, originally produced by the performance of the movement itself. And when such an idea is attended to, when, in popular language, we think hard enough of how the movement would "feel" and look if it were performed, then, so close is the connection between sensory and motor processes, the movement is instituted afresh. The movement is willed by attending to the idea of it. This is the familiar doctrine expounded by James in Chapter XXVI of his "Psychology" (189). Recently it has been pointed out that the "willing" of a movement by no means always or even usually involves preliminary attention to a movement idea (*e.g.* 445). This is undoubtedly true. Nearly or quite all the movements executed by a man in the ordinary course of a day are movements that he has made many, many times before. And movements that have been repeatedly made come to be made in response to stimuli that through association have been substituted for the original processes inducing movement. When I see my handkerchief on the floor I do not need to think beforehand of what stooping and picking it up will feel like; the sight of that object in that position sets off the appropriate movement directly. When the soldier hears the command "Halt!" he does not first think of stopping; the sound stops him. But the important consideration is not what conditions determine old movements, movements that have been many times performed by the individual. The superiority of an animal consists largely in its power to learn new movements rapidly. And whenever we ourselves learn really new movements, we find that an essential part of the process is the presence of a movement idea in the focus of attention.

Such processes as those involved in learning the typewriter, in learning to play golf, in acquiring any new set of muscular adjustments, certainly involve calling up in the form of ideas the sensory experiences obtained from actually moving. We have to "think" where the fingers must go, how the arms must swing; the trainer who instructs us puts forth every effort to suggest to us the proper look and feel of the movements themselves. He must, of course, in so doing recall to us the ideas of the movements already familiar to us which are most nearly similar to the required new ones. Where nothing similar can be found, the training is likely to fail. The difficulty experienced by an average human being in learning to move his ears consists essentially in the fact that, never having done anything remotely similar to moving his ears, he has no movement idea to call up. He cannot move them because he cannot "imagine" how it would feel to move them.

Thus the power to attend to a memory idea of the sensations formerly involved in the performance of a movement is a very important factor in the rapid acquisition of new movements. And one reason why the lower animals in general learn new movements but slowly may be connected with a

lack of development of the power to attend to movement
ideas. For the slight development of this power in most of
the lower animals there is at least one obvious reason. The
life of an animal in natural conditions demands that its
attention shall be constantly directed outward. It is en-
gaged in continual watchfulness for food and enemies. The
stimuli which come to it from external objects demand all
its mental energies; the successful animal is the wide-awake,
alert animal. How can it, with every available avenue of
sense wide open to the external world, with every unit of
mental capital invested in watching and listening and smell-
ing, spare any mental energy to attend to the sensations from
its own movements? It sees the prey, it makes an elaborate
series of movements in response to the sight; but if it were to
attend for one instant to the sensations from the movements
themselves, there would be a relaxation of its watchfulness
of external things that might mean the escape of the prey.
But unless it attends to the sensations resulting from movement, it will not reproduce them in idea. That which is
unattended to when originally experienced is ordinarily not
recalled.

It would thus seem as though one condition which must be
fulfilled if movement ideas are to play an important part in a
creature's experience were that the animal should, for a time
at least, be set free from the pressure of the practical hand-to-
hand struggle for the means of existence, and thus enabled
in safety to attend to its own movement sensations. Animal
play, at first thought, offers an instance of such liberation
from practical necessities. But as Groos has shown, animal
play is not so unpractical as it looks (154). It is simply the
exercise of the same instincts upon which in other circumstances the animal's welfare depends. The attention is
absorbed in external objects quite as much in play as in

the actual chase or warfare. The kitten watches the string, for which she has no practical use, as intently as she watches the bird for which she does have a practical use; the dogs rolling over and over each other are nearly as absorbed in each other's movements as if they were in deadly combat.

That relief from practical necessity which will serve the purpose we are considering is to be found not in play, but in infancy. If a creature spends the period during which its nervous system is undergoing most rapid development in a state of complete shelter and protection from external danger, with all its vital needs supplied, then the nervous energy which under other conditions would be expended in the processes underlying attention to external stimuli is free to be so devoted that attention will be directed toward the creature's inner experiences. The human baby, while he may be interested in lights and sounds, in external impressions, does not need to be alert and watchful lest he miss his dinner or be dined on himself; his attention is free to be expended on his own movement experiences as well as on anything else. That young children do go through a stage of intense interest in the sensations resulting from their own movements is a fact made clear from many observations. The curious period of "self-imitation" in the child when it repeats for an indefinite period the same movement or sound, over and over again (8), is very likely a period of vivid attention to movement sensations; and just as the movement will take place if we attend exclusively to the idea of it, so here the child's developed attention to the sensations resulting from the movement reinstates the movement itself.

That the prolonged period of human infancy is of advantage to the intellectual life of man because it means plasticity, the absence of fixed instincts that would take the place of acquisition by individual experience, was first pointed out by

Fiske (126). But quite as important is the fact that in prolonged infancy we have the opportunity for acquiring the habit of that attention to our own movements which is the prerequisite for the movement idea. There are, as we have seen, various ways of learning by experience — slow ways that do not involve ideas, and the rapid way that does. The great advantage of man over most of the lower animals is not so much in the fact as in the method of his learning. One of the most vital meanings of the long period of helplessness and dependence constituting human infancy lies in the fact that by relieving from the necessity of attending exclusively to external objects, it renders possible attention to the sensations resulting from movement; and thus, by supplying an essential condition for the revival of such sensations in idea, it opens the way for the control of movement through the movement idea.

CHAPTER XIII

Some Aspects of Attention

THE student absorbed in reading "does not hear" an approaching footstep. That is, a stimulus which would under other circumstances produce an effect loses a great part of its influence because of the fact that another stimulus is already upon the field. This other stimulus need not be more intense, that is, need not involve more physical energy, than the one which is gnored. It does not win the victory by a mere swamping of its rival through its superior quantity. A man may walk along city streets, his eyes and ears bombarded with brilliant lights and loud sounds, and yet the centre of his consciousness may be a train of ideas, representing in their physical accompaniment in his cortex a quantity of energy insignificant compared with that of the external stimuli pouring in upon him. Psychologists commonly express this fact by saying that while the strength of a stimulus conditions the intensity of the mental process accompanying it, the *clearness* of that process depends upon *attention*.

§ 96. *The Interference of Stimuli*

Attention, then, is the name given to a device, whatever its nature, whereby one stimulus has its effectiveness increased over that of another whose physical energy may be greater. What happens in the simpler forms of animal life when two stimuli, requiring different reactions, operate simultaneously? We may quote from Jennings the facts about Paramecium. "If the animal is at rest against a mass of vegetable matter or a bit of paper, . . . and it is then struck with the tip of a glass rod, we find that at first it may not react to the latter stimulus at all." "A strong blow on the anterior end causes the animal to leave the solid and give the typical avoiding reaction." "If specimens showing the contact reaction are heated, it is found that they do not react to the heat until a higher temperature is reached than that necessary to cause a definite reaction in free-swimming specimens." "On the other hand, both heat and cold interfere with the contact reaction. Paramecia much above or much below the usual temperature do not settle against solids with which they come in contact, but respond instead by a pronounced avoiding reaction." "Specimens in contact with a solid react less readily to chemicals than do free specimens. . . . On the other hand, immersion in strong chemicals prevents the positive contact reaction." "The contact reaction may completely prevent the reaction to gravity," and to water currents. It also modifies the reaction to the electric current. While a part of the influence exerted by the contact reaction on other responses may be purely physical, due to the fact that an actual secretion of mucus may occur whereby the animal "sticks fast" to the solid, yet this alone does not explain the facts, for the cilia that are not attached do not behave normally. The reaction to gravity regularly yields whenever opposed to the action of any other stimulus (211, pp. 92 ff.).

Sometimes the action of one form of stimulation merely affects the form of the response to another, as in the case where abnormal temperature causes the avoiding instead of the positive reaction to be given to solids. In other cases, reaction to one of the stimuli is suppressed or weakened. The facts suggest that the influential stimulus is either the *one that is on the field first* (the contact reaction may prevent response to temperature, or abnormal temperature may modify the contact reaction), or the *one that is the more important* (gravity yields always to other stimuli).

In some higher animals the effects of interference of stimuli have been noted. The earthworm will not respond to light if feeding (91) or mating (179). In the turbellarian *Convoluta roscoffensis* light is victorious over heat in determining reaction. The animals in their positively phototropic phase will remain in the heated light end of a vessel until they perish. Light and gravity are more nearly balanced in their effects. Convoluta is negatively geotropic, yet if the brightest region is below the surface, the animals will go there. But if this region is only a little brighter than the surface, they will stay at the surface, gravity dominating (140). The sea urchin shows in its behavior a somewhat similar relation between mechanical and chemical stimulation. If weak acid is dropped into the water containing specimens of Arbacia, their spines begin to interlace. A slight shaking will restore them to the normal position, but if more acid be added, no mechanical stimulation will overcome the effect of the chemical (409). Various facts concerning the interrelations of gravity and light as stimuli have been noted in Chapter IX. A very interesting case of the suppression of one reaction by another is reported by Holmes in his observations on the water insect Ranatra. The positive response of this insect to light, very precise and striking, may be wholly suspended when the animal is feeding, when a number of individuals are collected, when the insect stops to clean itself, or even "by the sudden appearance of a large object in the field of vision," behavior which is strongly suggestive of the "distraction of attention" in a human being (186). Roubaud, in a study of the behavior of some species of flies that live on the seashore, feeding on dead fish and the like, says that they will abandon the "head-on" position which they regularly assume toward the wind, if attracted by the odor of food (370).

Wherever we find that one class of stimuli regularly yields to another if the two act together, it is safe to assume that the prepotent stimulus is more important to the organism's welfare than the vanquished one. And while we cannot without more ado call such cases of the interference of stimuli as are found in very simple animals cases of attention, and ascribe to their psychic accompaniments all the characteristics of attention as a feature of our own experience, yet we may assert that they have in common with attention the significance of being *a device to secure reaction to the most vitally important of several stimuli acting at once upon the organism.*

§ 97. *Methods of securing Prepotency of vitally Important Stimuli*

An inanimate object acted upon by several forces at once is determined in its motion by their relative intensity. Conceivably, an extremely simple form of animal life, when subjected to two stimulations acting together, would also respond in a way answering precisely to the relative strength of the two. It is easy to see what would be the disadvantage of such a state of affairs for the animal. The weaker of the two stimuli might be of far greater significance for organic welfare than the stronger. For example, it would often be important that an animal should be able to respond to a very faint food stimulus rather than to any of the stronger forces acting upon it. Evidently a prime need of animal life is some arrangement whereby weak but important stimuli shall be given the preference in determining reaction over stronger but less vitally necessary ones. *Sense organs* are one such device. The comparatively slight amount of chemical energy coming from a bit of food may have its effectiveness for the nervous system greatly increased through its reception by a structure adapted to use the whole of it to advantage. Light stimulation involves a quantity of energy that is insignificant in comparison with the grosser forces acting on an organism; yet falling on the retina, the energy is economized and magnified through the stored-up chemical forces it sets free. Thus a weak stimulus may by a sense organ be made powerful to determine reaction. Another arrangement to the same effect is the peculiarity of the nervous system whereby, through an arrangement akin to the summation of faint stimuli, *a moving stimulus*, one acting successively upon neighbor ng points of a sensitive surface, *produces an effect disproportionate to its intensity*. A moving stimulus is a vitally important stimulus; it means life, and hence may mean food or danger. The response to it is in most cases adapted rather to its importance than to its physical strength   A third arrangement for the securing of reaction to vitally important stimulation lies in the existence of *preformed connections* in the nervous system, which bring it about that the *path of the excitation produced by one stimulus is clear to the motor apparatus*, while that of another is closed. Reactions of this sort we call instinctive. The nesting bird responds to the sight of building material rather than to that of objects offering equally strong stimulation to the optic nerve; the cat sits at the mouse hole, the parent animal responds to the faintest cry of the offspring, because these stimuli have the right of way by virtue of inherited nervous connections.

Finally, a weak stimulus may determine reaction and be victorious over a stronger one because of *nervous pathways formed throught he individual's own experience*. The conse-

U

quences of reaction to it in the individual's past may operate to secure reaction to it in the future. To the cat in a puzzle box, the string that must be pulled to let it out offered originally no stronger stimulus to action than any other object in sight; but after sufficient experience the string comes to dominate the situation and determine the cat's behavior. If the experience of consequences is slowly acquired, by many repetitions, the process of reacting to an object originally indifferent may be unaccompanied by any ideas of the consequences of such reaction. If it is rapidly acquired, we know that we human beings at least accompany our reactions by calling up the results of our past reactions in the form of memory ideas.

§ 98. *The Peculiar Characteristics of Attention as a Device to secure Prepotency*

We have suggested that attention is a means of securing reaction to the vitally important stimuli acting upon an organism. Does reaction to a stimulus always mean attention to the sensation accompanying that stimulus?

This question may best be answered by examining the characteristics of the attention process as we know it. In attention, the details of the object attended to become clear and distinct. That is, attention is a state where discrimination is improved. Further, attention involves varying degrees of effort, and these are marked by varying intensity of certain bodily processes. Attention under difficulties is accompanied by a rigid position of the body, by holding the breath, and by various muscular effects, aside from the processes which, like frowning, are concerned with the adaptation of the sense organ to receive an impression. These general bodily effects of attention are all such as to suggest that the body is to be kept as quiet as possible during the attentive state. In other words, no reaction is to be made to the object attended to except such as may be necessary to allow its being carefully discriminated from other objects. *Attention, in its intenser degrees, at least, seems to involve a state of suspended reaction.*

Not every case, then, of response adapted to the vital importance of a stimulus is a case that suggests as its psychic aspect attention to the accompanying sensation. When, for example, a reaction of especial speed is made to contact with a moving stimulus, the speed of the reaction would itself indicate that the sensations produced are not attended to. The proper situation for attention would be the situation in which the reaction needs to be suspended until the stimulus is fully discriminated. Now such careful discrimination does not appear to be characteristic of reactions that are largely based on inherited nervous structures. Many facts concerning the instincts of animals, that is, their inherited reactions, indicate that these are extremely rough adjustments of behavior to environment until refined by individual experience. Hudson observed, for example, that newly born lambs on the South American plains had a tendency to run away from any object that approached them, and to follow any object that receded from them. They would follow his horse for miles as he rode along, and would run away from their own mothers when the latter moved toward them. He explained this as adapted to the fact that ordinarily their first duty, on making their appearance in the world, is to keep up with the receding herd, while an approaching object is more likely to be an enemy (188). Later, this rough adjustment is modified; they learn by experience not to run away from their mothers, and not to follow indiscriminately any leader.

If it is true that instinct unmodified by experience is

adapted to general rather than to special features of environment, it seems likely that the phenomena of attention as we know them are found chiefly in connection with those responses to vitally important stimulation which are determined, in part, at least, by the individual experience of the reacting animal, for these are the responses requiring most careful discrimination among stimuli, and the delay of reaction until such discrimination has been made.[1] Putting the matter in a slightly different way, we may say that purely inherited responses can be adapted only to certain broad, roughly distinguished classes of stimuli, for these alone are common to the experience of all members of the species. Nothing but individual experience can bring to light the importance for welfare of certain particular stimuli, for the significance of these would vary with the experience of each individual animal. Among the lower animals, attention probably reaches its highest pitch where the response most needs to be suspended in order that the stimulus may be fully discriminated. The rabbit or wild bird crouching motionless close to the ground, watching each movement of a possible enemy, suggests strongly to our minds a condition of breathless attention. Whether such an interpretation is the true one depends very much, I should say, on the extent to which past individual experience has refined the animal's powers of discrimination. Mere "freezing to the spot" may be an inherited reaction, useful in time of danger, but more anal-

---

[1] In this connection Franz's recent experimental demonstration that the frontal lobes, long regarded as the seat of the neural processes underlying attention, are concerned in the functioning of recently learned reactions, is of especial interest. Franz found that cats and monkeys which had been trained to work mechanisms lost the power to do so when the frontal lobes were extirpated, although habits of older date, such as responding to a call, were preserved (136, 136 a).

ogous in its psychic aspect to the blank emptiness of the hypnotic trance than to alert, watchful attention.

Yet although, in so far as attention is a state favoring discrimination of stimuli, it is involved in that part of an animal's behavior which is derived from individual experience, since pure instinct discriminates but roughly; in so far as it is still one of the devices for securing reaction to stimuli of vital importance, its root must lie in instinct. No object wholly unrelated to some fundamental instinct can hope to secure attention, for the great classes of vitally important stimuli have all of them preformed paths in the nervous system by which their reactions are secured. What individual experience does is to refine upon the adaptations which instinct makes possible; to bring about the connection of certain stimuli, originally indifferent, with the performance of an instinctive response, or to produce a checking of the instinctive response when certain individual peculiarities of a stimulus that would otherwise call it forth become evident. For instance, an animal learns by experience to come at the call of a human being who feeds it; the sound, originally without effect on its reactions, has come to be connected with the nervous mechanism of an instinct. The chick pecking at small objects on the ground learns by experience to inhibit this instinctive response with reference to objects having certain peculiarities originally undiscriminated, but now in some way emphasized through painful circumstances accompanying his previous encounter with them.

The most fundamental characteristic of attention, then, is perhaps that aspect of it which has been called *abstraction*, the diminished effectiveness of stimuli not attended to. By virtue of this aspect we recognize that attention belongs with instinct as being concerned in securing the prepotency of vitally important stimulation. On the other hand, the further characteristic of attention, namely, that it is a state of suspended reaction involving careful discrimination of stimuli, suggests that its functioning is connected rather with the refining and modifying influence of individual experience acting on instinct, since here alone do we find delayed reaction and accurate stimulus discrimination.

The highest grade of attention, the final triumph of vital importance over mere intensity of stimulation, is to be found where the focus of attention is occupied by an idea or train of ideas. When a process purely centrally excited holds the field and makes the individual deaf and blind to powerful external stimuli pouring in upon his sense organs, then he is superior to the immediate environment at least. This form of attention occurs, probably, only when the vital importance of the idea attended to has been learned through that most rapid form of individual acquisition of experience which involves the revival of the past in idea. It has been called derived attention. The ideas attended to are held in the focus of consciousness and analyzed through the power of associated ideas. The inventor holds to his problem, the student to his task, in spite of distractions, because of the consequences which he thinks of as likely to result. It seems unlikely that attention in this final form occurs among the lower animals. While ideas are probably present to some extent in the minds of the higher mammals, they are hardly so far freed from connection with external stimuli that the animal can shut out the world of sense from its consciousness and dwell in a world of ideas.

BIBLIOGRAPHY

The following is a list of the books and articles consulted in the preparation of this work. Not all of them are cited in the text.

1. ADAMS, G. P., 1903. On the negative and positive phototropism of the earthworm, *Allolobophora fœtida*, as determined by light of different intensities. Am. Jour. Physiol., vol. 9, p. 26.

2. ADERHOLD, R., 1888. Beitrag zur Kenntniss richtender Kräfte bei der Bewegungen niederer Organismen. Jena. Zeitschr. f. Naturwiss., Bd. 22, S. 310.

3. ALLABACH, L. F., 1905. Some points regarding the behavior of Metridium. Biol. Bull., vol. 10, p. 35.

4. ALLEN, J., 1904. . The associative processes of the guinea-pig. Jour. Comp. Neur. and Psych., vol. 14, p. 293.

5. ANDREÆ, E., 1903. Inwiefern werden Insekten durch Farbe u. Duft der Blumen angezogen? Beihefte z. botan. Zentralblatt, Bd. 15, S. 427.

6. AXENFELD, D., 1896. Die Röntgenschen Strahlen dem Insektenauge sichtbar. Cent. f. Physiol., Bd. 10, S. 436.

7. —— 1899. Quelques observations sur la vue des arthropodes. Arch. ital. biol., t. 31, p. 370.

8. BALDWIN, J. M., 1894. Mental development: methods and processes. New York.

9. BARDEEN, C. R., 1901. Physiology of *Planaria maculata*. Am. Jour. Physiol., vol. 5, p. 1.

10. —— 1901. Function of the brain in *Planaria maculata*. Ibid., vol. 5, p. 175.

11. BATESON, W., 1887. Notes on the senses and habits of some crustacea. Jour. Mar. Biol. Assoc. United Kingdom, vol. 1, p. 211.

12. —— 1887. On the sense-organs and perceptions of fishes. Ibid., vol. 1, p. 225.

13. BEER, TH., 1892. Die Accommodation des Vogelauges. Pflügers Arch., Bd. 53, S. 175.

14. BEER, TH., 1894. Die Accommodation des Fischauges. Ibid., Bd. 58, S. 523.

15. —— 1897. Die Accommodation des Kephalopodenauges. Ibid., Bd. 67, S. 541.

16. —— 1898. Die Accommodation des Auges bei den Reptilien. Ibid., Bd. 69, S. 507.

17. —— 1898. Vergleichend-physiologische Studien zur Statocysten-Function, I. Ueber den angeblichen Gehörsinn u. das angebliche Gehörorgan der Crustaceen. Ibid., Bd. 73, S. 1.

18. —— 1898. Die Accommodation des Auges bei den Amphibien. Ibid., Bd. 73, S. 501.

19. —— 1899. Vergleichend-physiologische Studien u. s. w., II. Versuche an Crustaceen. Ibid., Bd. 74, S. 364.

20. BEER, TH., BETHE, A., u. VON UEXKÜLL, J., 1899. Vorschläge z. einer objektivirender Nomenclatur in der Physiologie des Nervensystems. Biol. Cent., Bd. 19, S. 517.

21. BELL, J. C., 1906. The reactions of the crayfish. Harvard Psych. Studies, vol. 2, p. 615.

22. —— 1906. The reactions of the crayfish to chemical stimuli. Jour. Comp. Neur. and Psych., vol. 16, p. 299.

23. BENTLEY, I. M., 1899. The memory image and its qualitative fidelity. Am. Jour. Psych., vol. 11, p. 1.

24. BERT, P., 1869. Sur la question de savoir si tous les animaux voient les mêmes rayons que nous. Arch. de physiol., t. 2, p. 547.

25. BERTKAU, P., 1885. Ueber die Augen u. ein als Gehörorgan gedeutetes Organ der Spinnen. Sitzungsber. d. niederrhein. Gesellsch., Bd. 42, S. 218, 282.

26. BERRY, C. S., 1906. The imitative tendencies of white rats. Jour. Comp. Neur. and Psych., vol. 16, p. 333.

27. BETHE, A., 1894. Ueber die Erhaltung des Gleichgewichtes. Biol. Cent., Bd. 14, S. 95.

28. —— 1898. Das Centralnervensystem von *Carcinus moenas*, II. Arch. f. mikr. Anat., Bd. 51, S. 447.

29. —— 1898. Die anatomische Elemente des Nervensystems u. ihre physiologische Bedeutung. Biol. Cent., Bd. 18, S. 843.

30. BETHE, A., 1898. Dürfen wir den Ameisen u. Bienen psych-ische Qualitäten zuschreiben? Pflügers Arch., Bd. 70, S. 15.

31. —— 1900. Noch einmal über d. psychischen Qualitäten der Ameisen. Ibid., Bd. 79, S. 39.

32. —— 1902. Die Heimkehrfähigkeit der Ameisen u. Bienen. Biol. Cent., Bd. 22, S. 193, 234.

33. BIGELOW, H. B., 1904. The sense of hearing in the goldfish, *Carassius auratus*. Am. Nat., vol. 38, p. 275.

34. BINET, A., 1894. The psychic life of micro-organisms. Authorized translation. Chicago.

35. BOHN, G., 1902. Contributions à la psychologie des anné-lides. Bull. Inst. gén. psych., Paris, t. 2, p. 317.

36. —— 1903. Observations biologiques sur les arénicoles. Bull. Mus. d'hist. nat., t. 9, p. 62.

37. —— 1903. Sur les mouvements oscillatoires des *Convoluta roscoffensis*. C. r. Acad. Sci., Paris, t. 137, p. 576.

38. —— 1903. Les *Convoluta roscoffensis* et la théorie des causes actuelles. Bull. Mus. d'hist. nat., t. 9, p. 352.

39. —— 1903. Actions tropiques de la lumière. C. r. Soc. Biol., Paris, t. 55, p. 1440.

40. —— 1903. Sur la phototropisme des artiozoaires supérieurs. C. r. Acad. Sci., Paris, t. 137, p. 1292.

41. —— 1903. De l'évolution des connaissances chez les ani-maux marins littoraux, I. Les crustacés. Bull. Inst. gén. psych., Paris, t. 3, p. 590.

42. —— 1904. Coopération, hiérarchisation, intégration des sensations chez les artiozoaires. C. r. Acad. Sci., Paris, t. 138, p. 112.

43. —— 1904. Intervention des influences passées dans les mouvements actuels d'un animal. C. r. Soc. Biol., Paris, t. 56, p. 789.

44. —— 1904. Les premières lueurs de l'intelligence. Bull. Inst. gén. psych., Paris, t. 4, p. 419.

45. —— 1904. Periodicité vitale des animaux soumis aux oscillations du niveau des hautes mers. C. r. Acad. Sci., Paris, t. 139, p. 610.

46. —— 1904. Oscillations des animaux littoraux synchrones des mouvements de la marée. Ibid., t. 139, p. 646.

47. Bohn, G., 1904. Mouvements de manège en rapport avec les mouvements de la marée. C. r. Soc. Biol., Paris, t. 57, p. 297.

48. —— 1904. Attractions et répulsions dans un champ lumineux. Ibid., t. 57, p. 315.

49. —— 1904. Influence de la position de l'animal dans l'espace sur les tropismes. Ibid., t. 57, p. 351.

50. —— 1904. L'anhydrobiose et les tropismes. C. r. Acad. Sci., Paris, t. 139, p. 809.

51. —— 1904. Théorie nouvelle du phototropisme. Ibid., t. 139, p. 890.

52. —— 1905. Les réceptions oculaires. Bull. Inst. gén. psych., Paris, t. 5, p. 171.

53. —— 1905. Les causes actuelles et les causes passées. Rev. scient., t. 3, pp. 353, 389.

54. —— 1905. Mouvements rotatoires d'origine oculaire. C. r. Soc. Biol., Paris, t. 58, p. 714.

55. —— 1905. Attractions et oscillations des animaux marins sous l'influence de la lumière. Mémoires Inst. gén. psych., Paris, vol. 1, p. 110.

56. —— 1905. Des tropismes et des états physiologiques. C. r. Soc. Biol., Paris, t. 59, p. 515.

57. —— 1905. L'éclairement des yeux et les mouvements rotatoires. Essais et erreurs dans les tropismes. Ibid., t. 59, p. 564.

58. —— 1905. Impulsions motrices d'origine oculaire chez les crustacés. Bull. Inst. gén. psych., Paris, t. 5, p. 42.

59. —— 1906. Les tropismes, les réflexes, et l'intelligence. L'année psych., t. 12, p. 137.

60. —— 1906. Sur les courbures dues à la lumière. C. r. Soc. Biol., Paris, t. 61, p. 420.

61. —— 1906. Sur les mouvements de roulement influencés par la lumière. Ibid., t. 61, p. 468.

62. —— 1906. Mouvements en relation avec l'assimilation pigmentaire chez les animaux. Ibid., t. 61, p. 527.

63. —— 1907. L'influence de l'éclairement passé sur la matière vivante. Ibid., t. 62, p. 292.

64. —— 1906. Observations sur les papillons du rivage de la mer. Bull. Inst. gén. psych., Paris, t. 6, p. 285.

65. BOHN G., 1907. Le rhythme nycthéméral chez les actinies. C. r. Soc. Biol., Paris, t. 62, p. 473.

66. —— 1907. Les état physiologiques des actinies. Bull. Inst. gén. psych., Paris, t. 7, p. 81.

67. BONNIER, G., 1905. L'accoutumance des abeilles et la couleur des fleurs. C. r. Acad. Sci., Paris, t. 141, p. 988.

68. BOUVIER, E. L., 1901. Les habitudes de Bembex. L'année psych., t. 7, p. 1.

69. BOYS, C. V., 1880. The influence of a tuning fork on the garden spider. Nature, vol. 23, p. 149.

70. BREUER, J., 1891. Ueber die Function der Otolithen-Apparate. Pflügers Arch., Bd. 48, S. 195.

71. BUNTING, M., 1893. Ueber die Bedeutung der Otolithenorgane für d. geotropischen Functionen von *Astacus fluviatilis.* Ibid., Bd. 54, S. 531.

72. BUTTEL-REEPEN, H. VON, 1900. Sind die Bienen Reflexmaschine? Biol. Cent., Bd. 20, S. 97, 177, 209.

73. CALKINS, M. W., 1905. The limits of genetic and comparative psychology. British Jour. Psych., vol. 1, p. 261.

74. CARPENTER, F. W., 1905. Reactions of the pomace fly to light, heat, and mechanical stimulation. Am. Nat., vol. 39, p. 157.

75. CLAPARÈDE, E., 1901. Les animaux sont-ils conscients? Rev. phil., t. 51, p. 24. Trans. in Internat. Quart., vol. 8, p. 296.

76. —— 1903. La faculté d'orientation lointaine (Sens de direction, sens de retour). Arch. de psych., t. 2, p. 133.

77. —— 1905. La psychologie comparée est-elle légitime? Ibid., t. 5, p. 13.

78. CLARK, G. P., 1896. On the relation of the otocysts to equilibrium phenomena in *Gelasimus pugilator* and *Platyonichus ocellatus*. Jour. Physiol., vol. 19, p. 327.

79. COLE, L. J., 1901. Notes on the habits of pycnogonids. Biol. Bull., vol. 2, p. 195.

80. —— 1907. An experimental study of the image-forming powers of various types of eyes. Proc. Amer. Acad. Arts and Sciences, vol. 42, p. 335.

81. —— 1907. Influence of direction *vs.* intensity of light in determining the phototropic responses of organisms.

Abstract in Jour. Comp. Neur. and Psych., vol. 17, p. 193.

82. COLE, L. W., 1907. Concerning the intelligence of raccoons. Jour. Comp. Neur. and Psych., vol. 17, p. 211.

83. CONRADI, E., 1905. Song and call-notes of English sparrows when reared by canaries. Am. Jour. Psych., vol. 16, p. 190.

84. CUÉNOT, L., 1891. Études morphologiques sur les échinodermes. Arch. de biol., t. 11, p. 521.

85. CYON, E., 1878. Experimentelle Untersuchungen über die Function der halbzirkelförmigen Canäle. Bibl. de l'école des hautes études, section des sciences naturelles, t. 18.

86. DAHL, F., 1883. Ueber die Hörhaare bei den Arachnoiden. Zool. Anz., Bd. 6, S. 267.

87. —— 1885. Das Gehör- und Geruchsorgan der Spinnen. Arch. f. mikr. Anat., Bd. 24, S. 1.

88. —— 1885. Versuch einer Darstellung der psychischen Vorgänge in der Spinnen. Vierteljahr. f. wiss. Phil., Bd. 9, S. 84, 162.

89. DARWIN, C. R., 1874. Descent of man and selection in relation to sex. New York.

90. —— 1877. Effects of cross and self-fertilization in the vegetable kingdom. New York.

91. —— 1883. The formation of vegetable mould through the action of worms, with observations on their habits. New York.

92. DAVENPORT, C. B., 1897–1899. Experimental morphology. 2 vols., New York.

93. DAVENPORT, C. B., and CANNON, W. B., 1897. On the determination of the direction and rate of movement of organisms by light. Jour. Physiol., vol. 21, p. 22.

94. DAVENPORT, C. B., and LEWIS, F. T., 1899. Phototaxis of Daphnia. Science, N.S., vol. 9, p. 368.

95. DAVENPORT, C. B., and PERKINS, H., 1897. A contribution to the study of geotaxis in the higher animals. Jour. Physiol., vol. 22, p. 99.

96. DEARBORN, G. v. N., 1900. The individual psycho-physiology of the crayfish. Am. Jour. Physiol., vol. 3, p. 404.

97. DELAGE, Y., 1887. Sur une fonction nouvelle des otocystes comme organes d'orientation locomotrice. Arch. de zool. expér., IIe série, t. 5, p. 1.

98. DELLINGER, O. P., 1906. Locomotion of Amœbæ and allied forms. Jour. Ex. Zool., vol. 3, p. 337.

99. DESCARTES, R., 1640, 1649. The page references in the text are to the translation in Torrey's The philosophy of Descartes in extracts from his writings. N.Y., 1892.

100. DREW, G. A., 1906. The habits, anatomy, and embryology of the giant scallop, *Pecten tenuicostatus*. Univ. of Maine Studies, no. 6.

101. —— 1907. The habits and movements of the razor-shell clam. Biol. Bull., vol. 12, p. 127.

102. DUBOIS, R., 1889. Sur le mécanisme des fonctions photo-dermatiques et photogéniques dans le siphon du *Pholas dactylus*. C. r. Acad. Sci., Paris, t. 109, p. 233.

103. —— 1890. Sur la perception des radiations lumineuses par la peau chez les protées aveugles des grottes de la Carniole. Ibid., t. 110, p. 358.

104. —— 1890. Sur la physiologie comparée des sensations gustatives et tactiles. Ibid., t. 110, p. 473.

105. —— 1890. Sur la physiologie comparée de l'olfaction. Ibid., t. 111, p. 66.

106. EDINGER, L., 1899. Haben die Fische ein Gedächtniss? Allgemeine Zeitung, Beilage, Oct. 21 and 23. (Translation in Smithsonian Report, 1899, p. 375.)

107. EIGENMANN, C. H., 1899. The blind fishes. Biol. Lectures, Marine Biol. Lab., Wood's Hole, 1899, p. 113.

108. EMERY, C., 1893. Zirpende und springende Ameisen. Biol. Cent., Bd. 13, S. 189.

109. ENGELMANN, T. W., 1879. Ueber Reizung des contraktilen Protoplasmas durch plötzliche Beleuchtung. Pflügers Arch., Bd. 19, S. 1.

110. —— 1882. Ueber Licht- und Farbenperception niedersten Organismen. Ibid., Bd. 29, S. 387.

111. —— 1887. Ueber die Functionen der Otolithen. Zool. Anz., Bd. 10, S. 439.

112. ENTEMAN, M. M., 1902. On the behavior of social wasps. Pop. Sci. Mo., vol. 61, p. 339.

113. ESTERLY, C. O., 1907. Reactions of copepods to light and to gravity. Am. Jour. Physiol., vol. 18, p. 47.

114. EWALD, K., 1892. Physiologische Untersuchungen über das Endorgan des Nervus octavus. Wiesbaden.

115. FABRE, J. H., 1879–1904. Souvenirs entomologiques. 9 vols. Paris.

116. FERTON, C., 1905. Notes detaillées sur l'instinct des hymenoptères mellifères et ravisseurs. Ann. Soc. entom. France, t. 74, p. 56.

117. FIELDE, A. M., 1901. A study of an ant. Proc. Philadelphia Acad. Nat. Sci., vol. 53, p. 425.

118. —— 1901. Further study of an ant. Ibid., vol. 53, p. 521.

119. —— 1903. Supplementary notes on an ant. Ibid., vol. 55, p. 491.

120. —— 1903. Artificial mixed nests of ants. Biol. Bull., vol. 5, p. 320.

121. —— 1903. A cause of feud between ants of the same species living in different communities. Ibid., vol. 5, p. 326.

122. —— 1904. Observations on ants in relation to temperature and to submergence. Ibid., vol. 7, p. 170.

123. —— 1904. The power of recognition among ants. Ibid., vol. 7, p. 227.

124. —— 1905. The progressive odor of ants. Ibid., vol. 10, p. 1.

125. FIELDE, A. M., and PARKER, G. H., 1904. The reactions of ants to material vibrations. Proc. Philadelphia Acad. Nat. Sci., vol. 56, p. 642.

126. FISKE, J., 1874. Outlines of cosmic philosophy. 2 vols., Boston.

127. FLEURE, H. J., and WALTON, C. L., 1907. Notes on the habits of some sea-anemones. Zool. Anz., Bd. 31, S. 212.

128. FLOURENS, P., 1842. Récherches expérimentales sur les propriétés et les fonctions du système nerveux dans les animaux vertébrés. Paris.

129. FOREL, A., 1874. Les fourmis de la Suisse. Zurich.

130. —— 1888. Sur les sensations des insectes. Recueil zool. suisse, t. 4, no. 2.

131. —— 1900–1901. Sensations des insectes. Rivista di

biologia generale, vol. 2, pp. 561, 641; vol. 3, pp. 7, 241, 401.

132. FOREL, A., 1904. Ants and some other insects. Trans. by W. M. Wheeler. Chicago.

133. —— 1906. La mémoire du temps chez les abeilles. Bull. Inst. gén. psych., Paris, t. 6, p. 258.

134. FOREL, A., and DUFOUR, H., 1902. Ueber die Empfindlichkeit der Ameisen für ultraviolett und Röntgensche Strahlen. Zool. Jahrbuch, Abth. f. Systematik, Bd. 17, S. 335.

135. FRANDSEN, P., 1901. Studies on the reactions of *Limax maximus* to directive stimuli. Proc. Amer. Acad. Arts and Sciences, vol. 37, p. 185.

136. FRANZ, S. I., 1906. Observations on the functions of the association areas (cerebrum) in monkeys. Jour. Am. Med. Assoc., vol. 47, p. 1464.

136a. —— 1907. On the functions of the cerebrum : the frontal lobes. Arch. of Psych., no. 2.

137. FRÖHLICH, A., 1904. Studien über die Statozysten wirbelloser Tiere, I. Versuche an Cephalopoden, und Einschlägiges aus der menschlichen Pathologie. Pflügers Arch., Bd. 102, S. 415.

138. —— 1904. Studien u. s. w., II. Versuche an Krebsen. Ibid., Bd. 103, S. 149.

139. —— 1905. Ueber den Einfluss der Zerstörung des Labyrinthes beim Seepferdchen, nebst einigen Bemerkungen über das Schwimmen dieser Tiere. Ibid., Bd. 106, S. 84.

140. GAMBLE, F. W., and KEEBLE, F., 1903. The bionomics of *Convoluta roscoffensis*, with special reference to its green cells. Quar. Jour. Micr. Sci., vol. 47, p. 363.

141. GARREY, W. E., 1905. A sight reflex shown by sticklebacks. Biol. Bull., vol. 8, p. 79.

142. GAUBERT, P., 1892. Récherches sur les organes des sens et sur les systèmes intégumentaires, glandulaires, et musculaires des appendices des Arachnides. Ann. des Sci. nat., 7e série, Zool., t. 13, p. 31.

143. GHINST, VAN DER, 1906. Quelques observations sur les actinies. Bull. Inst. gén. psych., Paris, t. 6, p. 267.

144. GILTAY, E., 1904. Ueber die Bedeutung der Krone bei den

Bluten u. über das Farbenunterschiedungsvermögen der Insekten, I. Jahrb. f. wiss. Bot., Bd. 40, S. 368.

145. GLASER, O. C., 1907. Movement and problem solving in *Ophiura brevispina*. Jour. Exp. Zool., vol. 4, p. 203.

146. GOLDSMITH, M., 1905. Récherches sur la psychologie de quelques poissons littoraux. Bull. Inst. gén. psych., Paris, t. 5, p. 51.

147. GOLTZ, F., 1870. Ueber die physiologische Bedeutung der Bogengänge des Ohrlabyrinthes. Pflügers Arch., Bd. 3, S. 172.

148. GRABER, V., 1882. Die chordotonalen Sinnesorgane u. das Gehör der Insekten, I. Arch. f. mikr. Anat., Bd. 20, S. 506.

149. —— 1883. Die chordotonalen u. s. w., II. Ibid., Bd. 21, S. 65.

150. —— 1883. Fundamentalversuche über d. Helligkeits- u. Farbenempfindlichkeit augenloser u. geblendeter Thiere. Sitzungsber. d. kais. Akad. d. Wiss., Wien, math.-naturwiss. Klasse, Bd. 87, Abth. 1, S. 201.

151. —— 1884. Grundlinien zur Erforschung des Helligkeits- und Farbensinns der Thiere. Prag und Leipzig.

152. —— 1889. Ueber die Empfindlichkeit einiger Meerthiere gegen Riechstoffe. Biol. Cent., Bd. 8, S. 743.

153. GROOM, T. T., and LOEB, J., 1890. Der Heliotropismus der Nauplius von *Balanus perforatus* und die periodischen Tiefenwanderungen pelagischer Tiere. Ibid., Bd. 10, S. 160.

154. GROOS, K., 1898. The play of animals. Trans. by E. L. Baldwin. New York.

155. GURLEY, 1902. The habits of fishes. Am. Jour. Psych., vol. 13, p. 408.

156. HACHET-SOUPLET, P., 1900. Examen psychologique des animaux. Paris.

157. HANDL, A., 1887. Ueber d. Farbensinns der Thiere u. die Vertheilung der Energie im Spektrum. Sitzungsber. d. kais. Akad. d. Wiss., Wien, math.-naturwiss. Klasse, Bd. 94, S. 935.

158. HARGITT, C. W., 1906. Experiments on the behavior of tubicolous annelids. Jour. Exp. Zool., vol. 3, p. 295.

159. HARGITT, C. W., 1907. Further observations on the behavior of tubicolous annelids. Abstract in Jour. Comp. Neur. and Psych., vol. 17, p. 199.

160. —— 1907. Notes on the behavior of sea-anemones. Biol. Bull., vol. 12, p. 274.

161. HARPER, E. H., 1905. Reactions to light and mechanical stimulation in the earthworm, *Perichaeta bermudensis*. Ibid., vol. 10, p. 17.

162. HARRINGTON, N. R., and LEAMING, E., 1899. The reaction of Amœba to lights of different colours. Am. Jour. Physiol., vol. 3, p. 9.

163. HENSEN, V., 1863. Studien über das Gehörorgan der Decapoden. Zeit. f. wiss. Zool., Bd. 13, S. 319.

164. —— 1899. Wie steht es mit der Statozysten-Hypothese? Pflügers Arch., Bd. 74, S. 22.

165. HERRICK, C. J., 1903. The organ and sense of taste in fishes. Bull. U.S. Fish Comm., vol. 22, p. 237.

166. HERRICK, F. H., 1895. The American lobster. Ibid., vol. 15, p. 1.

167. HERTEL, E., 1904. Ueber Beeinflussung des Organismus durch Licht, speziell durch die chemisch wirksamer Strahlen. Zeit. f. allg. Physiol., Bd. 4, S. 1.

168. HESSE, R., 1896. Untersuchungen über die Organe der Lichtempfindungen bei niederen Thieren, I. Die Organe der Lichtempfindungen bei den Lumbriciden. Zeit. f. wiss. Zool., Bd. 61, S. 393.

169. —— 1897. Untersuchungen u. s. w., II. Die Augen der Platyhelminthen, insonderheit der tricladen Turbellarien. Ibid., Bd. 62, S. 549.

170. —— 1897. Untersuchungen u. s. w., III. Die Sehorgane der Hirudineen. Ibid., Bd. 62, S. 671.

171. —— 1898. Die Lichtempfindung des Amphioxus. Anat. Anz., Bd. 14, S. 556.

172. —— 1898. Untersuchungen u. s. w., IV. Die Sehorgane des Amphioxus. Zeit. f. wiss. Zool., Bd. 63, S. 456.

173. —— 1899. Untersuchungen u. s. w., V. Die Augen der polychäten Anneliden. Ibid., Bd. 65, S. 506.

174. —— 1900. Untersuchungen u. s. w., VI. Die Augen einiger Mollusken. Ibid., Bd. 68, S. 379.

x

175. HESSE, R., 1901. Untersuchungen u. s. w., VII. Von den Arthropodenaugen. Ibid., Bd. 70, S. 347.

176. —— 1902. Untersuchungen u. s. w., VIII. Weitere Thatsachen. Allgemeines. Ibid., Bd. 72, S. 565.

177. HOBHOUSE, L. T., 1901. Mind in evolution. London.

178. HODGE, C. F., and AIKINS, H. A., 1895. The daily life of a protozoan. Am. Jour. Psych., vol. 6, p. 524.

179. HOFFMEISTER, W., 1845. Die bis jetzt bekannten Arten aus der Familie der Regenwürmer. Braunschweig.

180. HOLMES, S. J., 1900. Habits of *Amphithoe longimana* Smith. Biol. Bull., vol. 2, p. 165.

181. —— 1901. Phototaxis in Amphipoda. Am. Jour. Physiol., vol. 5, p. 211.

182. —— 1902. Observations on the habits of *Hyallella dentata*. Science, N.S., vol. 15, p. 529.

183. —— 1903. Phototaxis in Volvox. Biol. Bull., vol. 4, p. 319.

184. —— 1903. Sex recognition among amphipods. Ibid., vol. 5, p. 288.

185. —— 1905. The selection of random movements as a factor in phototaxis. Jour. Comp. Neur. Psych., vol. 15, p. 98.

186. —— 1905. The reactions of Ranatra to light. Ibid., vol. 15, p. 305.

187. HOLT, E. B., and LEE, F. S., 1901. The theory of phototactic response. Am. Jour. Physiol., vol. 4, p. 460.

188. HUDSON, W. H., 1895. The naturalist in La Plata. London.

189. JAMES, W., 1890. The principles of psychology. 2 vols. New York.

190. JANET, C., 1893. Note sur la production des sons chez les fourmis et sur les organes qui les produisent. Ann. Soc. ent. France, t. 62, p. 159.

191. —— 1894. Sur les nerfs de l'antenne et les organes chordotonaux chez les fourmis. C. r. Acad. Sci., Paris, t. 118, p. 814.

192. —— 1893–1905. Les fourmis, les guêpes et les abeilles. Paris.

193. JENNINGS, H. S., 1897. Studies on reactions to stimuli in unicellular organisms, I. Reactions to chemical, os-

motic, and mechanical stimuli in the ciliate protozoa.
Jour. Physiol., vol. 21, p. 258.

194. —— JENNINGS, H. S., 1899. Studies, etc., II. The
mechanism of the motor reactions of Paramecium. Am.
Jour. Physiol., vol. 2, p. 311.

195. —— 1899. Studies, etc., III. Reactions to localized stimuli
in Spirostomum and Stentor. Am. Nat., vol. 33, p. 373.

196. —— 1899. The behavior of unicellular organisms. Biol.
lectures, Marine Biol. Lab., Wood's Hole, 1899, p. 93.

197. —— 1899. The psychology of a protozoan. Am. Jour.
Psych., vol. 10, p. 503.

198. —— 1899. Studies, etc., IV. Laws of chemotaxis in
Paramecium. Am. Jour. Physiol., vol. 2, p. 355.

199. —— 1900. Studies, etc., V. On the movements and motor
reflexes of the flagellata and ciliata. Ibid., vol. 3, p. 229.

200. —— 1900. Reactions of infusoria to chemicals: a criticism. Am. Nat., vol. 34, p. 259.

201. —— 1900. Studies, etc., VI. On the reactions of Chilo-
monas to organic acids. Am. Jour. Physiol., vol. 3, p. 397.

202. —— 1902. Artificial imitations of protoplasmic activities
and methods of demonstrating them. Jour. Applied
Micros., vol. 5, p. 1597.

203. —— 1902. Studies, etc., IX. On the behavior of fixed
infusoria (Stentor and Vorticella) with special reference
to the modifiability of protozoan reactions. Am. Jour.
Physiol., vol. 8, p. 23.

204. —— 1904. Physical imitations of the activities of Amœba.
Am. Nat., vol. 38, p. 625.

205. —— 1904. The behavior of Paramecium. Additional
features and general relations. Jour. Comp. Neur. and
Psych., vol. 14, p. 441.

206. —— 1904. Contributions to the study of the behavior of
lower organisms. Carnegie Institution Publications.
Washington.

207. —— 1905. Modifiability in behavior, I. Behavior of sea-
anemones. Jour. Exp. Zool., vol. 2, p. 447.

208. —— 1905. The method of regulation in behavior and in
other fields. Ibid., vol. 2, p. 473.

209. —— 1905. The basis for taxis and certain other terms in the

behavior of infusoria. Jour. Comp. Neur. and Psych., vol. 15, p. 138.

210. —— JENNINGS, H. S., 1906. Modifiability in behavior, II. Factors determining direction and character of movement in the earthworm. Jour. Exp. Zool., vol. 3, p. 435.

211. —— 1906. Behavior of the lower organisms. New York.

212. —— 1907. Habit formation in the starfish. Abstract in Jour. Comp. Neur. and Psych., vol. 17, p. 190.

213. JENNINGS, H. S., and JAMIESON, C., 1902. The movements and reactions of pieces of ciliate infusoria. Biol. Bull., vol. 3, p. 225.

214. JENNINGS, H. S., and MOORE, E. M., 1902. On the reactions of infusoria to carbonic and other acids, with special reference to the causes of the gatherings spontaneously formed. Am. Jour. Physiol., vol. 6, p. 233.

215. JENSEN, P., 1893. Ueber den Geotropismus niederer Organismen. Pflügers Arch., Bd. 53, S. 428.

216. JORDAN, H., 1905. Einige neuere Arbeiten auf dem Gebiete der "Psychologie" wirbelloser Thiere. Biol. Cent., Bd. 25, S. 451, 473.

217. JUDD, C. H., 1905. Movement and consciousness. Yale Psych. Studies, N.S., vol. 1, p. 199.

218. KEEBLE, F., and GAMBLE, F. W., 1902. The colour physiology of the higher crustacea. Phil. Trans. Roy. Soc., London, vol. 196B, p. 295.

219. KELLOGG, V. L., 1907. Some silk-worm moth reflexes. Biol. Bull., vol. 12, p. 152.

220. KIENITZ-GERLOFF, 1898. Prof. Plateau und die Blumentheorie. Biol. Cent., Bd. 18, S. 417.

221. KINNAMAN, A. J., 1902. Mental life of two *Macacus rhesus* monkeys in captivity. Am. Jour. Psych., vol. 13, pp. 98, 173.

222. KLINE, L. W., 1899. Suggestions toward a laboratory course in comparative psychology. Ibid., vol. 10, p. 399.

223. KÖRNER, O., 1905. Können die Fische hören? Beiträge zur Ohrenheilkünde, S. 93.

224. KORANYI, A. VON, 1892. Ueber die Reizbarkeit der Froschhaut gegen Licht und Wärme. Cent. f. Physiol., Bd. 6, S. 6.

225. KRAUSE, W., 1897. Die Farbenempfindungen der Amphioxus. Zool. Anz., Bd. 20, S. 513.

226. KREIDL, A., 1893. Weitere Beiträge zur Physiologie des Ohrlabyrinthes. Sitzungsber. d. kais. Akad. d. Wiss., Wien, math.-naturwiss. Klasse, Abth. 3, Bd. 102, S. 149.

227. —— 1895. Ueber die Schallperception der Fische. Pflügers Arch., Bd. 61, S. 450.

228. —— 1896. Ein weiterer Versuch über das angebliche Hören eines Glockenzeichens durch die Fische. Ibid., Bd. 63, S. 581.

229. LECAILLON, A., 1904. Sur la biologie et la physiologie d'une araignée (*Chiracanthum carnifex*). L'année psych., 1903, pp. 10, 63.

230. LEE, F. S., 1894. A study of the sense of equilibrium in fishes. Jour. Physiol., vol. 15, p. 311.

231. LEHNERT, G. H., 1891. Beobachtungen an Landplanarien. Arch. f. Naturgeschichte, Bd. 57, S. 306.

232. LOCKE, J., 1689. Essay on the human understanding.

233. LOEB, J., 1888. Die Orientirung der Tiere gegen das Licht. Sitzungsber. d. phys.-med. Ges., Würzburg, 1888, S. 1.

234. —— 1888. Die Orientirung der Tiere gegen die Schwerkraft der Erde. Ibid., S. 5.

235. —— 1890. Der Heliotropismus der Tiere und sein Uebereinstimmung mit dem Heliotropismus der Pflanzen. Würzburg.

236. —— 1890. Weitere Untersuchungen über den Heliotropismus der Tiere. Pflügers Arch., Bd. 47, S. 391.

237. —— 1891. Untersuchungen zur physiologischen Morphologie der Tiere, I. Ueber Heteromorphose. Würzburg.

238. —— 1891. Ueber Geotropismus bei Tieren. Pflügers Arch., Bd. 49, S. 177.

239. —— 1893. Ueber künstliche Unwandlung positiver heliotropischer Tiere in negativ heliotropische und umgekehrt. Ibid., Bd. 54, S. 81.

240. —— 1894. Beiträge zur Gehirnphysiologie der Würmer. Ibid., Bd. 56, S. 247.

241. —— 1894. Zur Physiologie und Psychologie der Actinien. Ibid., Bd. 59, S. 415.

242. LOEB, J., 1897. Zur Theorie der physiologischen Licht- und Schwerkraftwirkungen. Ibid., Bd. 66, S. 439.

243. —— 1900. Comparative physiology of the brain and comparative psychology. New York.

244. —— 1904. The control of heliotropic reactions in fresh water crustaceans by chemicals. Univ. of Cal. Pub., vol. 2, p. 1.

245. —— 1906. Ueber die Erregung von positivem Heliotropismus durch Säure, insbesondere Kohlensäure, und von negativem Heliotropismus durch ultraviolette Strahlen. Pflügers Arch., Bd. 115, S. 564.

246. —— 1906. Ueber die Summation heliotropischer und geotropischer Wirkungen bei den auf der Drehschiebe ausgelöster compensatorische Kopfbewegungen. Ibid., Bd. 116, S. 368.

247. —— 1907. Concerning the theory of tropisms. Jour. Exp. Zool., vol. 4, p. 151.

248. LUBBOCK, J., 1883. Ants, bees, and wasps. New York.

249. —— 1883. On the sense of colour among some of the lower animals, I. Jour. Linn. Soc., London, Zool., vol. 16, p. 121.

250. —— 1884. On the sense of colour, etc., II. Ibid., vol. 17, p. 205.

251. —— 1888. On the senses, instincts, and intelligence of animals, with special reference to insects. New York.

252. LUKAS, F., 1905. Psychologie der niedersten Thiere. Wien und Leipzig.

253. LYON, E. P., 1898. The functions of the otocyst. Jour. Comp. Neur. and Psych., vol. 8, p. 238.

254. —— 1904. On rheotropism, I. Rheotropism in fishes. Am. Jour. Physiol., vol. 12, p. 149.

255. —— 1905. On the theory of geotropism in Paramecium. Ibid., vol. 14, p. 421.

256. —— 1906. Note on the geotropism of Arbacia larvæ. Biol. Bull., vol. 12, p. 21.

257. —— 1906. Note on the heliotropism of Palæmonetes larvæ. Ibid., vol. 12, p. 23.

258. McCOOK, H. C., 1889–1893. American spiders and their spinning work. 3 vols.

259. MASSART, J., 1891. Récherches sur les organismes inférieurs, III. La sensibilité à la gravitation. Bull. Acad.
roy. Belgique, t. 22, p. 158.

260. MAST, S. O., 1903. Reactions to temperature changes in
Spirillum, Hydra, and fresh-water planarians. Am.
Jour. Physiol., vol. 10, p. 165.

261. —— 1906. Light reactions in *Stentor cœruleus*. Jour.
Exp. Zool., vol. 3, p. 359.

262. —— 1907. Light reactions in lower organisms, II. Volvox.
Jour. Comp. Neur. and Psych., vol. 17, p. 99.

263. MAYER, A. G., and SOULE, C. G., 1906. Some reactions of
caterpillars and moths. Jour. Exp. Zool., vol. 3, p. 415.

264. MAYER, A. M., 1874. Researches in acoustics. Am. Jour.
Science and Arts, III Series, vol. 8, p. 89.

265. MENDELSSOHN, M., 1895. Ueber den Thermotropismus
einzelliger Organismen. Pflügers Arch., Bd. 60, S. 1.

266. —— 1902. Récherches sur la thermotaxie des organismes
unicellulaires. Jour. de physiol. et de pathol. gén., t. 4,
p. 393.

267. —— 1902. Récherches sur l'interférence de la thermotaxie avec d'autres tactismes et sur la mécanisme du
mouvement thermotactique. Ibid., t. 4, p. 475.

268. —— 1902. Quelques considérations sur la nature et la
role biologique de la thermotaxie. Ibid., t. 4, p. 489.

269. MEREJKOWSKY, C., 1881. Les crustacés inférieurs distinguent-ils les couleurs? C. r. Acad. Sci., Paris, t. 93,
p. 1160.

270. METCALF, M. M., 1900. Hearing in ants. Science, N.S.,
vol. 11, p. 194.

271. MILLS, T. W., 1894–1896. The psychic development of
young animals and its physical correlations. Montreal.

272. —— 1898. The nature and development of animal intelligence. New York.

273. —— 1899. The nature of animal intelligence and the
methods of investigating it. Psych. Rev., vol. 6, p.
262.

274. MINKIEWICZ, C., 1907. Chromotropism and phototropism.
Trans. in Jour. Comp. Neur. and Psych., vol. 17, p. 89.

275. MITSUKURI, K., 1901. Negative phototaxis and other

properties of Littorina as factors in determining its habitat. Annot. zool. japonenses, 4.

276. Möbius, K., 1873. Die Bewegungen der Thiere und ihr psychischer Horizont. Schrift. d. naturwiss. Ver. f. Schleswig-Holstein, Bd. 1, S. 113.

277. Montaigne, M. de, 1580. Essays. Florio's translation.

278. Moore, A., 1903. Some facts concerning geotropic gatherings of Paramecium. Am. Jour. Physiol., vol. 9, p. 238.

279. Morgan, C. L., 1891. Animal life and intelligence. Boston.

280. —— 1894. Introduction to comparative psychology. London.

281. —— 1896. Habit and instinct. London.

282. —— 1900. Animal behaviour. London.

283. Morse, M., 1906. Notes on the behavior of Gonionemus. Jour. Comp. Neur. and Psych., vol. 16, p. 450.

284. Müller, H., 1873. Die Befruchtung der Blumen durch Insekten und die gegenseitigen Anpassungen beider. Leipzig.

285. —— 1882. Versuche über d. Farbenliebhaberei der Honigbiene. Kosmos, Bd. 6, S. 273.

286. Murbach, L., 1903. The static function in Gonionemus. Am. Jour. Physiol., vol. 10, p. 201.

287. Nagel, W. A., 1892. Die niederen Sinne der Insekten. Jena.

288. —— 1892. Der Geschmacksinn der Actinien. Zool. Anz., Bd. 15, S. 334.

289. —— 1893. Versuche zur Sinnesphysiologie von *Beroe ovata* und *Carmarina hastata*. Pflügers Arch., Bd. 54, S. 165.

290. —— 1894. Beobachtungen über den Lichtsinn augenloser Muscheln. Biol. Cent., Bd. 14, S. 385.

291. —— 1894. Experimentelle sinnesphysiologische Untersuchungen an Coelenteräten. Pflügers Arch., Bd. 57, S. 495.

292. —— 1894. Vergleichend physiologische und anatomische Untersuchungen über d. Geruchs- und Geschmacksinn und ihre Organe. Zoologica, Heft 18.

293. —— 1896. Der Lichtsinn augenloser Thiere. Jena.

294. NAGEL, W. A., 1899. Review of Loeb: Vergleichende Gehirnphysiologie u. s. w. Zool. Cent., Bd. 6, S. 611.

295. NORMAN, W. W., 1900. Do the reactions of the lower animals against injury indicate pain sensation? Am. Jour. Physiol., vol. 3, p. 271.

296. NUEL, J. P., 1904. La vision. Paris.

297. ―― 1905. La psychologie comparée est-elle légitime? Réponse à M. Claparède. Arch. de psych., t. 5, p. 326.

298. OLTMANNS, F., 1892. Ueber die photometrischen Bewegungen der Pflanzen. Flora, Bd. 75, S. 183.

299. OELZELT-NEWIN, A., 1906. Beobachtungen über das Leben der Protozoen. Zeit. f. Psych. und Physiol. der Sinnesorgane, Bd. 41, S. 349.

300. OSTWALD, W., 1903. Zur Theorie der Richtungsbewegungen niederer schwimmender Organismen, I. Pflügers Arch., Bd. 95, S. 23.

301. ―― 1906. Zur Theorie u. s. w., II. Ibid., Bd. 111, S. 452.

302. ―― 1907. Zur Theorie u. s. w., III. Ueber die Abhängigkeit gewisser heliotropischer Reaktionen von der inneren Reibung des Mediums, sowie u. d. Wirkung "mechanischer Sensibilatoren." Ibid., Bd. 117, S. 384.

303. PARKER, G. H., 1896. The reactions of Metridium to food and other substances. Bull. Mus. Comp. Zool., Harvard, vol. 29, p. 105.

304. ―― 1901. Reactions of copepods to various stimuli and the bearing of this on daily depth migrations. Bull. U. S. Fish Com., vol. 21, p. 103.

305. ―― 1902. Hearing and allied senses in fishes. Ibid., vol. 22, p. 45.

306. ―― 1903. The sense of hearing in fishes. Am. Nat., vol. 37, p. 185.

307. ―― 1903. The phototropism of the mourning cloak butterfly, *Vanessa antiopa* Linn. Mark Anniversary Volume, p. 453.

308. ―― 1903. The skin and the eyes as receptive organs in the reactions of frogs to light. Am. Jour. Physiol., vol. 10, p. 28.

309. ―― 1904. The function of the lateral-line organs in fishes. Bull. Bureau of Fisheries, vol. 24, p. 183.

310. PARKER, G. H., 1905. On the stimulation of the integumentary nerves of fishes by light. Am. Jour. Physiol., vol. 14, p. 413.

311. —— 1907. The interrelation of sensory stimuli in Amphioxus. Abstract in Jour. Comp. Neur. and Psych., vol. 17, p. 197.

312. PARKER, G. H., and ARKIN, L., 1901. The directive influence of light on the earthworm, *Allolobophora fœtida*. Am. Jour. Physiol., vol. 5, p. 151.

313. PARKER, G. H., and BURNETT, F. L., 1901. The reactions of planarians with and without eyes to light. Ibid., vol. 4, p. 373.

314. PARKER, G. H., and METCALF, C. R., 1906. The reactions of earthworms to salts. Ibid., vol. 17, p. 55.

315. PATTEN, W., 1893. On the morphology of the brain and sense organs of Limulus. Quar. Jour. Micr. Sci., vol. 35, p. 1.

316. PEARL, R. J., 1903. The movements and reactions of fresh-water planarians. Ibid., vol. 46, p. 509.

317. —— 1904. On the behavior and reactions of Limulus in early stages of its development. Jour. Comp. Neur. and Psych., vol. 14, p. 138.

318. PEARL, R. J., and COLE, L. J., 1901. The effect of very intense light on organisms. Report Mich. Acad. Sci., 1901, p. 77.

319. PEARSE, A. S., 1906. Reactions of *Tubularia crocea*. Am. Nat., vol. 40, p. 401.

320. PECKHAM, G. W. and E. G., 1887. Some observations on the mental powers of spiders. Jour. Morph., vol. 1, p. 383.

321. —— 1894. The sense of sight in spiders, with some observations on the color sense. Trans. Wis. Acad. Sciences, Arts, and Letters, vol. 10, p. 231.

322. —— 1898. On the instincts and habits of the solitary wasps. Wis. Geol. and Nat. Hist. Survey, Bull. 2.

323. —— 1905. Wasps, social and solitary. Boston.

324. PERRIS, E., 1850. Mémoire sur le siège de l'odorat dans les articulés. Ann. sci. nat., Zool., Série 3, t. 14, p. 149.

325. PIÉRON, C., 1904. Du role du sens musculaire dans l'orien-

tation de quelques espèces de fourmis. Bull. Inst. gén. psych., Paris, t. 4, p. 168.

326. PIÈRON C., 1904. Contribution à l'étude du problème de la reconnaissance chez les fourmis. C. r. 6ᵉ Congrès internat. de Zool., p. 482.

327. —— 1906. Contribution à la psychologie des actinies. Bull. Inst. gén. psych., Paris, t. 6, p. 40.

328. PLATEAU, F., 1885. Récherches expérimentelles sur la vision chez les arthropodes. Les insectes distinguent-ils la forme des objets? Bull. Acad. roy. Belgique, IIIe série, t. 10, p. 231.

329. —— 1886. Récherches sur la perception de la lumière par les myriapodes aveugles. Jour. de l'anat. et de la physiol., t. 22, p. 431.

330. —— 1887. Observations sur les mœurs du *Blaniulus guttulatus*. C. r. Soc. ent. Belgique, t. 31, p. 81.

331. —— 1887. Récherches expérimentelles, etc., I. Bull. Acad. roy. Belgique, t. 14, p. 407.

332. —— 1887. Récherches expérimentelles, etc., II. Ibid., t. 14, p. 545.

333. —— 1888. Récherches expérimentelles, etc., III. Ibid., t. 15, p. 28.

334. —— 1888. Récherches expérimentelles, etc., IV. Ibid., t. 16, p. 159.

335. —— 1888. Récherches expérimentelles, etc., V. Ibid., t. 16, p. 395.

336. —— 1895. Comment les fleurs attirent les insectes, I. Ibid., t. 30, p. 466.

337. —— 1896. Comment, etc., II. Ibid., t. 32, p. 505.

338. —— 1897. Comment, etc., III. Ibid., t. 33, p. 301.

339. —— 1899. La choix des couleurs par les insectes. Mémoires Soc. zool. France, t. 12, p. 336.

340. —— 1899. La vision chez *l'Anthidium manicatum*. Ann. Soc. ent. Belgique, t. 43, p. 452.

341. —— 1902. Observations sur les erreurs commises par les hymenoptères visitant les fleurs. Ibid., t. 46, p. 113.

342. PLATT, J. B., 1899. On the sp. gr. of Spirostomum, Paramecium, and the tadpole in relation to the problem of geotaxis. Am. Nat., vol. 33, p. 31.

343. POLLOCK, W. H. (with addendum by Romanes), 1883. On indications of the sense of smell in Actiniæ. Jour. Linn. Soc. London, Zool., vol. 16, p. 474.

344. PORTER, J. P., 1904. A preliminary study of the psychology of the English sparrow. Am. Jour. Psych., vol. 15, p. 313.

345. —— 1906. Further study of the English sparrow and other birds. Ibid., vol. 17, p. 248.

346. —— 1906. The habits, instincts, and mental powers of spiders, genera Argiope and Epeira. Ibid., vol. 17, p. 306.

347. POUCHET, 1872. De l'influence de la lumière sur les larves de diptères privées d'organes extérieurs de la vision. Rev. et mag. de zool., IIe série, t. 23, pp. 110, 129, 183, 225, 261, 312.

348. POUCHET and JOUBERT, 1875. La vision chez les Cirrhipèdes. C. r. et Mémoires Soc. Biol., VIe série, t. 2, p. 245.

349. PRENTISS, C. W., 1901. The otocyst of decapod crustacea. Bull. Mus. Comp. Zool., Harvard, vol. 36, p. 165.

350. PREYER, W., 1886. Ueber die Bewegungen der Seesterne. Mitth. a. d. zool. Stat. zu Neapel, Bd. 7, S. 27, 191.

351. PRITCHETT, A. H., 1904. Hearing and smell in spiders. Am. Nat., vol. 38, p. 859.

352. PÜTTER, A., 1900. Die Reizbeantwortungen der ciliaten Infusorien. Zeit. f. allg. Physiol., Bd. 3, S. 406.

353. —— 1900. Studien über Thigmotaxis bei Protisten. Arch. f. Anat. u. Physiol., physiol. Abth., Supplementband, S. 243.

354. RÁDL, E., 1901. Ueber d. Phototropismus einiger Arthropoden. Biol. Cent., Bd. 21, S. 75.

355. —— 1901. Untersuchungen über d. Lichtreactionen der Arthropoden. Pflügers Arch., Bd. 87, S. 418.

356. —— 1903. Untersuchungen über die Phototropismus der Tiere. Leipzig.

357. —— 1905. Ueber das Gehör der Insekten. Biol. Cent., Bd. 25, S. 1.

358. —— 1906. Einige Bemerkungen und Beobachtungen über die Phototropismus der Tiere. Ibid., Bd. 26, S. 677.

359. RASPAIL, X., 1899. On the sense of smell in birds. Trans. in Smithsonian Report, 1899, p. 367.

360. RAWITZ, B., 1888. Der Mantelrand der Acephalen. Jena. Zeit., Bd. 22, S. 415.

361. RHUMBLER, L., 1898. Physikalische Analyse von Lebens-erscheinungen der Zelle, I. Bewegung, Nahrungsauf-nahme, Defäkation, Vacuolen-Pulsation und Gehäusebau bei lobosen Rhizopoden. Arch. f. Entwicklungsmech., Bd. 7, S. 103.

362. —— 1905. Zur Theorie der Oberflächenkräfte der Amöben. Zeit. f. wiss. Zool., Bd. 83, S. 1.

363. RILEY, C. V., 1895. The senses of insects. Nature, vol. 52, p. 209.

364. ROMANES, G. J., 1883. Animal intelligence. New York.

365. —— 1885. Jellyfish, starfish and sea-urchins. New York.

366. —— 1885. Mental evolution in animals. London.

367. —— 1887. Experiments on the sense of smell in dogs. Nature, vol. 36, p. 273.

368. ROMANES, G. J., and EWART, J. C., 1881. Observations on the locomotor system of Echinodermata. Phil. Trans. Roy. Soc., London, vol. 172, pt. 3, p. 855.

369. ROSENTHAL, J., 1905. Physiologie und Psychologie. Biol. Cent., Bd. 25, S. 713, 741.

370. ROUBAUD, 1907. Instincts, adaptation, résistance au milieu chez les mouches des rivages maritimes. Bull. Inst. gén. psych., Paris, t. 7, p. 61.

371. ROUSE, J. E., 1906. The mental life of the domestic pigeon. Harvard Psych. Studies, vol. 2, p. 580.

372. ROYCE, J., 1903. Outlines of psychology. New York.

373. RYDER, J. A., 1883. Primitive visual organs. Science, N.S., vol. 2, p. 739.

374. SCHNADER, M., 1887. Zur Physiologie des Froschgehirns. Pflügers Arch., Bd. 41, S. 75.

375. SCHNEIDER, G. H., 1905. Die Orientirung der Brieftauben. Zeit. f. Psych. u. Physiol. d. Sinnesorgane, Bd. 40, S. 252.

376. SCHNEIDER, K. C., 1905. Grundzüge der vergleichender Tierpsychologie. Biol. Cent., Bd. 25, S. 666, 701.

377. SCHRÖDER, C., 1901. Experimentelle Studien über Blüten-besuch, besonders der *Syritta pipiens* L. Allg. Zeit. f. Ent., Bd. 6, S. 181.

378. Schwarz, F., 1884. Der Einfluss der Schwerkraft auf die Bewegungsrichtung von Chlamydomonas und Euglena. Sitzungsber. d. deutsch. bot. Gesell., Bd. 2, S. 51.

379. Semon, R., 1904. Die Mneme als erhaltendes Princip im Wechsel des organischen Geschehens. Leipzig.

380. Sewall, H., 1884. Experiments on the ears of fishes with reference to the function of equilibrium. Jour. Physiol., vol. 4, p. 339.

381. Sharp, B., 1884. On the visual organs in Lamellibranchiata. Mitth. a. d. zool. Station zu Neapel, Bd. 5, S. 447.

382. Sherrington, C. S., 1906. The integrative action of the nervous system. New York.

383. Shufeldt, R. W., 1900. Notes on the psychology of fishes. Am. Nat., vol. 34, p. 275.

384. Small, W. S., 1899. Notes on the psychic development of the young white rat. Am. Jour. Psych., vol. 11, p. 80.

385. —— 1899. An experimental study of the mental processes of the rat, I. Ibid., vol. 11, p. 133.

386. —— 1900. An experimental study, etc., II. Ibid., vol. 12, p. 206.

387. Smith, A. C., 1902. The influence of temperature, odors, light, and contact on the movements of the earthworm. Am. Jour. Physiol., vol. 6, p. 459.

388. Sosnowski, J., 1899. Untersuchungen über die Veränderungen der Geotropismus bei *Paramecium aurelia*. Bull. Internat. Acad. Sci., Cracovie, 1899, p. 130.

389. Spaulding, E. G., 1904. An establishment of association in hermit crabs, *Eupagurus longicarpus*. Jour. Comp. Neur. and Psych., vol. 14, p. 49.

390. Stahl, E., 1878. Ueber d. Einfluss des Lichtes auf die Bewegungserscheinungen der Schwärmsporen. Bot. Zeit., Bd. 36, S. 715.

391. Steiner, J., 1888. Die Functionen des Centralnervensystems und ihre Phylogenese, II Abth., Fische. Braunschweig.

392. Strasburger, E., 1878. Die Wirkung des Lichtes und der Warme auf Schwärmsporen. Jena. Also in Jena. Zeit., n. F., Bd. 5, S. 572.

393. THORNDIKE, E. L., 1898. Animal intelligence. Psych. Rev. Monograph Supp., vol. 2, no. 4.

394. —— 1899. A note on the psychology of fishes. Am. Nat., vol. 33, p. 923.

395. —— 1899. The instinctive reactions of young chicks. Psych. Rev., vol. 6, p. 282.

396. —— 1899. A reply to "The nature of animal intelligence and the methods of investigating it." Ibid., vol. 6, p. 412.

397. —— 1901. The mental life of the monkeys. Psych. Rev. Monograph Supp., no. 15.

398. TIEDEMANN, F., 1815. Beobachtungen über d. Nervensystem und d. sensiblen Erscheinungen der Seesterne. Deutsches Arch. f. d. Physiol., Bd. 1, S. 161.

399. TITCHENER, E. B., 1902. Were the earliest organic movements conscious or unconscious? Pop. Sci. Mo., vol. 60, p. 458.

400. —— 1905. The problems of experimental psychology. Am. Jour. Psych., vol. 16, p. 208.

401. TORELLE, E., 1903. The response of the frog to light. Am. Jour. Physiol., vol. 9, p. 466.

402. TORREY, H. B., 1904. Biological studies on Corymorpha, I. *C. palma* and its environment. Jour. Exp. Zool., vol. 1, p. 395.

403. —— 1904. Habits and reactions of *Sagartia davisi*. Biol. Bull., vol. 6, p. 203.

404. TOWER, W. L., 1906. Evolution in chrysomelid beetles of the genus Leptinotarsa. Carnegie Pub.

405. TOWLE, E., 1900. A study in the heliotropism of Cypridopsis. Am. Jour. Physiol., vol. 3, p. 345.

406. TREMBLEY, A., 1744. Mémoires pour servir à l'histoire d'un genre de polypes d'eau douce. Paris.

407. TRIPLETT, N. B., 1901. The educability of the perch. Am. Jour. Psych., vol. 12, p. 354.

408. TURNER, C. H., 1906. A preliminary note on ant behavior. Biol. Bull., vol. 12, p. 31.

409. UEXKÜLL, J. VON, 1897. Ueber Reflexe bei den Seeeigeln. Zeit. f. Biol., Bd. 34, S. 298.

410. —— 1897. Der Schatten als Reiz fur *Centrostephanus longispinus*. Ibid., Bd. 34, S. 319.

411. UEXKÜLL, J., VON, 1900.　Die Wirkung von Licht und Schatten auf die Seeeigeln.　Ibid., Bd. 40, S. 447.

412. —— 1900.　Ueber die Stellung der vergleichender Physiologie zur Hypothese der Tierseele.　Biol. Cent., Bd. 20, S. 497.

413. VASCHIDE, N., and ROUSSEAU, P., 1902.　Études expérimentales sur la vie mentale des animaux.　Rev. scient., t. 19, pp. 737, 777.

414. —— 1903.　Études, etc.　Ibid., t. 20, p. 321.

415. VERWORN, M., 1891.　Gleichgewicht und Otolithenorgan. Pflügers Arch., Bd. 50, S. 423.

416. —— 1899.　Psycho-physiologische Protistenstudien.　Jena.

417. —— 1899.　General physiology.　Trans. by F. S. Lee. London.

418. WAGNER, G., 1904.　On some movements and reactions of Hydra.　Quar. Jour. Micr. Sci., vol. 48, p. 585.

419. WARREN, E., 1900.　On the reaction of *Daphnia magna* to certain changes in its environment.　Ibid., vol. 43, p. 199.

420. WASHBURN, M. F., 1904.　A factor in mental development. Phil. Rev., vol. 13, p. 622.

421. WASHBURN, M. F., and BENTLEY, I. M., 1906.　The establishment of an association involving color discrimination in the creek chub, *Semotilus atromaculatus*.　Jour. Comp. Neur. and Psych., vol. 16, p. 113.

422. WASMANN, E., 1891.　Die zusammengesetzten Nester und gemischter Kolonien der Ameisen.　Münster.

423. —— 1891.　Zur Frage nach den Gehörsvermögen der Ameisen.　Biol. Cent., Bd. 11, S. 26.

424. —— 1893.　Lautäusserungen der Ameisen.　Ibid., Bd. 13, S. 39.

425. —— 1897.　Vergleichende Studien über d. Seelenleben der Ameisen und der höheren Tiere.　Freiburg i. B.　Trans., St. Louis, 1905.

426. —— 1899.　Die psychischen Fähigkeiten der Ameisen. Zoologica, Heft 26.

427. —— 1899.　Instinkt und Intelligenz im Thierreich.　Freiburg i. B.　Trans., St. Louis, 1903.

428. —— 1900.　Einige Bemerkungen zur vergleichenden

Psychologie und Sinnesphysiologie. Biol. Cent., Bd. 20, S. 342.

429. WATKINS, G. P., 1900. Psychical life in protozoa. Am. Jour. Psych., vol. 11, p. 166.

430. WATSON, J. B., 1903. Animal education. Univ. of Chicago Contributions to Philosophy, vol. 4, no. 2.

431. —— 1907. Kinæsthetic and organic sensations: their rôle in the reactions of the white rat to the maze. Psych. Rev. Monograph Supp., vol. 8, no. 2.

432. WEIR, J., 1899. The dawn of reason. New York.

433. WELD, L. D., 1899. The sense of hearing in ants. Science, N.S., vol. 10, p. 766.

434. WÉRY, J., 1904. Quelques expériences sur l'attraction des abeilles par les fleurs. Bull. Acad. roy. de Belgique, pt. 1, p. 1211.

435. WHEELER, W. M., 1899. Anemotropism and other tropisms in insects. Arch. f. Entwicklungsmech., Bd. 8, S. 373.

436. —— 1900. A study of some Texan Ponerinæ. Biol. Bull., vol. 2, pp. 1, 43.

437. —— 1903. Ethological observations on an American ant. Jour. für Psych. und Neur., Bd. 2, S. 31, 64.

438. WHITMAN, C. O., 1898. Animal behavior. Biol. Lectures, Marine Biol. Lab., Wood's Hole, 1898, p. 285.

439. WILL, F., 1885. Das Geschmacksorgan der Insekten. Leipzig.

440. WILLEM, V., 1891. Sur les perceptions dermatologiques. Bull. scient. de la France et de la Belgique, t. 23, p. 329.

441. —— 1892. De la vision chez les mollusques gastéropodes pulmonés. Arch. de biol., t. 12, p. 57.

442. —— 1892. Les gastéropodes percoivent-ils les rayons ultra-violets? Ibid., t. 12, p. 99.

443. —— 1892. Observations sur la vision et les organes visuels de quelques mollusques prosobranches et opisthobranches. Ibid., t. 12, p. 123.

444. WILSON, E. B., 1891. The heliotropism of Hydra. Am. Nat. vol. 25, p. 413.

445. WOODWORTH, R. S., 1906. The cause of a voluntary move-

ment. No. 12 in Studies in philosophy and psychology by former students of Charles Edward Garman. Boston.

446. WUNDT, W., 1894. Lectures on human and animal psychology. Trans. by J. E. Creighton and E. B. Titchener. London.

447. YERKES, A. W., 1906. Modifiability of behavior in *Hydroides dianthus*. Jour. Comp. Neur. and Psych., vol. 16, p. 441.

448. YERKES, R. M., 1900. Reactions of Entomostraca to stimulation by light, I. Am. Jour. Physiol., vol. 3, p. 157.

449. —— 1901. Reactions, etc., II. Reactions of Daphnia and Cypris. Ibid., vol. 4, p. 405.

450. —— 1901. The formation of habits in the turtle. Pop. Sci. Mo., vol. 58, p. 519.

451. —— 1902. A contribution to the physiology of the nervous system in the medusa *Gonionemus murbachii*, I. The sensory reactions of Gonionemus. Am. Jour. Physiol., vol. 6, p. 434.

452. —— 1902. A contribution, etc., II. The physiology of the nervous system. Ibid., vol. 7, p. 181.

453. —— 1902. Habit formation in the green crab, *Carcinus granulatus*. Biol. Bull., vol. 3, p. 241.

454. —— 1903. The instincts, habits, and reactions of the frog, I. Associative processes of the green frog. Harvard Psych. Studies, vol. 1, p. 579.

455. —— 1903. The instincts, etc., II. Reaction time of the green frog to electrical and tactual stimuli. Ibid., vol. 1, p. 598.

456. —— 1903. The instincts, etc., III. Auditory reactions of frogs. Ibid., vol. 1, p. 627.

457. —— 1903. Reactions of *Daphnia pulex* to light and heat. Mark Anniversary Volume, p. 361.

458. —— 1904. The reaction time of *Gonionemus murbachii* to electric and photic stimuli. Biol. Bull., vol. 6, p. 84.

459. —— 1904. Space perceptions of tortoises. Jour. Comp. Neur. and Psych., vol. 14, p. 17.

460. —— 1904. Inhibition and reinforcement of reactions in the frog. Ibid., vol. 14, p. 124.

461. YERKES, R. M., 1905. Concerning the genetic relations of types of action. Ibid., vol. 15, p. 132.

462. —— 1905. The sense of hearing in frogs. Ibid., vol. 15, p. 279.

463. —— 1905. Animal psychology and criteria of the psychic. Jour. Phil., Psych., and Sci. Methods, vol. 2, p. 141.

464. —— 1905. Bahnung und Hemmung der Reactionen auf tactile Reize durch akustische Reize beim Frosche. Pflügers Arch., Bd. 107, S. 207.

465. —— 1906. Objective nomenclature, comparative psychology, and animal behavior. Jour. Comp. Neur. and Psych., vol. 16, p. 380.

466. —— 1906. Mutual relations of stimuli in the frog, *Rana clamata* Daudin. Harvard Psych. Studies, vol. 2, p. 545.

467. —— 1906. Bohn's studies in animal behavior. Jour. Comp. Neur. and Psych., vol. 16, p. 231.

468. —— 1906. Concerning the behavior of Gonionemus. Ibid., vol. 16, p. 457.

469. —— 1907. The dancing mouse. New York.

470. YERKES, R. M., and AYER, J. B., 1903. A study of the reactions and reaction time of the medusa *Gonionemus murbachii* to photic stimuli. Am. Jour. Physiol., vol. 9, p. 279.

471. YERKES, R. M., and HUGGINS, G. E., 1903. Habit formation in the crawfish, *Cambarus affinis*. Harvard Psych. Studies, vol. 1, p. 565.

472. YUNG, E., 1892. La fonction dermatoptique chez le ver de terre. C. r. et Trav. Soc. Helv. Sci. nat., 1892, p. 127.

473. —— 1893. La psychologie de l'escargot. Ibid., 1893, p. 127.

474. —— 1903. Récherches sur le sens olfactif de l'escargot (*Helix pomatia*). Arch. de Psych., t. 3, p. 1.

475. ZENNECK, J., 1903. Reagiren die Fische auf Töne? Pflügers Arch., Bd. 95, S. 346.

476. ZIEGLER, H. E., 1900. Theoretisches zur Tierpsychologie und vergleichenden Neuropathologie. Biol. Cent., Bd. 20, S. 1.

INDEX

INDEX OF NAMES

The numbers refer to the pages on which the work of the writers is cited, whether their names appear in the text or not.

Animal Behavior

The Dancing Mouse

A STUDY IN ANIMAL BEHAVIOR BY

ROBERT M. YERKES, Ph.D.

Instructor in Comparative Psychology, Harvard University

The book deals with the evolution of activity and with the principles and methods of the study of animal behavior and comparative psychology. Just as a detailed study of the frog is made the basis of courses in comparative anatomy, so Dr. Yerkes makes a complete survey of the structure, characteristics, effects of breeding and environment, etc., of the dancing mouse, with an account of its sensitiveness to different stimuli, its receptivity of training, the methods of measuring its intelligence, the permanence of changes in its behavior, etc., the foundation of work in comparative psychology.

Cloth, xxi + 290 pages, illus., index, 12mo, $1.25 net

CRITICAL COMMENT

"Dr. Yerkes' book is a most interesting example of modern laboratory methods and can be read with profit by any one, on account of the accurate methods of observation and careful deductive reasoning which it shows. An elaborate, painstaking system of experiments was carried on with over 400 mice, with the object of determining muscular coördination, structural peculiarities, strength of the special sense organs, habit formation, educability, and strength of memory of these little animals. Some experiments were also undertaken along the line of inherited peculiarities. Dr. Yerkes states that, owing to an unfortunate epidemic of intestinal trouble which broke out among his mice, all of them except a single pair died within a few weeks, thus putting a stop to the experiments which he hoped to complete. The work is, therefore, really only a preliminary study, but it will be read with much interest by all students of comparative psychology." — *Jour. of Amer. Med. Ass'n.*

"The subject of this study is the so-called dancing mouse which is found in China and Japan, an animal which goes through a series of movements, whirling and circling, which have all the appearances of calculated dancing. For the study of hereditary tendencies and the relations of anatomical structure to intelligence, this animal is an instrument ready made for the psychologist, and Dr. Yerkes' careful and exhaustive study has been pronounced of the utmost scientific value. The book is the first of a series of works on animal behavior."
— *The Times.*

"This book is as useful, perhaps, as a disclosure of the methods by which the behavior and intelligence may be studied as for what it contributes concerning the particular animal under investigation. To people who have not followed the recent developments in this field of science the book is a revelation." — *Review of Reviews.*

PUBLISHED BY

THE MACMILLAN COMPANY

Sixty-four and Sixty-six Fifth Avenue, New York